THE NATURE OF
CAMBRIDGE

Edited by Mark Hill

2022

piscespublications

Published 2022 by Pisces Publications

First published 2022.

British-Library-in-Publication Data
A catalogue record for this book is available from the British Library.

ISBN 978-1-874357-07-5

Designed and published by Pisces Publications

Visit our bookshop
www.naturebureau.co.uk/bookshop/

Pisces Publications is the imprint of NatureBureau,
36 Kingfisher Court, Hambridge Road, Newbury, Berkshire RG14 5SJ
www.naturebureau.co.uk

Printed and bound by Gomer Press, UK

Front cover Main: Bee Orchid *Ophrys apifera* [Bob Jarman]. Below left to right: Hornet Hoverfly *Volucella zonaria* [Chris Kirby-Lambert], Peregrines *Falco peregrinus* [Akua Reindorf], Harvest Mouse *Micromys minutus* [Mark Hows].
Back cover: View north-east over the northern edge of Cambridge, showing its position on the fen edge [Pat Doody].

Contents

The NatHistCam project

The Cambridge Natural History Society (CNHS) was founded in 1857 as Cambridge Entomological Society and its activities include talks, excursions and surveys. In 2019 it held its 100th Conversazione, its annual exhibition, with over a hundred displays from local organisations and individuals. Membership is open to all and has always included many of the major naturalists based in the area. Many CNHS members are active in recording flora or fauna (or both), either professionally or in their spare time, and the Society has in years past organised species recording projects. In the 1920s and 30s CNHS published several monographs on groups of invertebrates in Cambridgeshire and it was responsible for two editions of *The geology and soils of Cambridgeshire* (King & Nicholson 1946; Hay & Perrin 1960). Since 2004 it has been running annual field surveys of sites in or near Cambridge. Reports of these are on its website and are also published in *Nature in Cambridgeshire*.

The idea of a publication on the natural history of Cambridge was first raised at a meeting of the Council of CNHS in autumn 2014, where it was received favourably. By autumn 2015 the project

Figure 1.1 Logo designed for the project by Sam Motherwell.

was beginning to take shape, with Mark Hill, then President of the CNHS, providing ideas on timescale, survey area and possible outputs. These were presented to, and agreed by, the Council of CNHS in September 2015. It was decided that the project should have its own steering committee and website, and that people from outside the CNHS, specifically from other local natural history and conservation groups, should be involved. Much discussion followed and by the end of the year a planning group had come together, with the geographical scope (the 8 km × 8 km survey area) agreed. The key objectives were to create a snapshot of the flora and fauna of Cambridge city and its immediate environs in a historical context and to increase public awareness of the diversity of plants, animals and fungi in the city. In the process, we hoped to engage people in recording biodiversity in their local patches and to collate recent records of a wide range of taxa found in the city and make these records available.

Work began in earnest at the beginning of 2016 with a small steering committee, which met in Cambridge's biodiversity hub, the David Attenborough Building. Core members, who were involved from start to finish were Monica Frisch, Mark Hill, Bob Jarman, Duncan Mackay, Chris Preston, Paul Rule, Jonathan Shanklin and Olwen Williams. Others were involved at different stages and with different roles. A comprehensive list is in the acknowledgements. NatHistCam was chosen as the name of the project as, at the time, it produced no hits in Google. We created a website, and persuaded Sam Motherwell, a local artist, to create a logo for us, which he generously did for no charge (Figure 1.1). The project was formally launched at the CNHS Conversazione in June 2016, which coincided with the publication of the issue of *Nature in Cambridgeshire* containing an article about the project (Hill 2016).

Data collection

We recorded species and their habitats in a variety of ways. The helpful staff at the Cambridgeshire and Peterborough Environmental Records Centre (CPERC) created a recording page for use by

NatHistCam. Our website advertised surveys and encouraged people to submit sightings of fauna and flora. By autumn 2020, over 2000 records of about 1000 species had been submitted to the CPERC NatHistCam page, with a handful of recorders responsible for most of them. We also decided to survey private gardens in the inhabited monads and devised a protocol for doing so. We then modified this protocol to learn about wildlife in college gardens by interviewing gardening staff.

Press publicity in December 2016 drew attention to our survey of **Mistletoe** *Viscum album* which generated about 120 reports (see chapter 5). We continued to get some press coverage, mostly in the form of interviews on Radio Cambridgeshire, but we never succeeded in getting large numbers of the general public involved either in specific surveys or more generally. Some enthusiastic new members joined the steering group and we began accumulating data.

Our website, hosted by Mackays of Cambridge and managed by Monica Frisch, continued to develop, with the addition of blog postings about the wildlife of our area (referred to hereafter as the NHC area). These were at first intermittent, but by winter 2016 Olwen Williams was posting a monthly round-up of sightings. She emailed around 135 people each month requesting sightings, with about 30 people contributing regularly. Bob Jarman wrote monthly reports focussing mainly on birds, drawing on his expertise and that of other members of Cambridgeshire Bird Club, and highlighting some of their noteworthy records. Others also contributed from time to time, resulting in at least two blogs in most months. A full list of the blogs is on the website.

Certain themes emerged from the records submitted in response to Olwen's requests. Not surprisingly these were mostly reports of species that were seen as notable or interesting to the recorder, though some noted the appearance of common plants or birds, such as early spring flowers or the arrival of **Swifts**. Table 1.1 is based on sightings reported in Olwen's blog, not on an analysis of all the data. However, these records contributed to the impressive lists of Butterflies and Odonata which are reported on in chapters 8 and 10, as well as giving an indication of the variety of species being noticed and noted within the NHC area. Not least in importance was the obvious pleasure many people had, both in sending their findings (and queries) and in receiving news of their city's wildlife, often accompanied by photographs.

Some reports were of species previously recorded in the city but which had not been seen for many years. There were also reports of the arrival of a plant or an animal new to the city and possibly moving north through climate change. These include the very distinctive **Wasp Spider** *Argiope bruennichi*, the **Willow Emerald Damselfly** *Chalcolestes viridis*, four species of bee and various other insects. Some species were thought to have arrived with building materials, or other human activity, such as **Cottongrass** *Eriophorum angustifolium*, normally found in acid bogs, which was planted beside a new lake.

From the outset we planned to record plants, including bryophytes, systematically in all 64 monads (1-km squares) of the NHC area. The objective was to identify presence at the monad level, not a detailed study of abundance. These records were complete by the end of 2019 (Table 1.2). We made a separate survey of plants on Cambridge walls in 2020. Date ranges for the animal groups started in 2000 (molluscs) and ended in 2021 (birds and spiders).

For most animal groups we either relied on lead recorders such as Mark Hows for small mammals and Steve Allain for amphibians and reptiles, or pulled records together from scattered sources. As animals tend to be mobile, we did not explicitly use the monad structure of the NHC area, but aimed nevertheless to keep within its boundary, thus excluding most of Milton Country Park and all of Madingley Wood and Wandlebury Country Park.

It became apparent that several moth traps were operating in the city, but moth recorders were not pooling their records and the county recorder had a large backlog to catch up with. Spurred on by Annette Shelford, Sam Buckton and Duncan Mackay, a moth trap was set up in the Botanic Garden and recorded weekly by a team from our project and Cambridge University. Paul Rule rose to the challenge of recording invertebrates and his wonderful photographs were published on our website and gave a flavour of the rich fauna in less well-known groups.

We did not make our own bird records but relied on Bob Jarman and the Cambridgeshire Bird Club, who provided a comprehensive species list (chapter 13). Some very interesting records resulted from 'noc-mig', the recording and identification, by experts, of flight calls of overflying migrants. Bob Jarman also undertook surveys of overwintering **Blackcaps**, singing **Mistle Thrushes** (recently Red-listed) and **Rooks** (Jarman and Preston 2020).

Table 1.1 Some of the interesting species reported in Olwen Williams's blogs in response to requests for sightings.

Species	Scientific name	Notes
Common Tamarisk-moss	*Thuidium tamariscinum*	A woodland moss previously recorded in the NHC area in a lawn on Paradise Island from 1958 to 1964
Balloonwort (Liverwort)	*Sphaerocarpos* sp.	Last record 1802
Fungus	*Leucopaxillus rhodoleucus*	Only two other British records
Rust on Moon Carrot	*Puccinia libanotidis*	Rare rust fungus on red-listed host
Bristly Stonewort	*Chara hispida*	Last record 1997
Bog Stitchwort	*Stellaria alsine*	Last record 1988
Broad-leaved Helleborine	*Epipactis helleborine*	No previous confirmed record
Dodder	*Cuscuta epithymum*	Last record 1898
Whorled Water-milfoil	*Myriophyllum verticillatum*	Last record 1902
Purple Emperor (female)	*Apatura iris*	Vagrant
Small Blue Butterfly	*Cupido minimus*	Last record 2004
Jersey Tiger Moth	*Euplagia quadripunctaria*	First recorded in 1920s but recent expansion north
Scarce Gold Conch Moth	*Phtheochroa schreibersana*	Last record 1920
Glow-worm	*Lampyris noctiluca*	Only in Cherry Hinton Chalk pit
Musk Beetle	*Aromia moschata*	An iridescent green beetle, local in Britain
Western Conifer Seed Bug	*Leptoglossus occidentalis*	Introduced into Europe from the USA in 1999; first British records 2007
Southern Green Shieldbug	*Nezara viridula*	First recorded in Britain in 2003
Willow Emerald Damselfly	*Chalcolestes viridis*	First recorded breeding in Britain in 2007
Ivy Bee	*Colletes hederae*	First recorded in Britain in 2001, now common in NHC area
Tree Bumblebee	*Bombus hypnorum*	First recorded breeding in Britain in 2001
Violet Carpenter Bee	*Xylocopa violacea*	Native to southern Europe; first recorded breeding in Britain in 2007; in NHC area 2020
White-faced Mason Bee	*Osmia cornuta*	First recorded in Britain in 2017
Wasp Spider	*Argiope bruennichi*	First recorded on S coast of Britain in 1922; recently moving north
Common Sandpiper	*Actitis hypoleucos*	Uncommon passage migrant
Great White Egret	*Ardea alba*	Increasing range
Red Kite	*Milvus milvus*	Range expanding from west; one breeding record
Swift	*Apus apus*	Declining migrant whose arrival is usually noted
Wheatear	*Oenanthe oenanthe*	Uncommon passage migrant

Table 1.2 Date ranges for species reported in chapters 4–14.

Taxonomic group	Start	End	Comment
Vascular plants	2000	2019	2020 data for walls
Mosses, liverworts	2010	2019	
Fungi	2001	2019	rusts, smuts, mildews 2017–2020
Lichens	2010	2018	
Butterflies, moths	2016	2020	
Caddisflies	2010	2020	
Beetles	2016	2020	
Bugs (Hemiptera)	2016	2019	
Dragonflies, damselflies	2009	2020	mainly 2018–2020
Sawflies, bees, wasps, ants	2015	2020	
Flies (Diptera)	2015	2019	
Spiders	2016	2021	
Molluscs	2000	2020	
Fish	2016	2019	Environment Agency surveys
Amphibians, reptiles	2010	2019	
Birds	2015	2021	
Mammals	2016	2019	

At the end of 2019, survey work was largely complete, although data continued to be collected in order to fill in gaps where we had little information on certain groups. Nevertheless, a project of this nature is never complete as the flora and fauna of any area is always changing, sometimes swiftly. For example, **Little Egrets** first appeared in Britain in significant numbers only 30 years ago. Now they can be seen regularly in the NHC area and the related **Great White Egret** has also expanded its range, one being seen over Cambridge in October 2020. Who knows what changes there will be in the next 30 years? Indeed, one of the purposes of the NHC project was to collect data against which future changes can be measured. Within the next 30 years Cambridge is likely to grow in both population and extent. We hope there will still be plenty of flora and fauna for people to study and enjoy.

The study area

The NHC area is an 8 km square centred on the junction of Mill Road and Covent Garden (Figure 1.2). This is about 1 km east-south-east of the historic city centre and reflects the fact that the city has expanded more in the east than the west.

Chapter 3 provides an overview of the development of the city.

Land use maps and aerial photography show that about 43% of the area is built up. Using data from the CEH Land Cover Map 2007 (Morton *et al.* 2014) the 64 monads have been classified according to the percentage of urban land cover at that time (Figure 1.3). This shows that 23 monads, almost entirely peripheral, were primarily rural (less than 20% urban), while another 27 were 50% or more urban. Several of the formerly rural areas have subsequently been built on, notably near Trumpington in south Cambridge and the West Cambridge Site and Eddington in the west and north-west. Monads are given names and brief descriptions.

A more recent Land Cover Map (Morton *et al.* 2020) shows the extent of the built-up area, together with land cover in 2019 (Figure 1.4). Recent building was mainly on peripheral arable land, leaving significant areas of open space within the city, especially grassland along the banks of the river Cam and associated with the colleges. The research carried out into the flora and fauna of our area indicates that even the urban areas contain plenty of varied habitats.

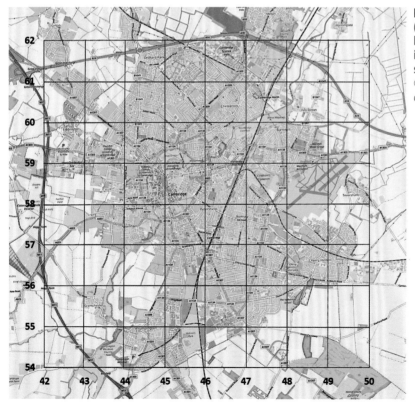

Figure 1.2 The NHC area (from OpenStreetMap). Grid lines are spaced at 1 km intervals, and the 64 1-km squares are called monads.
© (OpenStreetMap contributors; cartography licensed as CC BY-SA).

TL4261 Girton S, Girton Coll N, A14	TL4361 development on former NIAB land, A14	TL4461 Orchard Park, allotments, A14, lake	TL4561 King's Hdges Rec Grnd, A14, busway	TL4661 Science Park, busway	TL4761 Sewage wks, railway sidings, A14	TL4861 River Cam S of Baits Bite lock, A14	TL4961 Horningsea farmland
TL4260 Eddington N, Girton Coll S	TL4360 Girton SE & NIAB	TL4460 Arbury W, Histon Road	TL4560 Arbury E, N Cambridge Academy	TL4660 Chesterton N	TL4760 Ditton Meadows, Camb North rail	TL4860 Fen Ditton	TL4960 farmland E of Fen Ditton, A14
TL4259 Eddington S, Madingley Road P&R	TL4359 Ascension Burial Grnd, Chrchill Coll, Obsrvatries	TL4459 Castle Hill, Jesus Grn W	TL4559 Midsummer Common, Jesus Grn E	TL4659 Stourbridge Common W, Chesterton S	TL4759 Stourbridge Common E, Barnwell Lake	TL4859 City Cemetery	TL4959 Newmarket Road P&R
TL4258 West Cambridge Site, Coton footpath	TL4358 Adams Rd, Cavendish Laboratory	TL4458 City centre and Backs	TL4558 Christ's & Parker's Pieces, Midsummr C	TL4658 Petersfield, Mill Rd Cemetery	TL4758 Coldham's Common	TL4858 Airport main part	TL4958 Teversham, Airport E
TL4257 Laundry Farm	TL4357 Newnham W, Bolton's Pit	TL4457 Coe Fen, Paradise, Newnham E	TL4557 Botanic Gdn, Newtown, Downing Coll	TL4657 Rail station, Coleridge Rec Grnd, Clifton Rd	TL4757 Cherry Hinton Brook, lakes, Terr Army Pit	TL4857 Coldham's Lane, lakes	TL4957 Cherry Hinton NE
TL4256 between Grantchester & M11	TL4356 Grantchester Meadows	TL4456 Camb Lakes Golf Course, River Farm	TL4556 Empty Common, Brookl Ave, Accordia	TL4656 Homerton Coll, Cherry Hinton Rd W, allotments	TL4756 Cherry Hinton Rd E, St Bede's Sch	TL4856 Cherry Hinton Hall, Cherry Hinton W	TL4956 Cherry Hinton SE, Fulbourn Hospital
TL4255 Grantchester W, M11	TL4355 Grantchester main part with church & R Cam	TL4455 Trumpington Hall, Trumpington Road	TL4555 Clay Farm N, Long Road	TL4655 Addnbrke's, Biomed Campus N, Nightgl Pk W	TL4755 Nightingale Park E, Qu Edith's Way	TL4855 East & West Pits	TL4955 Peterhouse Technology Park, farmland
TL4254 Cantelupe Farm, M11, Bourn Brook	TL4354 Byron's Pool, Trumpington Meadows	TL4454 Trumpington village & church, P&R	TL4554 Clay Farm S, Hobson's Park	TL4654 Nine Wells, Biomedical Campus S	TL4754 Babraham Rd P&R	TL4854 Beechwood, Gogs Golf Course W	TL4954 Roman Rd, Gogs Golf Course E

Figure 1.3 Monads of the NHC area, with grid references and short descriptions. The monads are coloured according to the amount of urban and suburban land cover in the CEH Land Cover Map 2007: 0%–19% blue, 20%–49% green, 50%–100% orange.

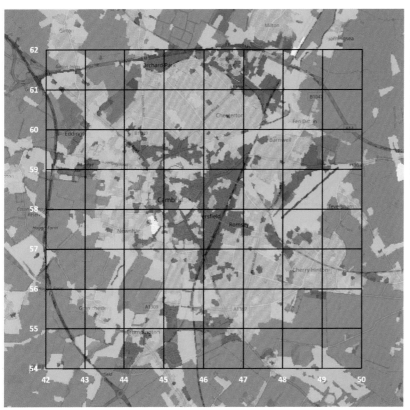

Figure 1.4. Land cover of the NHC area according to the CEH Land Cover map LCM2019, all of which is based on images dated 2019. Blackish is urban; grey is suburban; blue is freshwater; brown is arable; green is grass; red is woodland; yellow is fen or marsh (only Coe Fen and Milton Country Park in our area).

Habitats in the NHC area

A major factor in the biodiversity of Cambridge is the wide range of habitats found within the 64 sq km of the study area. It may seem surprising that an urban area has so many different habitats. But this results both from the physical geography, particularly the river and its many streams (see chapter 2) and from the development of the city, with housing ranging from dense Victorian terraces to large detached houses and the concentration of college buildings in large grounds (see chapter 3). This means that there are many niches for many different species. In addition, some species are opportunists and will spread into areas not typically associated with them if they consider the habitat is suitable. An example is the **Peregrine**, a bird of prey. The RSPB's website says 'The strongholds of the breeding birds in the UK are the uplands of the north and west and rocky seacoasts'. Yet this species breeds successfully at an urban site within the NHC area, having discovered that tall buildings are a satisfactory substitute for precipitous cliffs, as well as in a chalk quarry.

Water and wetland

The River Cam more or less bisects the study area from south-west to north-east, running through 12 of the 64 monads (almost a fifth). In addition to the main river, there are various tributaries: Bin Brook, Bourn Brook, Cherry Hinton Brook, Coldham's Brook, Hobson's Brook, and innumerable ditches. A map of the watercourses is in chapter 2.

While water quality may affect the suitability of the river and brooks as plant habitats, there are areas which support a wide range of aquatic and semi-aquatic plants as well as invertebrates and the range of fauna which feed on them. Surveys have shown that **Water Voles** are found in several of these streams. They probably persisted in some of them throughout the period when there were many **Mink** (which are now controlled, see chapter 16) on the river. **Otters** are now frequent on the Cam. Also associated with watercourses and ponds are bats, which feed on invertebrates.

Cherry Hinton Brook and Hobson's Brook are notable for being chalk streams, with their sources in springs at Giant's Grave in Cherry Hinton, and Nine Wells respectively. Chalk streams are important habitats for fish and species of invertebrates which need very clean water. Globally chalk streams are rare, with 85% of the world's chalk rivers being found in the United Kingdom, mainly in southern and eastern England.

Maps and aerial photos show several lakes, the largest of which are the three flooded quarries to the south-east of the railway line. Just inside the NHC area is the lake north of Orchard Park. Several of the new developments around Cambridge incorporate lakes and other water features, both for amenity and for flood alleviation, for example the University West Cambridge Site, Eddington, the Biomedical Campus and Trumpington Meadows. In addition to these are various ponds of assorted sizes in the college grounds as well as garden ponds. Many of these are important for ducks and are home to a variety of exotic waterfowl as well as to common species such as **Moorhen** and **Mallard**. Together these water bodies mean that Cambridge is remarkably good for Odonata. Our survey of damsel- and dragonflies has revealed that 24 species can be found in our area. The smaller water-bodies are also valuable habitat for amphibians.

The lakes in the south-east are important for migrating and wintering wildfowl. They are not currently open to the public; one being used by the Territorial Army and the remaining two being leased to Cherry Hinton and District Angling Club. As a result they are relatively undisturbed – however without access it is not certain what species they hold. There are recent records of **Water Rail** from the adjacent Cherry Hinton Brook. The other lakes in the NHC area are also important for waterfowl, with a thriving colony of about 30 breeding pairs of **Black-headed Gulls** at Hobson's Park.

There are no significant areas of marsh in our area but there are areas of wet grassland on several of the commons and at Skaters' Meadow and some areas flood in very wet seasons.

Water abstraction is a concern for many of the streams in Cambridge, while invasive species, particularly **Floating Pennywort** *Hydrocotyle ranunculoides* and **Himalayan Balsam** *Impatiens glandulifera* present management challenges and many opportunities for volunteer work parties. These issues are discussed further in chapter 16.

Woodlands

There are very few woods within the 64 sq km of the study area, and no ancient woodland. The Beechwoods on the southern fringe of the area were planted in the 1840s and extended in 1992 with the planting of a new wood on the western (town) side. This plantation, mainly of beech trees, is notable for a large population of **White Helleborine** *Cephalanthera damasonium*, an orchid also found elsewhere in the Cambridge area, and some unusual species of **Hawkweed** *Hieracium* spp. – almost all Hawkweeds are rare in Cambridgeshire.

Paradise Local Nature Reserve is important as an example of wet woodland, while Byron's Pool LNR and the Adams Road Bird Sanctuary are also well-wooded, but fairly small. There are many smaller areas of woodland, for example at Barnwell West LNR, in the grounds of Cherry Hinton Hall and on Coldham's Common. Many have developed from scrub, while some were planted. Hedgerows and scrub, particularly good habitat for invertebrates and birds, are found on most of the commons, along the streams and ditches, and in many gardens, public and private.

While there may only be small areas of woodland, there are plenty of trees in Cambridge. The City Council estimate tree canopy cover as 17% (ADAS 2013) and the most frequent trees across the city as a whole are **Ash** *Fraxinus excelsior*, followed by species of *Prunus* (cherries and plums). Among the various street trees are some less common species, such as **Ginkgo** *Ginkgo biloba* along Mill Road, and **Manna Ash** *Fraxinus ornus* trees on Perne Road.

The Cambridge University Botanic Garden has many fine specimen trees, as do many colleges. The size of college gardens means that trees can grow naturally to a great height and some of the colleges have magnificent specimen trees. Good examples are the **Chichester Elms** *Ulmus × hollandica* in Queens' College which are over 34 metres tall, and the sprawling **Oriental Plane** *Platanus orientalis* tree in Emmanuel College. The surveys of college gardens and a report on the wildlife of the Botanic Garden are in chapter 15.

The grounds of Cherry Hinton Hall contain some interesting species and a tree trail has been produced describing them. There is also a tree trail for the Accordia development on Brooklands Avenue.

Grasslands

Grasslands in the NHC area range from carefully tended formal lawns, especially in the colleges, through more lightly managed amenity grassland such as Parker's Piece and other public open spaces, to semi-natural grasslands on the various commons

alongside the river and in some of the local nature reserves, and remnants of good chalk grassland. An aerial photograph also shows many playing fields, which provide green open space but are botanically species-poor.

Because of the colleges there are large areas of unbuilt land in the heart of the city. The management of these is very diverse, with some areas being carefully-manicured lawns and well-tended flowerbeds and borders. Other colleges have land used for grazing while yet others favour gardening for wildlife. King's College converted part of their back lawn, stretching down to the river, into a wildflower meadow in 2018 and it is being surveyed for biodiversity. The summer 2020 survey by the college revealed 46 species of invertebrate including 13 true bugs and 13 pollinators. One of the objectives of the Backs Management Plan is to create a biodiverse corridor through the city and several colleges are planning wildflower meadows.

Our surveys of the college gardens highlight the importance of these large areas for wildlife (see chapter 15). At Corpus Christi for a number of years **Mallard** have been breeding in New Court and the Porters escort the ducklings across the road! The college land at Leckhampton, to the west of Grange Road, is extensive and a haven for wildlife. The 7.5 acres include vegetable gardens, and are managed without the use of metaldehyde slug control, herbicides or pesticides and include wildflower areas. There is a **Badger** sett (one of several within the city) and other mammals reported include **Muntjac**, **Foxes** and **Rabbits** (from adjacent fields). One of the biggest Badger setts in our area is in Newnham College.

The Botanic Garden is an interesting mixture of areas created to explain aspects of botany, such as the systematic beds, lawns, lakes, ponds and streams, and areas of less-managed land. As a result it supports a good range of fauna and wild flora, which is being monitored. Its staff organise regular moth trapping and periodic surveys. Chapter 15 outlines the fauna and fauna of the Botanic Garden in more detail.

Many of the new housing developments, at Eddington, Clay Farm and Trumpington Meadows, include open spaces for informal recreation. At several of the more recent developments efforts have been made to create a variety of habitats to encourage wildlife and promote sustainability.

Domestic gardens, because of their quantity, are a significant habitat in urban and suburban areas.

They vary greatly in size and suitability for wildlife and the NHC surveys demonstrate both how different one garden can be from another and how rich some are. Paul Rule's study of his own garden showed just how many species of invertebrate can be found in a suburban garden (see chapter 15). Not only were the number of species impressive but it attracted media interest. Paul's garden was filmed by Cambridge TV in November 2016 and one of our press releases resulted in a short mention of it on BBC1's Autumn Watch in 2020.

In urban areas, churchyards and cemeteries are also important patches of grassland and even if quite small, can be valuable for wildlife and often attractive (see chapter 15). Most are well-tended, while Little St Mary's has favoured wild flowers. One of the larger churchyards is that surrounding St Andrew's Church in Chesterton, which is also one of the more botanically interesting. Both churchyards and cemeteries often contain introduced plants, which have been planted on graves as memorials, and which may then spread.

The land alongside the River Cam includes several large areas of common land: Coe Fen and Sheep's Green, Jesus Green, Stourbridge Common and Ditton Meadows. These vary in character from grassland and avenues of trees on Jesus Green to the species-rich ditches which criss-cross Ditton Meadows. This reflects their history and management. Preston (2008) describes the pressures resulting in some of the riparian commons being levelled with domestic rubbish during the 19th century in order to reduce the problems caused by flooding. As a result Jesus Green is relatively level with few ditches, though it still floods occasionally, while Coe Fen and Sheep's Green still have meandering streams and ditches and flood periodically. Many of these riparian commons are grazed.

Unimproved grassland is scarce in our area but there are nevertheless some areas of relatively species-rich grassland. Barnwell East, for example, has supported five species of orchid and **Adder's-tongue Fern** *Ophioglossum vulgatum* though lack of grazing means scrub and invasive plants are problematic, despite volunteer management.

There are remnants of chalk grassland at the margins of the study area. Possibly the best are to be found in the south-east of the study area, where the Gog Magog Golf Course is a SSSI and the southern end of West Pit also contains a small area with rare chalk grassland species.

Arable land

The growth of Cambridge has mainly been at the expense of arable land (see chapter 3). The late 20th century saw major growth in the north and north-east, with the Arbury estates, Kings Hedges and Orchard Park converted to housing since the 1950s. Arable land now remaining in the NHC area is in the peripheral monads, and is increasingly being developed for housing, industry or academia. Major developments since 2010 are the University's West Cambridge Site and Eddington in the west and north-west, and Trumpington Meadows and Clay Farm in the south.

In the north and west of our area, farmland is mostly in rotations of winter arable crops such as winter wheat, winter barley, winter oilseed rape and winter beans, with very little over-wintered stubble for birds to feed on. In the south-east on the drier chalk hills, spring crops such as spring barley and spring linseed often follow winter stubble or bare fields which, until recently, attracted migrating **Dotterels** in late April.

As a consequence of rapid urban development, arable habitats, important for farmland breeding birds such as **Corn Bunting**, **Grey Partridge** and **Yellowhammer**, are becoming rare in our area. Nevertheless, two monads in the north-east of the project area are the best places locally to see **Roe Deer**.

Brownfield sites and semi-industrial areas

Railway sidings, sites of old buildings and the areas around factories and other industrial areas provide ideal habitat for ruderal species of plants which like disturbed ground. When urban land has been recently abandoned there is little competition from other plants and annual plants may find the conditions to their liking. Later, more competitive plants may get established. In Cambridge, where calcareous soils predominate, **Weld** *Reseda luteola*, **Brambles** *Rubus fruticosus* agg. and shrubs such as **Cotoneasters** *Cotoneaster* spp. and **Butterfly-bush** *Buddleja davidii* take over. This was very obvious at East Pit in the years following the landscaping work carried out by the Wildlife Trust when they turned the area into a nature reserve. East Pit is a disused quarry which provides steep cliffs for nesting birds and areas of bare Chalk. These attract specialist species, both mosses and invertebrates. Other former quarries are now overgrown, such as Lime Kiln Close, flooded or developed.

Built-up areas

While built-up areas may be expected to be poorer in flora and fauna, they do provide some distinctive habitats such as walls, paving and even drains. The fern flora includes species found in drains which provide the cool damp conditions suitable for **Hart's-tongue** *Asplenium scolopendrium* and other ferns.

In addition, construction work may introduce new substrates which provide different habitats. They may also introduce plant species from elsewhere. For example, some plants of sandy soils, more usually associated in eastern England with the Breckland, have been found in Cambridge and they have probably come in with builders' sand sourced from Suffolk.

Another benefit to wildlife of urban areas is the population of wildlife-loving people who feed the birds, put up bird boxes, create wildlife-friendly gardens and generally try to care for the wildlife sharing their gardens. Developers seeking planning permission to build houses are increasingly expected to create habitats in mitigation for land lost to wildlife, for example by using sustainable urban drainage schemes to manage rainwater and incorporating bird and bat boxes into their developments.

At the David Attenborough Building on the University's New Museums Site in central Cambridge, bat roosting spaces have been incorporated into the artworks created with waste slate from the roofing industry, there are green roofs, unfortunately not readily accessible to human beings, and even a couple of water features in the courtyards at third floor level. These were all deliberately included to create extra habitat for invertebrates, birds, bats and other flora and fauna.

The natural history of the NHC area depends on the overall physical environment and how this is changing. Here we give a simplified description of the underlying geology and its modification by glacial action and the river systems that cross through it. The chapter concludes with a discussion of the changing climate of the area.

Geology and landscape

Famous for its riverside location in the Cam Valley and for its nearby Chalk hills, Cambridge is also very much a fen edge city. The inland extent of fenland is not clearly defined as it varies depending on local conditions but a general guide is where the land currently rises to c.5 m above sea level (O.D.), shown on maps as the 5 m contour. In Cambridge, this includes the River Cam to just above Jesus Lock (Figure 2.1), although fenland conditions may well have extended further south at various times. Only small strips of land along the river, in the north-east, are under 5 m, whilst most of the NHC area lies in the wider Cam Valley between 10 and 20 m O.D. In

contrast, the Chalk slopes of the Gog Magog Hills to the south (rising to c.73 m in the NHC area), show the city's position at the foot of the degraded Chalk escarpment known, further to the south-west, as the Chilterns. These three elements of its location (the hills, the fenland and, very significantly, the river) reflect the city's underlying geology and the resulting topography.

The present landscape developed in five major stages. The first produced the Chalk and underlying Gault clay (together forming the bedrock) c.110 to c.90 million years ago (mya) during the Cretaceous Period. The second was a long period of time during which the land was above sea level, resulting in erosion of the bedrock and tectonic movements associated with the formation of the Alps tilting the land to the south-east. The third was the Anglian glaciation c.480,000 to c.425,000 years ago (ya) during the Pleistocene Epoch, when an ice sheet c.1 km thick travelled across the Cambridge area, causing erosion and depositing various glacial sediments. The fourth stage saw further erosion

Figure 2.1 Location of Cambridge on the fen edge: view looking north with Nine Wells LNR in centre foreground, at the base of the Chalk hills. The Isle of Ely, Peterborough and Norfolk can be seen in the distance. (© Cambridgeshire Geological Society [contains Image © Google, OS data © Crown copyright and database right 2017])

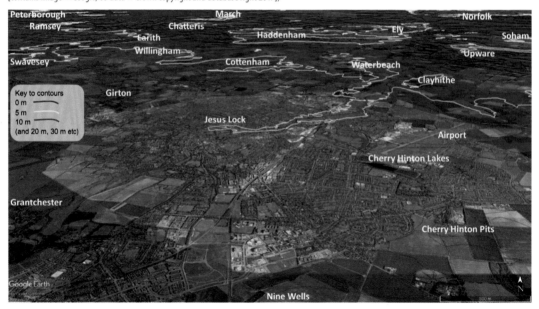

Figure 2.2 View north-east over the northern edge of the city, showing its position on the fen edge. The Cam flows past Ditton Meadows and Fen Ditton before heading towards the fenland around Waterbeach. (PD).

of the bedrock by thermokarst (freeze-thaw) processes and the creation of an evolving river system that deposited a complex series of sands and gravels under the cold climates of the later part of the Pleistocene Epoch, ending c.11,700 ya. More recently, during the Holocene Epoch, the fifth stage saw the accumulation of peat in river valleys around the fen edge at various times (Figure 2.2) followed by deposition of alluvium over the last c.2,000 years. The local fluvial Pleistocene and Holocene deposits are now classified as the Cam Valley Formation.

The Cretaceous bedrock (the 'solid' geology)

The Gault clay and the Chalk form the bedrock at the surface in Cambridge, both dating from the Cretaceous Period. The Gault clay dates from c.110 to c.100 mya and the Chalk from c.100 to c.90 mya. Each formed from sediments in relatively shallow seas (rather than deep oceans), although they are significantly different in their composition due to changing environmental conditions. Overall, the Gault clay has a much higher percentage of clay minerals and a lower percentage of calcium carbonate than the Chalk.

The bedrock in this region has been tilted slightly (1–2°) downwards to the south-east due to tectonic movements associated with the formation of the Alps. Erosion has, therefore, removed the Chalk and exposed the underlying Gault clay in the north-west whereas the Chalk is deeper in the south-east. Generally, the Gault clay is at the surface to the west of the river and the Chalk to the east,

although there are still small areas of Chalk to the west. To the east of the river, erosion has removed the Chalk in a few places and the Gault clay is now at the surface, generally forming lower land, such as at Christ's Pieces, Parker's Piece and the northern part of Coldham's Common, where it underlies Barnwell Lake. Near to the river, patches of much younger deposits, mostly river gravels and silts, cover the bedrock. The Gault clay is generally a dark, relatively stiff, calcareous mudstone that forms a lime-rich, loamy and clayey soil with impeded drainage. It has been used for brickmaking, producing (because of its high calcium carbonate content) the characteristic pale-coloured bricks, sometimes called 'Cambridge Whites', from which many Cambridge houses are made. Local, small-scale brickpits include the now-flooded Bolton's Pit.

Overlying the Gault clay, there is a complex series of Chalk horizons that form an escarpment with a north-west facing scarp (steeper) slope. Chalk is one of only a few rocks that consist almost entirely of the remains of plants (and, to a lesser extent, animals) and its formation occurred in specific conditions that have given it unique characteristics (see Box 2.1). Its high alkalinity has a major effect on the soils it develops and also on the nature of its groundwater, with this influence reaching a considerable distance downstream.

The oldest of the Chalk horizons, lying above the Gault clay, is the West Melbury Marly Chalk, which is found along much of the south-eastern fen edge. It has a high 'mud' (clay mineral) content

Box 2.1 Ammonites and algae: the formation of the Chalk

At the beginning of the Late Cretaceous (c.100 mya) global sea levels were the highest they have been during the last 600 million years and the climate was exceptionally warm, with a carbon dioxide-rich atmosphere and high sea temperatures. These conditions, together with a stable, shelf sea environment that lasted a significant amount of time (Hey & Perrin 1960), resulted in an abundance of marine algae called coccolithophores. The Chalk is a soft, porous limestone mostly composed of consolidated fragments of coccoliths, the very small plates made of calcium carbonate that formed their exoskeletons. Other fossils are also present including those of much larger animals such as the ammonite found at Cherry Hinton East Pit in 1961. It measures 700 mm across and is now on display at the Sedgwick Museum (Figure 2.3).

Figure 2.3 The large *Pachydiscus sp.* ammonite found at East Pit, Cherry Hinton in 1961. (© 2021 Sedgwick Museum of Earth Sciences, Reproduced with permission)

The Chalk in the NHC area formed over a period of c.10 million years, during which time the local environment underwent changes that have given the strata differing qualities, particularly in mineral content and therefore, permeability. With a deepening of the sea and corresponding increase in distance from land, there was a reduction in the amount of eroded material (such as clay minerals) in seabed deposits. The younger Chalk is, therefore, generally more 'pure' (with less clay) than the older. The older strata, with more clay content, form the Grey Chalk (previously, the Lower Chalk) whilst the younger comprise the White Chalk (previously, the Middle and Upper Chalk). In addition, cyclical changes in solar energy input and associated algal blooms resulted in deposition of irregular bands with varying ratios of clay and calcium carbonate (Catt 2010). One marl (clay) band is of particular interest as it is associated with deposits found in other parts of the world that represent anoxic conditions linked to a significant extinction event for marine species. This is the horizon known as the Plenus Marls (named after its fossil belemnites), underlying the Melbourn Rock. It can be seen, along with other differently coloured bands, in the cliffs at Cherry Hinton East Pit, designated as a Local Geological Site for its geodiversity (Figure 2.4).

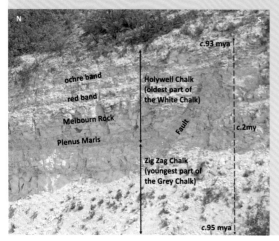

Figure 2.4 Cherry Hinton East Pit: geological succession shown in c.3 m of cliff face. The Plenus Marls and Melbourn Rock are notable, marking the change from the Grey Chalk below to the younger White Chalk above. A fault can be seen to the right in the photo: the land to the north has moved downward relative to that to the south (identification of horizons by Dr P. Friend). (CD).

making it less permeable than most of the Chalk and, therefore, subject to waterlogging. At the base of the Chalk, however, lies a shallow band of pebbly, greenish-grey, marly sand which is named the Cambridge Greensand as it only occurs locally (in Bedfordshire, Hertfordshire and Cambridgeshire). Less resistant than the Gault clay and Chalk, it would have been more easily eroded in the river valley along the edge of the Chalk escarpment.

Its high phosphate content brought considerable wealth to the area (see Box 2.2), accompanied by a significant impact on the landscape.

The West Melbury Marly Chalk forms most of the land under 20 m on the east side of the river, from Fen Ditton south to Trumpington. West of the river, it occurs around Grantchester and it forms the eastern end of the small ridge that extends north-west from Castle Hill. The West Melbury

Marly Chalk generally produces a shallow, lime-rich soil although both neutral and calcareous grassland occur on it, a reflection of the variation in its drainage properties and topography, the latter moderated significantly by phosphate diggings in many areas of the city. In the Cherry Hinton area, the West Melbury Marly Chalk was quarried for lime for use in cement making from the end of the 19th century. Four cement works were involved, the last one to close being the Norman Cement Works in 1984. Three of the disused pits were allowed to flood, the northernmost by 1925 and the other two in the late 1980s, becoming Cherry Hinton Lakes, now the largest amount of open water in the NHC area. The lakes are filled by groundwater only as they have no permanent water courses flowing into them, other than, possibly, a few artificial drains (McGill 2015).

The next youngest Chalk horizon, the Totternhoe Stone, is a hard band of sandy, grey rock more resistant to erosion than the softer West Melbury Marly Chalk below. As well as forming a distinctive break in slope around the Gog Magogs at *c*.15 m O.D., it creates a series of springs due to its location above the impermeable West Melbury Marly Chalk and its many fissures which give it a high water-conducting capacity. The waters of Giant's Grave at Cherry Hinton and those of Nine Wells LNR arise from springs in the Totternhoe Stone. The latter has been designated as a Local Geological Site for these geological features. Sometimes called Burwell Rock due to the

Box 2.2 Pterosaurs and the mining rush for 'coprolites'

The Cambridge Greensand formed *c*.99 mya. It is noted for its many pterosaur fossils, but is better known for its high content of calcium phosphate nodules, generally known as 'coprolites'. These formed from phosphatised organic remains of many types of animals, as shown by the fossils they contain, including mollusc shells, fish teeth and reptile bones (Lee *et al*. 2015) as well as true coprolites (fossilised 'dung'), particularly those of fish (Friend 2008). The remains were rolled around in a very shallow sea forming nodules deposited in a sandy environment. The phosphate, also found (but to a lesser extent) in the Gault clay below, was exploited for its value as fertilizer from the 19th century onwards and dug from many areas along the fen edge. The remains of the diggings formed an irregular surface, looking similar to 'ridge and furrow', that still influences the ecology of many areas including parts of Trumpington Meadows, Coldham's Common (Figure 2.5), the ridge west from Castle Hill and around Grantchester.

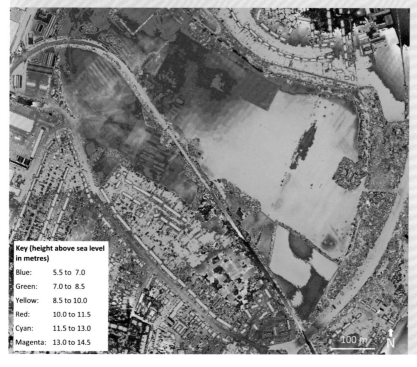

Figure 2.5 Lidar image showing 'ridge and furrow' pattern left by coprolite diggings, Coldham's Common. (Derived from Environment Agency 1m DSM Lidar under Open Government License v3.0 by Richard Cushing 2020)

Key (height above sea level in metres)

Blue:	5.5 to 7.0
Green:	7.0 to 8.5
Yellow:	8.5 to 10.0
Red:	10.0 to 11.5
Cyan:	11.5 to 13.0
Magenta:	13.0 to 14.5

100 m   N

Figure 2.6 Chalk 'clunch' incorporated into one of the walls of Peterhouse College. (CD).

significant quarries in that village, the Totternhoe Stone is well known for its use as a building stone in Cambridge as well as much further afield. It is generally called 'clunch' (Figure 2.6), although this term has sometimes been applied to any of the local Chalk used as 'stone'. It has been quarried in several places including East Pit (Figure 2.7) and West Pit at Cherry Hinton. The former was worked until as late as the 1980s. Above the Totternhoe Stone is

the Zig Zag Chalk, which forms the lower slopes of the Gog Magog Hills. Seen in the lower part of the cliffs at East Pit, it has a lower clay content than the West Melbury Marly Chalk and is, therefore, more permeable.

Forming the slightly steeper slopes above c.40 m O.D. is a white, shell-rich Chalk containing hard nodules, the Holywell Nodular Chalk (the oldest unit of the White Chalk). At its base is another band of hard Chalk, the Melbourn Rock, which forms the terrace-like feature on which Beechwoods LNR is situated (Figure 2.8). As with the Totternhoe Stone, it can give rise to springs such as those in Melbourn, the Cam Valley village after which it is named. The purest Chalk in the NHC area, and the youngest bedrock, is the New Pit Chalk, occurring above c.60 m O.D. It is a harder, blocky Chalk that covers the tops of the hills, including the area of Wandlebury and most of the Roman Road. As you climb the escarpment, small pieces of flint, crystalline nodules of the mineral quartz, start to occur in this younger Chalk.

The varying porosity of the Chalk beds influences the presence of plant species adapted to maximise water uptake and retention. Low clay-mineral content is reflected by the distribution of those species that tolerate limited nutrient levels. In general, deep, moist and moderately base-rich soils occur on the lower slopes grading into thin, dry and strongly base-rich soils higher up. The degree of slope, and associated vulnerability to erosion, also has an impact with soil only developing where the gradient is less than about 36°. Soils on the upper slopes of the Gog Magog Hills are mostly thin, immature calcareous soils but very steep slopes

Figure 2.7 View of Cherry Hinton East Pit showing its position near the base of the Chalk hills. Totternhoe Stone has been quarried from the base and Melbourn Rock can be seen on the cliff faces. (PD).

Figure 2.8 Beechwoods LNR lies on the terrace-like outcrop of the hard band of Chalk, the Melbourn Rock, on the slopes of the Gog Magog Hills. (CD).

where bare ground would occur, along with suitably adapted plants and invertebrates, are not present in this part of the escarpment. However, the cliff faces of some Chalk quarries such as Cherry Hinton West Pit, contain areas of almost bare rock where only 'raw soils' develop providing a similar environment.

During the *c*.90 million years since the youngest Chalk formed, the land in this area has risen above sea level due to uplift and no younger bedrock has formed (or, at least, survived). Weathering and erosion have changed the topography but ice sheets have had the greatest impact in the last *c*.2.6 million years since the start of the Quaternary Period. The effects of the last half a million years are significant in the landscape of today.

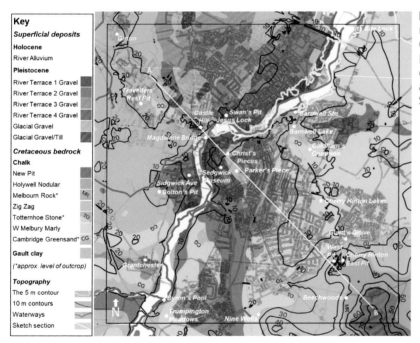

Figure 2.9 Geology map with contours. (© Cambridgeshire Geological Society [contains OS data © Crown copyright and database right 2017 and 2021, and British Geological Survey materials © UKRI 2021]).

Figure 2.10 Sketch section (8.8 km length, with vertical exaggeration) showing topography in relation to geology. Complexity and depth of Holocene and Pleistocene deposits and structural features (e.g. peat, buried channels) not shown. (© Cambridgeshire Geological Society [based on Google Earth elevation data © Google 2020 and British Geological Survey materials © UKRI 2018]).

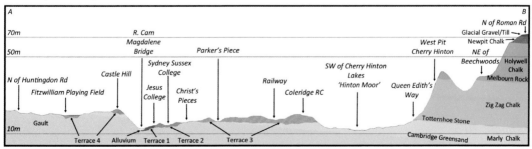

The Pleistocene ('Ice Age') 'superficial' geology

During the dynamic climate changes of the last *c*.480,000 years (the latter part of the Pleistocene) the Cambridge area has experienced a wide range of environments including glacial and tundra conditions as well as periods when steppe grassland, boreal forest and temperate woodland developed (Boreham 2002a). Erosion and deposition have changed the landscape, modifying the topography of the bedrock and providing a wider range of substrates and soils.

During the Anglian glaciation, ending *c*.425,000 ya, an ice sheet covered all of East Anglia, eroding the Chalk escarpment and depositing large amounts of glacial material. On top of the Gog Magog Hills, there are patches of Glacial Gravel, including larger 'cobbles' some of which (e.g. Millstone Grit from the Pennines) were carried considerable distances. Finer material, of more local origin, is also present, possibly dating from before and after the Anglian (Boreham 2004). These deposits have developed a variety of soils, with differing drainage and mineral properties depending on the proportion of clay, chalk or sand. This can be seen in the south-east of the NHC area (Figure 2.11) where the chalk soils near the Roman Road have incorporated this glacial material (Moulton soils), making them darker in colour. These 'hill-top' deposits have protected the underlying bedrock thus reducing its erosion: 'the hills of today are the valleys of the past' (Boreham 2004). The Anglian glaciation also saw the erosion of now-buried channels in the bedrock. Several have been found in the NHC area (Boreham 2002a) infilled with a variety of deposits that are often buried themselves and not visible at the surface.

The low ridge of Gault clay and Chalk running north-west from Castle Hill is partly covered by a large area of gravel that extends north, past Huntingdon Road towards Girton. Broadly referred to as the 'Observatory Gravels' (Worssam & Taylor 1969), this is a complex series of deposits that vary in character, origin and age. A buried channel with gravels dated to the Anglian glaciation (Boreham 2002a) underlies younger gravels, some of which are from the late Wolstonian stage, *c*.200,000 ya, and generally thought to be associated with a river that flowed north-west prior to the establishment of the current river system (Lee *et al.* 2015). These younger gravels contain Palaeolithic flint tools that are similar to others of late Wolstonian age found along the fenland margin. West & Gibbard (2017) suggested that they represent the southern limit of fenland ice during the Tottenhill glaciation. The gravels contain significant periglacial features, including ice-wedge formations that indicate permafrost conditions typical of cold stages of the Pleistocene. Gravels have been extracted from numerous pits on the ridge, with one of them, Travellers' Rest Pit at *c*.21–26 m O.D. just south of Huntingdon Road, being designated a geological SSSI due to its fossiliferous cold stage gravels (Marr 1920). These 'gravels' contain a variety of other material including sand and silt and generally develop free-draining (Moulton) soils where they overlie Chalk.

The course and strength of the river system continued to change in response to climatic cycles. Cold stages produced fast-flowing (high-energy) meltwater that caused erosion of the valley and deposition of large amounts of gravel along braided river channels. During the (much shorter) warmer, temperate stages, low-energy conditions resulted in the accumulation of finer material. The gravels of the Cam Valley consist mostly of rounded to angular flint, with some non-local

Figure 2.11 Near the top of the Gog Magog Hills showing the change in soil colour due to mixing of paler Chalk and darker glacial material. (CD).

Box 2.3 Hippos and horses: the River Terraces of the Cam

Four Terraces are currently mapped by the British Geological Survey, based, mostly, on their elevation within the river valley. However, each contains a complex collection of deposits and dating is often difficult due to older deposits sometimes becoming incorporated into newer material. Representing stages in the formation of the river valley, the Terraces provide an insight into past environments and the species present:

4th (Oldest) Found on Castle Hill, Huntingdon Road and along Newmarket Road. Fossils include **Woolly Mammoth, Red Deer** and **Roe Deer** (Worssam & Taylor 1969). Dating probably to *c.*300,000 to 200,000 ya, during a Wolstonian cold stage (Lee *et al.* 2015).

3rd Found at Trumpington and Arbury and covering large areas in the east of the city, including an important geological research site near Barnwell Abbey. At Grantchester Church, the gravels represent an ancient course of the Bourn Brook (Boreham & Leszczynska 2019). Remains include **Aurochs, Woolly Rhino, Woolly Mammoth, Straight-tusked Elephant, Spotted Hyena, Lion, Grey Wolf, Giant Deer** (once called Irish Elk), **Brown Bear** and **Hippopotamus.** These species represent a variety of environments and climates. Deposits include organic muds, sands, marl and flinty gravel, and show a wide range of dates (Lee *et al.* 2015) including the cold stage of the late Wolstonian *c.*180,000 ya, the Ipswichian interglacial *c.*120,000 ya and the early Devensian glaciation *c.*80,000 ya.

2nd Widely spread from the valley of the Bourn Brook and Trumpington to the city centre and Chesterton. A key research site was Sidgwick Avenue where a ***Bison priscus*** skull (Figure 2.12) was found that was radiocarbon dated to *c.*38,000 ya, the middle of the Devensian glaciation (Boreham *et al.* 2010).

10cm

Figure 2.12 Part of a bison skull, found at a site on Sidgwick Avenue and now on display in the Sedgwick Museum. © 2021 Sedgwick Museum of Earth Sciences. Reproduced with permission.

The current valley of Hobson's Brook held the main course of the river, incising down into the gravels of the older 3rd Terrace below (Boreham & Leszczynska 2019).

1st (Youngest) Found in narrow strips along the river. Near the site of Barnwell Station, remains from an arctic-alpine flora and fauna gave an uncalibrated radiocarbon date of *c.*19,500 ya (Godwin & Willis 1964), towards the end of the last glaciation, the Devensian. Species found (Marr & Gardner 1916) include **Reindeer, Woolly Rhino, Horse, Woolly Mammoth** (Figure 2.13), **Mountain Avens** *Dryas octopetala* and **Purple Saxifrage** *Saxifraga oppositifolia.*

Figure 2.13 Reconstruction of the Devensian landscape at Barnwell showing a pride of Lions following an attack on a juvenile Woolly Mammoth. (Permit Number CP20/085 British Geological Survey © UKRI 2020. All rights reserved.)

stone (glacial erratics). A series of River Terraces were formed when the river eroded the valley floor until it formed a new, lower floodplain, repeating this process several times. The oldest Terrace is, therefore, furthest away from the current river and at a higher level than the youngest. Four Terraces of the Cam are generally recognised although research continues to reveal that each consists of a complex collection of deposits (including loams, clays, silts and peats) that formed over varying periods of time as shown by the range of plant and animal remains found within them (Box 2.3). These river gravels have been quarried, for example at Swan's Pit on Milton Road, Chesterton (2nd Terrace), which was active into the 20th century. Overall, the gravel deposits have created higher and drier land used in the past for river crossings, settlements and agriculture. Free-draining, lime-rich loamy (Milton) soils are characteristic of the river gravels here but localised sandy soils can occur. An example of how the gravel deposits have significantly affected the ecology is in the area once called the 'Hill of Health', south of Huntingdon Road. Once popular with botanists for a wide range of conditions, it had a characteristic suite of plants of dry, gravelly soils, developed on deposits of the 4th Terrace as well as those of the 'Observatory Gravels' (Preston 2018).

During the last glaciation (the Devensian), ice-sheets did not reach the area but periglacial conditions continued as they had for most of the time since the Anglian glaciation, resulting in weathering of the frozen ground by freeze-thaw. The large 'hollow' (see the loop south in the 10 m contour in Figure 2.9), containing Coldham's Common in the north and what was once Hinton Moor in the south, was created by this 'thermokarst' erosion of the Chalk; a large lake, fed by Cherry Hinton Brook, formed here c.20,000 ya, behind the barrier created by the low ridge of River Terrace Gravels to the north (Boreham 1996).

The River Cam and the current landscape (the Holocene)

The current main course of the River Cam through Cambridge was probably established by c.14,000 ya, towards the end of the last glaciation, the Devensian (Gibbard et al. 2018). Although sea levels gradually decreased from the start of the Holocene c.11,700 ya, occasional marine incursions caused the back up of river water resulting in extensive freshwater marshes and the formation of

peat in the river valleys. At times, such as c.4,000 years ago, tidal conditions reached as far as the fen edge. The accumulation of peat occurred until c.2,000 ya in the lower part of the Cam Valley and it has been found under the alluvium at various places including Jesus Green (Boreham 2002a) and Byron's Pool (Boreham & Leszczynska 2019). Since c.2000 ya, a significant amount of alluvium (silt and mud) has been deposited on the floodplain and now underlies the river and its water meadows. It generally forms fertile loamy and clayey floodplain soils that produce good quality pasture, although groundwater gleys can form if waterlogging occurs.

Downstream from Cambridge, the Holocene alluvium has a modest gradient of c.0.4 m km^{-1} (Boreham 2002a). A similar gradient takes the river through the city centre, with a drop in elevation of only c.5 m over a distance of 12.5 km from where the river flows into the NHC area at Hauxton Junction in the south (c.10 m O.D.) to where it leaves at Baits Bite Lock in the north (c.5 m O.D.). In addition, abstraction from both the main river and its tributaries significantly reduces water flow. These two factors combine to produce a slow rate of flow, with a detrimental effect on water quality.

Four tributaries enter the Cam in the NHC area (Figure 2.14). The largest is the Bourn Brook, which drains the eastern slopes of the Western Plateau, the higher land to the west of the city. It arises in an area of Glacial Till, clay-rich material brought by ice during the Anglian glaciation, and cuts through sandstone bedrock (the Woburn Sands) near Bourn before flowing across Gault clay. It has a relatively steep gradient (Boreham 2002a) and joins the Cam at Byron's Pool.

Bin Brook, a clay stream, also drains the Western Plateau, with seasonal flows over mostly Gault clay but, in addition, also carries some water from chalk springs at Coton (Boreham 1991). It passes through the Backs and nearby college gardens to join the river south of Magdalene Bridge. It has cut a small valley with little in the way of a floodplain and, consequently, high flows during a heavy storm can cause significant flooding in Newnham where it also enters Full Brook to flow into the lake in Bolton's Pit.

The other two tributaries are classed as chalk streams due to their high content of calcium and carbonate ions obtained from the Chalk bedrock. Hobson's Brook, supplied by chalk springs to the south, runs along the valley that carried the main course of the Cam during the middle of the last

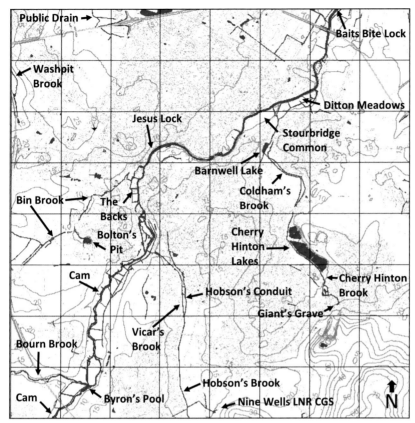

Public Drain →

Baits Bite Lock

← Washpit Brook

Ditton Meadows

Jesus Lock

Stourbridge Common

Barnwell Lake

Coldham's Brook

Bin Brook ← | The Backs

Bolton's Pit

Cherry Hinton Lakes

Cam

← Cherry Hinton Brook

Hobson's Conduit

Giant's Grave

Vicar's Brook

Bourn Brook

Cam | Byron's Pool

Hobson's Brook

Nine Wells LNR CGS

N

glaciation, the Devensian (Boreham & Leszczynska 2019). The brook has been diverted along an artificial channel called Hobson's Conduit that consequently gave its name to the brook. The stream that ran from Nine Wells was originally called Vicar's Brook and this name is still used for the branch that diverges from Hobson's Brook just north of Long Road to flow via Coe Fen, joining the river at the southern end of Sheep's Green (for a detailed map see Chapter 15).

Cherry Hinton Brook arises from the spring in the Totternhoe Stone at Giant's Grave (Figure 2.15)

Figure 2.15 The spring from the Totternhoe Stone at Giant's Grave, Cherry Hinton. (CD).

and flows through Cherry Hinton Park and past Cherry Hinton Lakes. Crossing Barnwell Road it becomes Coldham's Brook, which drains the northern part of this area of low-lying land. The flow in this section can be intermittent as the bank has become porous, with water escaping through to the main drains (Hawksley & Mungovan 2020). It is culverted under Newmarket Road, emerging into the Cam at the eastern end of Stourbridge Common.

In the north-west, Washpit Brook and the Public Drain both flow north, over Gault clay, their waters eventually emptying into the River Great Ouse.

The last few thousand years have brought significant, man-made changes to the courses, content and, subsequently, character of the waterways. The topography has also been modified by human use of the land, from the Neolithic ring ditches of burial mounds on the river terraces at Trumpington (Evans *et al.* 2018), to the numerous diggings for phosphates, clay and gravel, and the excavation of quarries for stone and lime. An impressive variety of building stones, brought to the area over, probably, thousands of years, have added to the 'geology'. Together, these relatively recent changes have caused habitat loss for many species. However, refuges have been created for some and there have even been gains for others: chalk grassland plants surviving in Chalk quarries, lichens living on limestone walls and gravestones, **Peregrines** using 'cliffs' formed by pits and tall buildings, and bats inhabiting the 'crevices' provided by many of the city's tiled roofs.

The geology of the area has played an integral role in the development of its landscape and ecology. A visit to the exhibits in the Sedgwick Museum of Earth Sciences reveals the fascinating, and continuing, interconnection between geological and biological history and the role of geology and landscape in the current local natural history.

The climate of Cambridge

According to Wikipedia the city has a maritime or oceanic climate, but equally it is at the edge of the driest region of England. Meteorologists regard the climate as the average of the weather of a site over periods of at least 30 years, and the period of the NHC survey needs to be viewed in this context.

Preston & Hill (2019) put the climate of Cambridgeshire into a wider British context. The climate of Cambridge will also be slightly different to that of the surrounding countryside due to the 'heat island' effect of the urban environment. The

effect is not as strong as that seen over London and is no more than 1°C in the mean. The micro-climate of individual sites plays a larger part in determining the suitable habitats for any species. Here we look in more detail at the climate of the city.

Several sites in the city have maintained weather records over the last 30 years. The longest running is the Cambridge University Botanic Garden (CUBG), which began taking formal records in 1889, though some earlier records exist. The main Meteorological Office station is the National Institute of Agricultural Botany (NIAB) site near Impington, just outside the NHC area, which has records since 1959. The British Antarctic Survey (BAS) run a testing and training weather station at their location in the west of Cambridge. More recently the CU Computer Laboratory have run a roof-top weather station at their West Cambridge site.

Cambridge has a generally equable climate, with mean winter temperatures around 5°C and mean summer temperatures around 18°C. Over the last 30 years no winter has experienced persistently sub-zero temperatures, though there have been shorter periods of frost, which may occur in most months apart from June to September. Mean minimum temperatures have a smaller range than mean maximum temperatures, largely reflecting the strong solar heating of summer. Only January and February have temperatures persistently below the growing temperature of grass.

The annual total rainfall of around 550 mm is only just a little wetter than that for a semi-arid region, which is defined as one receiving between 250 and 500 mm per year. Around 20% of the individual years over the last 60 years have had less than 500 mm of rainfall. Overall, the rainfall is relatively evenly distributed across the year, though it is least in the spring and most in the autumn. Over the last 30 years, monthly rainfall has usually been least in April, though over the full NIAB record it is February that has the least, belying its reputation of 'February fill dyke'. Very high monthly totals are often produced by single thunderstorm outbreaks. There are also periods of drought, which can occur at just about any time of year. The timing of these matters to wildlife, and what harms some species can benefit others.

Residents sometimes feel that Cambridge summers suffer from high humidity, though the evidence does not bear this out. The mean relative humidity in the BAS data (2010–2019) shows a variation from about 85% in winter to 70% in summer, which is not very different from that of our twinned city of Heidelberg. In Aberdeen it varies from about 90% in winter to 80% in summer. Most likely the feeling is a perception caused by the relatively slow adaptation of the human body to a short-lived period of change.

A few notable extreme events occurred during the main NHC recording period. On July 29, 2019 the CUBG and BAS recorded the highest daily maximum temperature yet recorded in the British Isles of 38.7°C. The end of February 2018 saw the 'Beast from the East'; however this was not a

Figure 2.16 Box plots showing (a) mean monthly rainfall at NIAB for the period 1990–2019, (b) the mean monthly temperature, (c) the mean maximum monthly temperature, (d) the mean minimum monthly temperature, (e) the extreme maximum temperature, (f) extreme minimum temperature at BAS for the period 2005–2020. The mean is shown by the solid line within the grey box, which marks the 25th and 75th percentiles. The whiskers show the 10th and 90th percentiles and the dots show outliers.

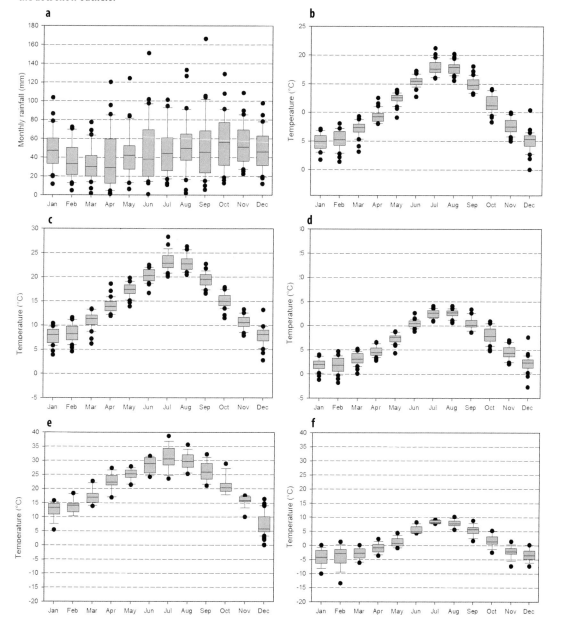

particularly cold event and did not produce the lowest recorded February or March temperatures. This event was followed by a notably dry June and July, with less than 1 mm of rainfall recorded in June.

Torrential rainfall producing flash floods has long been a feature of Cambridge weather. Bin Brook is notoriously prone to flooding and on occasion still rises to quite high levels despite attempts to control it. Future developments at Coton Countryside Reserve to provide new wetlands as a balancing system may finally alleviate this. Water levels in the River Cam are managed to largely prevent any significant overflow of the banks. On occasion the rainfall may win, so that Garret Hostel Lane was

30 cm deep in October 2001 and water levels were the same either side of Jesus Lock in May 1978.

We do not however live in a constant climate and ever-increasing amounts of greenhouse gases in the atmosphere are making significant changes. It is getting warmer. The signal in precipitation is less clear, but more intense rainfall is a likely consequence of the warmer temperatures. Although data series over periods of 30 years are sufficient to define climate, even longer periods are needed to say whether the climate is changing. For example many extreme rainfall events have return periods of over 100 years, although it is possible to make some statistical predictions based on shorter periods.

Table 2.1 Cambridge monthly weather data for the main recording period 2016–2019.

Mean maximum temperature (°C)

2016	8.7	8.8	10.0	12.4	17.7	19.7	23.2	23.9	21.8	15.0	9.6	9.4
2017	6.7	9.3	13.4	14.5	18.6	21.9	22.1	21.5	18.3	16.3	10.2	7.5
2018	8.5	5.9	8.7	14.2	19.1	22.0	26.7	23.1	19.9	15.8	11.4	9.8
2019	6.7	11.6	12.2	15.0	17.1	20.1	24.1	24.2	20.2	14.3	9.3	9.0

Mean minimum temperature (°C)

2016	2.6	1.9	1.9	3.6	7.8	11.4	13.1	12.7	12.6	7.2	2.4	2.4
2017	0.5	3.8	5.2	4.8	8.8	12.6	13.2	11.9	9.8	9.1	3.6	1.9
2018	2.4	-0.3	1.9	6.6	7.6	10.7	13.6	13.1	9.5	7.1	5.2	4.2
2019	1.0	1.7	4.5	2.8	6.6	10.8	13.4	12.7	10.2	6.9	3.6	3.0

Mean temperature (°C)

2016	5.6	5.4	6.0	8.0	12.8	15.6	18.2	18.3	17.2	11.1	6.0	5.9
2017	3.6	6.6	9.3	9.7	13.7	17.3	17.7	16.7	14.1	12.7	6.9	4.7
2018	5.5	2.8	5.3	10.4	13.4	16.4	20.2	18.1	14.7	11.5	8.3	7.0
2019	3.9	6.7	8.4	8.9	11.9	15.5	18.8	18.5	15.2	10.6	6.5	6.0

Monthly rainfall (mm)

2016	49.8	24.6	50.4	58.8	39.4	66.4	18.2	44.0	45.2	19.6	56.8	25.4
2017	48.0	43.4	29.8	12.8	64.8	59.0	94.8	64.2	58.6	22.4	36.6	70.8
2018	47.4	32.0	64.2	64.6	43.8	0.8	12.4	62.8	23.6	61.4	29.6	55.2
2019	22.1	26.6	37.4	10.8	41.4	79.2	43.4	35.8	62.4	78.0	57.0	75.4

Monthly sunshine hours

2016	49.9	109.6	33.9	177.9	208.5	132.7	206.0	215.6	131.3	111.6	98.9	58.4
2017	65.6	70.1	123.1	186.7	182.0	224.2	180.6	174.2	127.4	97.2	88.2	59.7
2018	73.3	114.6	80.1	128.9	252.2	221.7	270.2	185.4	184.4	147.7	92.5	68.2
2019	54.2	128.8	123.1	138.6	156.2	125.5	153.3	172.7	156.2	73.0	57.9	72.6

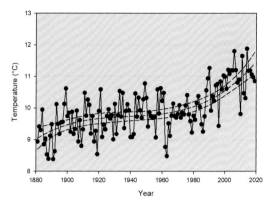

Figure 2.17 Mean annual temperature at CUBG. The central line is a polynomial regression to the points, with the dashed lines showing 95% confidence limits.

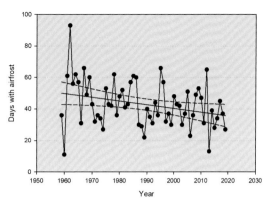

Figure 2.19 Number of air frosts each winter at NIAB. The solid line is a linear regression of the points, with the dashed lines showing 95% confidence limits.

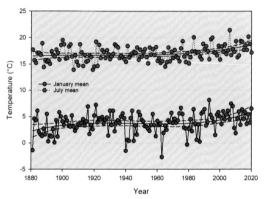

Figure 2.18 January and July mean temperatures at CUGB. The solid lines are a polynomial regression of the points, with the dashed lines showing 95% confidence limits.

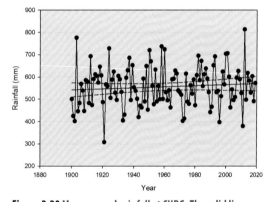

Figure 2.20 Mean annual rainfall at CUBG. The solid line is a linear regression of the points, with the dashed lines showing 95% confidence limits. A line parallel to the axis (i.e. no change) is also consistent with the data.

The changes to temperature are not simply a uniform increase. There are regional, centennial, decadal, seasonal and diurnal patterns to the changes. Figure 2.17 (updated from Carroll *et al.* 2008) shows the annual mean temperature at the Botanic Garden since 1880. There are clear inter-annual variations, but only a slow systematic increase until about 1980, when a more rapid increase began. With this rapidly warming climate the main NHC recording period will have seen many new species arrive that have only recently been able to survive. Few species are likely to have been lost as a direct consequence of climate change, but this may have compounded the difficulties for some. Temperature and moisture will affect the survival and growth rates of both predators and prey. Some plant species require winter chilling to ensure successful germination, whilst others will be

killed off by heavy frosts. What is a threat to some becomes an opportunity for others.

The mean curve hides some details. Datasets from the CUBG, NIAB and BAS have been amalgamated to provide a composite series of temperature, rainfall and sunshine. Mean summer and winter temperatures have risen at about the same rate on average. Mean July maxima have however risen more rapidly than mean July minima, whilst mean January minima have risen more rapidly than mean January maxima. There have been no very cold Januarys since 1987. Winters have become much milder, so that lying snow is now a rarity and there are fewer air frosts.

The mean monthly annual rainfall at the Botanic Garden since 1900 (Figure 2.20) shows a large inter-annual variation and perhaps some decadal variation. There is no significant long-term trend, although the regression does show a slight increase over the period. Occasional very dry years along with some very wet ones are noticeable in the record.

Meteorological Office measurements show that the UK has been getting sunnier over the last 100 years. The Cambridge record shown in Figure 2.21 is a composite of NIAB (1959–2010) and BAS (2010–2019) data, augmented by some measurements of sunshine from the CU Computer Laboratory during 2019 when the BAS instrument was not functioning. The short overlap suggested that the two series are similar; however the NIAB measurements used a conventional Campbell-Stokes sunshine card, whereas the BAS measurements use an electronic instrument. The observed trend demonstrates that Cambridge shares the sunnier trend of the UK, which is possibly caused by cleaner air.

Phenology was not part of the NHC studies, but has been reported elsewhere by Tim Sparks and others (e.g. 2008, 2013). One obvious indicator of change is lawn cutting – the last cut is coming later (often to the detriment of orchid rosettes) and the

first cut is coming earlier. Climate change really does affect us all.

Figure 2.21 Mean monthly sunshine hours for Cambridge. The solid line is a linear regression of the points, with the dashed lines showing 95% confidence limits.

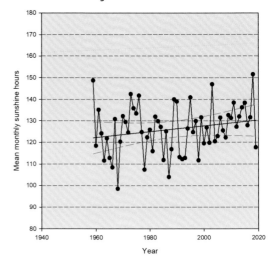

Cambridge is strikingly asymmetrical (Figure 1.2). Unlike London, it has not spread out in an even manner from the historic centre like a bacterial colony on an agar plate. The main axis through the city is a diagonal line running south-east to north-west. East of this line, large areas of housing have spread to meet the once separate villages of Cherry Hinton, Fen Ditton and Chesterton. These urban areas look uniform on the small-scale map but on the ground there are obvious differences between the Victorian terrace houses east of the railway station, the spacious pre-war estates further out along Perne Road and the more crowded post-war developments of Arbury in the north. To the west of the diagonal axis, large areas have been thinly populated until recently, although in some areas the developers are now rapidly making up for lost time. To cope with this asymmetry, the 8×8 km NHC area is itself offset, with its centre 1.2 km ESE of the town centre, Great St Mary's church and Market Hill. The explanation for the strange pattern of growth of the city lies deep in the history of its development.

Origins of the town

The origins of Cambridge as a town lie north of the River Cam, where the Roman settlement of Durolipons on Castle Hill was built on an existing Iron Age site. It was at the junction of two roads, one from Colchester which crossed the Cam at the bottom of the hill before heading towards Godmanchester, and the other, Akeman Street, which ran north-eastwards from Ermine Street to the Fens. Buildings spread out from this centre to create a town which Alison Taylor has described as a workaday place of modest significance (Bradley & Pevsner 2014). The area was to continue as a defensive and administrative centre, and it was here that Cambridge Castle was built in 1068, immediately after the Norman Conquest, and became the headquarters of the predatory Sheriff Picot (Figure 3.1).

By Picot's time, however, the northern settlement had been overtaken by the growth of a township established by the Saxons on the other, southern, side of the river. This was on raised ground in the Market Hill area, on the inside of the meander of the river. (To call this area a hill might seem to be a ludicrous exaggeration to modern readers, but in a low-lying town minor differences in height were very significant.) At some stage before the Conquest the outer limit of the town was defined, perhaps by a predecessor of the medieval King's Ditch, an artificial channel cut in an arc between the sites of the current Silver Street and Magdalene Bridges (Figure 3.2). By 875 the river

Figure 3.1 Cambridge Castle, drawn in about 1630 by an unknown artist. The trees lining the road have been recently pollarded on the left of the picture, whereas those further right show more regrowth. (Cambridge University Library MS Add. 2655. Reproduced by kind permission of the Syndics of Cambridge University Library).

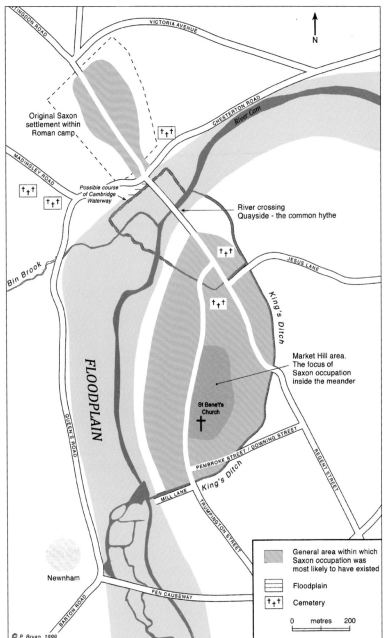

Figure 3.2 Saxon Cambridge, A.D. 800–1000, in relation to the modern road structure. The map shows the site of the original settlement to the north and the King's Ditch bordering the larger occupied area to the south. (Redrawn from Bryan 2008).

between the two settlements had been bridged and had given its name to the town. Thus placed, its inhabitants were well-placed to trade northwards along the navigable River Cam to the coast and also along an east-west route skirting the southern fringe of the Fens and linking East Anglia to the Midlands (to neither of which regions Cambridge truly belongs). Cambridge was sufficiently substantial to have been chosen as a county town when the shire counties were extended into former Mercian territory, probably in the early 10th century, and its wealth is demonstrated by the surviving Saxon tower of St Benet's church. By 1350 the town occupied the entire area between the river and the King's Ditch, and numerous lanes linked the hythes where goods were loaded and unloaded on the riverbank to the higher ground further east.

Development of the University

The scholars from Oxford who came to Cambridge in 1209 arrived in a thriving market town. By the end of the century the university which developed had been granted the land on the site of the current Senate House and Old Schools which still forms its formal administrative centre. It grew alongside, and probably in symbiotic relationship with, several substantial religious houses, many of them founded in the prosperous years of the 13th century. Some of these came to enclose significant green and garden spaces, such as those belonging to the Austin friars, on the land which is now the University's New Museums Site, and to the Franciscans, now the site of Sidney Sussex College. To the late medieval visitor the friaries might well have been more prominent than the colleges. The aggregation of students into colleges began slowly, with the

foundation of Peterhouse in 1284. This was on a site south of the King's Ditch, but most early colleges were based in the inhabited area north of the Ditch and immediately east of the river. The ability of the colleges to colonise this area perhaps suggests that the river-borne trade previously concentrated here was becoming less profitable. The foundation of King's College by Henry VI in 1441 was a pivotal moment, establishing a college on a lavish scale. The negotiations needed to acquire the land from a variety of owners took several years, but eventually it was possible to clear the site by sweeping away one parish church and numerous small streets and lanes. In the event much of this land was to remain open for centuries, as the only part of King Henry's design to be completed was the chapel, and that was finished almost 60 years after he had laid its foundation stone.

Figure 3.3 The central part of Richard Lyne's map of Cambridge, from the river on the west to the King's Ditch, pastures and arable fields to the east. The sites of the disused friaries of the White Friars (bottom left), Augustine Friars (bottom right) and Grey Friars (top right) are still labelled some 36 years after their suppression. (Cambridge University Library Digital Library. Reproduced by kind permission of the Syndics of Cambridge University Library).

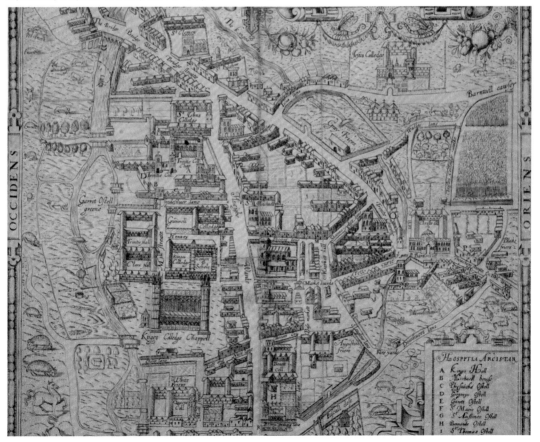

Figure 3.4 The same area of Cambridge shown in Figure 3.3, mapped by David Loggan in 1688 and reprinted *c.*1715. Despite the very different styles of the maps, the changes in the intervening century are clear, especially the formal development of the Backs west of the river but also the disappearance of the friaries and the loss of the King's Ditch for most of its length. (Cambridge University Library Digital Library. Reproduced by kind permission of the Syndics of Cambridge University Library).

Another large block of land further north was taken over in 1546 for Henry VIII's equally ambitious foundation, Trinity College. By then the federal structure of the University had become established, with a central (and until the 20th century often rather weak) University and numerous autonomous colleges. The colleges are independent foundations and vary greatly in age, size and wealth but all cherish their traditions and individual characteristics.

The first surviving pictorial map of Cambridge, by then an 'urbs celeberrima', was engraved by Richard Lyne in 1574 (Figure 3.3). Cows, sheep and horses graze pastures by the river, with pigs nearby in Swinecrofte; one man fishes with a rod from the riverbank and another with a net from a boat on the water; the map just extends to a cornfield at its eastern edge. No doubt these embellishments incorporate a degree of artistic licence, but this vivid and lively picture of a small town surrounded by agricultural land is not misleading – Hesse (2007) estimates that the medieval town occupied 3% of the area of the Cambridge parishes, with almost all the remainder being the agricultural hinterland. Lyne's map shows that the colleges now

dominated the area of former commercial land between the river and the High Street, a remarkable opening up of this formerly densely populated area and one which still gives the historic city centre much of its character. The map was drawn during a prolonged period of transition following the dissolution of the religious houses in 1538. Even before the Reformation two failing religious institutions had been converted to colleges, the nunnery of St Radegund (Jesus College, 1496) and the Hospital of St John (St John's College, 1516). By the end of the century three more colleges had taken over the sites of friaries, in some cases not before the friary buildings themselves had been demolished and their stone recycled.

David Loggan's map of Cambridge shows that by 1688 the riparian colleges had spread onto most of the land along the west bank of the river on which Lyne's angler was fishing (Figure 3.4). This area, from Newnham to the Bin Brook, was formerly a common pasture known as Long Green. King's College bought a large portion of this land from the Corporation and Lyne's map shows that it had enclosed one area by 1574; this is labelled 'Kynges College Back Sides' on John Hammond's

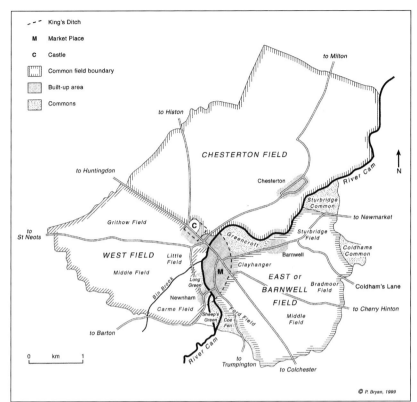

Figure 3.5 The common fields enclosing Cambridge before enclosure in the early 19th century. (Bryan 2008).

map of 1592. The different processes by which the three largest colleges, King's, Trinity and St John's, took over Long Green to create The Backs are set out by Hall & Ravensdale (1976); they provide an early example of the change from agricultural to amenity use which would be frequently replayed along the fringes of the town.

Cambridge's early natural history

One famous pair of engravings by Loggan depicts two of the three massive strip-cultivated open fields that all but encircled the town, West Field south of Huntingdon Road, Chesterton Field between Huntingdon Road and the River Cam and East or Barnwell Field south of the Cam (Figures 3.3, 3.5, 3.6). These three fields were subdivided into a few named large fields which were probably managed at different stages of the rotational cycle; they were worked from farms at the fringes of the Fields. This land was not available for building, and (unlike Long Green) very few individuals or institutions managed to encroach upon it. As the population of Cambridge grew but the area available for settlement remained more or less constant, the town became increasingly congested. This did

mean that the early botanists were able to find a wide range of habitats within an easy walk of the town. Many aquatic plants grew in the river and its associated ditches in the town. On the higher ground along Huntingdon Road there were gravel deposits, including the Hill of Health, with a characteristic flora which was rare elsewhere in the county. Madingley Wood, further west, was

Figure 3.6 Harvesting the West Fields. (Loggan 1690, scanned by P.H. Oswald).

Figure 3.7 Some of the plants lost when Hinton Moor was drained at the start of the 19th century. Top, left to right, Fen Orchid *Liparis loeselii*, recorded in 1660 'in the watery places' (FJR), Flea Sedge *Carex pulicaris* (PAS) and Marsh Helleborine *Epipactis palustris* (MG). Bottom, Oblong-leaved Sundew *Drosera intermedia*, also recorded 'about the watery places' (PAS).

much visited as the nearest site with a representative woodland flora (but one which is beyond the NHC area). Another popular walk was to Hinton Moor between Cambridge and Cherry Hinton, a calcareous wetland with some more acidic areas, and a fabulously species-rich area by modern standards (Figure 3.7), and beyond this to the chalk pits of Cherry Hinton. Further out (and on the fringe of our area) were the Gog Magog Hills, where the grassland on a thin chalk rendzina soil was exceptionally rich in rare species. All these areas were well known to John Ray in the 1650s and they constantly recur in the records of the older botanists.

Nineteenth century expansion eastwards

The barrier restricting the growth of the town was only lifted with the parliamentary enclosure of the town fields in the early 19th century. In both Cambridge and in Cambridgeshire as a whole, the landscape that had been familiar to all the earlier naturalists was transformed in the decades after enclosure. The town saw a wave of development which gradually carried it well beyond its former boundaries, allowing a reduction in the population density in the crowded centre (Figure 3.9). The

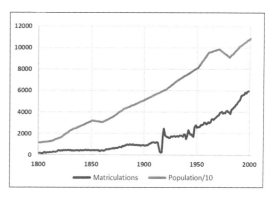

Figure 3.8 Matriculations, University of Cambridge, and total population of Cambridge, 1801–2001. Matriculation numbers are taken from Tanner (1917) and the supplements published subsequently at 5- or 10-year intervals, and population numbers from national census data. Between 1861 and 1921 and in 1981 the census took place during university vacations, hence the apparent dips in 1861 and 1981.

university also expanded greatly after a series of reforms in the mid-Victorian period, affecting university governance, college statutes, admissions, examinations and teaching staff. In one of the first of these changes, in 1850, the university

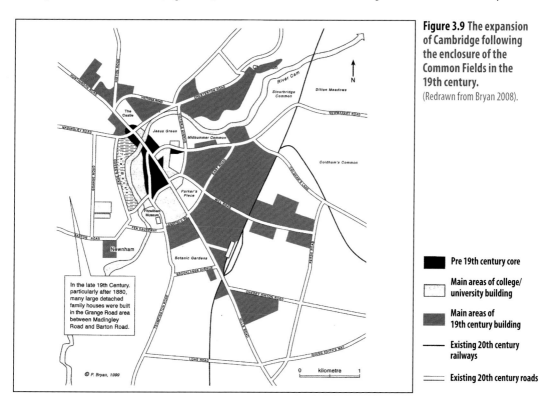

Figure 3.9 The expansion of Cambridge following the enclosure of the Common Fields in the 19th century.
(Redrawn from Bryan 2008).

In the late 19th Century, particularly after 1880, many large detached family houses were built in the Grange Road area between Madingley Road and Barton Road.

- ■ Pre 19th century core
- Main areas of college/university building
- ▨ Main areas of 19th century building
- —— Existing 20th century railways
- ══ Existing 20th century roads

© P. Bryan, 1999

0   kilometre   1

examinations were extended to cover subjects other than mathematics. This was one of the measures undertaken in the hope of pre-empting government action; other changes needed to be enforced by legislation on a university deeply resistant to change.

Before enclosure the land of the common fields had a range of different owners, including both institutions and private individuals. Some colleges had large acreages but their land was often scattered, reflecting long and varied histories of acquisition. On enclosure, any necessary roads

and footpaths were constructed and blocks of land allocated to the former owners. Those who had other rights (Lords of the Manor, tithe-owners) were also compensated with land, as were those with grazing rights (unless a common pasture was retained). In the process of enclosure, major land-owners were in a good position to safeguard their interests and the statutory allocation for tithe-owners was generous. The owners were then free to do what they liked with their new plots. In general, private individuals moved more rapidly to

Figure 3.10 Nineteenth and early 20th century housing in Cambridge. Top left: lowest quality houses, Gothic Street, Newtown, before demolition as slum-housing in 1950s; top right: terrace houses, Russell Place, Russell St, Newtown; middle left: superior terrace houses on Brookside, Newtown; middle right: 12 Grange Road, in the spacious development west of the river; bottom: inter-war council houses on Glebe Road, Cherry Hinton, 1935. (Cambridgeshire Collection, Cambridge Central Library).

build on the land close to the town; colleges built fewer, larger houses of higher quality and tended to oppose commercial development (and pubs). Thus the patterns of ownership at enclosure are sometimes still reflected in the character of the areas today. Almost all the cheap, high-density houses built before 1850 proved to be inadequate by 20th century standards and have been replaced, often in post-war slum clearance or urban renewal schemes, whereas many of the later Victorian houses are still happily occupied.

The necessary Act of Parliament for enclosure of the East Fields was passed in 1807 and the complex business of land allocation completed by 1811. Half the land was in private ownership, a consequence of the sale to the laity of the lands of Barnwell Priory at the Dissolution, and no institution had a large share. One of the main motivations for enclosure was agricultural improvement at a time of food shortages and high prices brought about by the Revolutionary and Napoleonic Wars (1793–1815). Hinton Moor appears to have been drained almost as soon as it became possible to do so. Building development in Cambridge started close to the town, in areas such as 'New Town' or Newtown (Figure 3.10). The land south of Newtown, allocated to Trinity Hall on enclosure, was bought by the University in 1831 for a new Botanic Garden, although work on the Garden could not begin until the tenant farmer's lease came to an end in 1844.

Further east, building between East Road and Newmarket Road followed so rapidly after enclosure that 'modern streets and property boundaries coincide precisely with most of the medieval furlong boundaries' (Hesse 2007). In 1845 the Eastern County Railway (ECR) arrived in Cambridge, with a station just east of the New Town, over a mile SE of the city centre. Other railway companies sought to build stations closer to the centre, and no less than 16 additional sites were suggested (Fellows 1948). Although some of these proposals attracted vociferous support, they were also strongly opposed. In the event those companies which succeeded in bringing new lines to Cambridge reached agreement with ECR to use the existing station. From 1870 onwards the main axis of development was along Mill Road to Romsey Town. By the time that Romsey Town was developed the medieval field boundaries had been lost, and the developments in this area show a regular grid of streets.

Chesterton Field was not enclosed until an Act of 1838 (with the land allocation in 1840), but its development followed a similar pattern to that of East Field. 'New Chesterton' started in the area immediately north of the Castle, between Chesterton Lane/Road and the new Victoria Road. These roads have larger houses along the main roads and more humble houses filling in the gaps, a pattern that had also characterised many of the areas developed from East Field. In 1912 the administrative arrangements were revised and Chesterton was added to the town of Cambridge.

From sewage and rubbish disposal to amenity use – the River Cam and its adjacent commons

The usual problems of disposing of waste in a crowded town were exacerbated in Cambridge by the flat nature of the site, which lacked rapidly running water in which waste could be deposited and carried away. Even in medieval times the King's Ditch became a notorious source of complaint (Roach 1959). Hobson's Conduit is now remembered for bringing fresh water to the town centre from chalk springs to the south in 1610, but its primary objective was to flush out the Ditch, which had become 'a great annoying' (Bushell 1938). The specific problem of the Ditch was solved as it was gradually covered over, but until the middle of the 19th century many tenements still relied on the visits of the scavengers' carts to collect the 'night soil'. One needs a strong stomach to read a report on the overcrowded conditions in the poorest parts of the town at this time (Ranger 1849). In Castle Street and Laxton's Yard, for example, 'several of the inhabitants have no privy, and deposit the soil in one corner of a small yard, covering it with ashes, from whence it is removed every five or six weeks … whilst, in some parts of the street, tubs are kept in the houses for receiving the soil: but the inhabitants complain bitterly of the effluvia'. Several of the occupants of River Lane solved the problem by throwing their excretions into the street.

Main sewers began to be built in Cambridge in 1823 and a network of sewers was established thereafter, but they all led into the Cam. However frequently the river was dredged, deposits rapidly developed in front of the sewage outfalls. Conditions were particularly noxious on Sundays when the mills were not working, the flow of the river was reduced as water built up in the mill ponds and the 'accumulation of filthy soil' became exposed to the sun. Cambridge, like any sensible mid-Victorian town with a sewage problem, sent for the architect of London's sewage system, Joseph Bazalgette. In a series of reports from 1866 onwards he proposed as a solution to the problem an intercepting sewer running along the east side of the river which would take the effluent to a sewage farm at Chesterton. Implementing his proposals was delayed for decades as the town and University argued about apportioning the costs, and a scheme was not approved until 1891 and completed by 1895. In April 1897 the Town Surveyor was able to report that the river was cleaner than he had ever known it. It cannot be a coincidence that punting as a recreational activity started on the river soon afterwards, in 1902–04 (Rivington 2012). The first interesting birds, **Curlew Sandpiper** and **Red-necked Phalarope**, were recorded at the sewage farm in 1896 but it was not until the 1920s that bird watchers came to appreciate its interest as a site for migrating species (Boyd 1957; Chapter 13 in this volume).

Those punting along the river in the early 20th century were still able to enjoy open vistas over the commons alongside the river. These had not only survived the threat from the railways but also an attempt in 1841 by the newly reformed Borough council to enclose them and make the higher ground available for building and market gardening, a plan which was shouted down at a tumultuous public meeting. Instead, there was a much more gradual transformation. Throughout the second half of the 19th century people were asked to dump their rubbish on the commons in the low-lying areas, as a way of raising the ground; in the early years they were even given 'from time to time the value of a pint of beer' to encourage them to do so. Eventually householders were discouraged from dumping the contents of their earth closets and other household refuse, although they remained a prime site for depositing 'road sweepings'. These were such a familiar feature that the young botanist I.H. Burkill (1893) was able to record 'with comparative ease' 99 plant species on ¾ acre of such deposits on Coe Fen. As a result of this landfill, and some more systematic drainage projects, there was a progressive loss of relic watercourses, ponds and ditches from the commons.

It was stock-keepers who had originally pressed for an improvement of the commons as grazing land, but as their condition improved there was an

increasing tension between their requirements and the pressure to use the commons as playgrounds. The isolated square Parker's Piece was set aside for recreation in 1877. Facilities for cyclists, runners, lady bathers and cricketers were provided on the riverside commons, and up to 300 ladies used the bathing facilities on hot summer days in 1900. The Cambridgeshire Volunteers acquired a rifle range on Coldham's Common in 1871, and a golf course was laid out there in 1876. It was said that balls sometimes had to be retrieved under rifle fire, and Bernard Darwin remembered the course as 'unspeakably muddy and unsavoury' and 'the worst course I have ever seen'; it was abandoned in 1902 (Morrison 2016). A new golf course was first marked out on the high ground of the Gog Magog Hills on the fringe of our area in 1898, on land owned by Gonville & Caius College. Photographs show that the course retained its character as open downland into the 1950s, despite some tree-planting in the 1930s to 'take away the bareness of the site'. However, there was much further tree planting between the late 1950s and 1999, as well as the spread of scrub. The tree-planting was supported by the Forestry Commission, the Countryside Commission and the County Council, and continued even after the site became an SSSI in 1986; it stopped only after English Nature intervened in 1999 (Morrison 2015).

Enclosure of the West Fields, and its sequel, 1802–1918

The West Fields lay in the parish of St Giles and were the first of the three town fields to be enclosed, with the Act passed in 1802 and the land allocated by 1805. However, in stark contrast to the East and Chesterton Fields, there was rather little development here following enclosure (Figure 3.11). The West Fields differed from the others in the predominance of collegiate owners. St John's had the largest share, much of it inherited from the medieval St John's Hospital. The plots of land along Queen's Road (the name came later) were all allocated to collegiate owners, reflecting the desire of the University (and doubtless the major colleges, which were much more influential than the University at the time) to safeguard and allow for the future enhancement of 'the present beauty of the walks' along the Backs (Guillebaud 2005, 2007).

At the north of the area, between Madingley and Huntingdon Roads, William Custance's large

Figure 3.11 The Backs in 2008, with the Wren Library, Trinity College in the distance. The 'beauty of the walks' remains 200 years after the enclosure of the adjacent West Fields (behind the photographer). (CDP).

house The Grove was built on the Hill of Health, destroying its botanical interest, and the University Observatory occupied another area of gravel deposits, far enough from the town to escape its smoky atmosphere. The bulk of the West Fields remained in agricultural use. This began to change in 1858, when St John's established its playing fields on the west side of Queen's Road, and other colleges rapidly followed suit. Five new colleges or analogous institutions had a more significant impact on the landscape, the first (Newnham College, 1875) intended for women and the others for men of particular Christian persuasions. Colleges began to issue building leases on plots in this area, to compensate for the decline in their agricultural income in the 1870s. They ensured that only large, detached houses, built of red brick with tiled roofs, were built along Grange Road and roads built to the west. In an era when shops customarily delivered orders to their middle-class customers, there was little need for shops; public houses were presumably unthinkable. By the First World War Grange Road had been extended northwards to Madingley Road and building had begun on Storey's Way (on private land, but along similar lines) to the north.

The contrast between the development of the West and East Fields is neatly summarised by the population for the two relevant parishes, given by Guillebaud (2006, 2007). In the western parish, St Giles, the population increased from 900 in 1801 to 3000 in 1911, whereas Barnwell, similar in size, increased from 250 in 1801 to 30,000 in 1911.

Steady expansion, 1918–1969

Cambridge continued to expand in the interwar years in the northern and eastern parts of the city, as in the preceding century. Large areas of housing were built along Milton Road, Newmarket Road and in particular along Cherry Hinton Road and Perne Roads. Council housing was now added to the private developments. The first substantial development also took place along Trumpington Road, south of the town. Fen Causeway was built in 1924–26, linking Trumpington Road to Newnham across Coe Fen and the River Cam, its construction made possible because of the availability of government grants to relieve unemployment. The objections of those concerned with 'the natural beauty of the fen' were brushed aside, but it was agreed not to attempt to drain the fen, 'a concession to people who took an interest in the growth of plants' (Preston & Sheail 2007). On the west side of the river, house building continued to be restricted to limited areas of spacious, high-quality houses in leafy streets. In response to the interwar expansion, the boundaries of the town were extended again in 1935, and Cherry Hinton and Trumpington, like Chesterton in 1912, were subsumed into the town.

Direct damage to Cambridge by bombing during the Second World War was very localised, with only 50 houses destroyed. In 1951, on the application of the Borough Council, Cambridge was granted the status of a city. Although its population was much too small to qualify under the usual criteria, it was recognised that its ancient university made it an exceptional case. On a visit to confer the honour, King George VI also attended a service of thanksgiving for the preservation of King's College Chapel from wartime destruction.

When house building started after the War, and the subsequent period of austerity, it continued in those areas where it had left off in 1938, although at higher density. Thus estates were built or expanded in the north (Arbury, Kings Hedges), in the east along Newmarket Road and in Cherry Hinton. Government planning came increasingly to influence development and the post-war policy was to restrict the growth of the town. As a result the surrounding villages expanded and a completely new settlement was established at Bar Hill, some 9 km north-west of the city. Whereas the typical worker before the War might have cycled to work, and returned home for lunch, the increasing tendency was to commute into

Cambridge by car. It was a change to which the town was in many ways ill-suited.

The University and colleges also expanded after 1918, although initially this was largely achieved by the infilling of existing sites. Notable exceptions were Clare College Memorial Court (1923) and, behind it, Giles Gilbert Scott's University Library building, opened in 1935. The latter not only had an immediate impact on the skyline but was significant in the longer term in marking the first significant presence of the University west of the river. This increased with the building of University departments on the Sidgwick site in the 1950s and seven new colleges were also built on this side of the river.

Another portent of future trends was the expansion of government institutes, often with close links to the University, and technology-related industrial firms. The institutes included the Plant Breeding Institute (1912), the National Institute of Agricultural Botany (1919), the Institute of Animal Physiology at Babraham (1948) and the Laboratory of Molecular Biology (1962). The Cambridge Scientific Instrument Company was the first of the technological companies. It was founded by Charles Darwin's youngest son Horace in 1881 and moved to a site on Chesterton Road in 1895 which provided room for expansion. It was followed by W.G. Pye (1897). Marshalls started as a small chauffeur-drive company in 1909, but it developed a serious interest in aviation in the 1920s and opened the current Cambridge Airport in 1937. Outside the town, agrochemical work was started at Hauxton in 1939 by Pest Control and taken over by Fisons in 1954.

Despite these developments, what can now be seen as a natural tendency of the city to expand was restricted in the 1950s and 1960s by planning policies aimed at discouraging industrial expansion as well as housing development. The refusal to allow IBM to establish its European research and development laboratories in the city was just one example of these restrictive policies (Segal Quince Wicksteed 1985). All this was to change in the following decades.

The 'Cambridge Phenomenon', 1970–2021

The last five decades have been a period of sustained growth and prosperity, and have led to a massive transformation in the appearance of many areas around the fringes of the town (Figure 3.12). During this time Cambridge, if not insulated, has at least been strongly buffered from the fluctuations in the national and international economy, and at times this has distinguished it rather sharply from other towns in Cambridgeshire and in East Anglia. There are many interrelated aspects to this growth.

The 'Cambridge Phenomenon' itself is the presence in and around the town of numerous 'high tech' businesses, particularly in the fields of electronics (including computing) and biotechnology (Figure 3.13). These characteristically employ relatively small numbers of highly educated and well-paid staff, concentrate on research and development rather than large-scale production, have many direct and indirect links to the University and have high rates of establishment and closure. These developments were triggered by a change in the University's attitude to collaboration with business in 1969 and the first Science Park was opened by Trinity College in 1973 (although two earlier projects along these lines had been stifled by planning restrictions). The ability of high-tech firms to attract and retain talented staff is tied to the general feeling that Cambridge is a desirable place to live in. It is certainly an expensive one, and this has resulted in its own problems for those employed in less well-paid sectors.

Cambridge University has also expanded, in line with the general increase in provision for higher education in Britain, which was accelerated by the Robbins Report in 1963, and its own success as a leading university. The focus of new development moved from the west side of the river to the West Cambridge Site, built on agricultural land further out in the former West Fields. Development started in the 1960s but has increased massively since 1999. Cambridge gained a second university in 1992 when Anglia Polytechnic University (now Anglia Ruskin) received university status; it had started as the Cambridge School of Art in 1858 and had undergone several earlier transformations. The city also has numerous language schools, sited here to cater for students attracted by Cambridge's reputation, and many schools and 'crammers'.

Of the numerous other institutions in Cambridge, the most visible expansion has been that of the Addenbrooke's Hospital complex. In 1950 Cambridge's hospitals employed just 48 'medical staff'. Addenbrooke's, founded on a site on Trumpington Street at the then south edge of the town in 1766, started to move to a new site at the current south edge of the town in 1962. It has been joined on the campus by other hospitals and research establishments such as the MRC

Figure 3.12 Cambridge in the early 21st century. (Redrawn and updated from Bryan 2008).

- Pre 19th century historic core
- Main areas of college/university buildings
- Existing 20th century roads
- Existing 20th century railways
- Main areas of the 19th century building
- Main areas of the 1900–1950
- Main areas of the 1950–2000
- Main areas of the 2000–2020
- Cambridge City Boundary

Figure 3.13 The grandest expression of the Cambridge Phenomenon is the glittering global headquarters of AstraZeneca. (MOH).

Laboratory of Molecular Biology and the global headquarters of AstraZeneca.

Housing developments have included much infilling within the city, plus larger developments in recent years on the outskirts of the existing built-up areas between Addenbrooke's and Trumpington (Clay Farm), on the west side of Trumpington (Trumpington Meadows) and south of Huntingdon Road in the north-west (Eddington). These more spacious developments have included areas of grassland and even lakes. The same is true of the larger areas of development outside the city, notably Cambourne, a large village 13 km west of Cambridge.

When I first came to Cambridge in 1973, from industrial Yorkshire, it struck me as a rather remote town, lying in scholarly isolation at the edge of the Fens. Its isolation had doubtless been increased by the closure of the railways to Bedford and Oxford in 1966 and to St Ives in 1970. Since then transport links have connected it much more effectively to the outside world. These included the M11 motorway to London, completed in 1980, the electrification of the two railway lines to London, the rail link to Stansted Airport, completed in 1991 at a time when the airport itself was expanding, and the upgrading of the A14 road which has re-established the town's historic position on the route from the east coast to the Midlands. Transport within the Cambridge area has not advanced so rapidly; indeed public transport has deteriorated although a 'guided bus' linking St Ives, Cambridge and Trumpington and running largely on former railway lines was opened in 2011. Transport problems are probably the main reason why Cambridge, despite its great expansion in other fields, has not become a major regional shopping centre.

In previous centuries the development of Cambridge has tended to take place in spurts, times of rapid growth followed periods of stability. If that pattern continues, we might expect that more stable times are over the horizon, but there is no sign as yet that they are coming into sight.

Sources

This chapter is based on the work of the many fine scholars who have investigated the development of Cambridge. The major source is *Cambridge: the shaping of the city* (Bryan 2008), together with *Cambridge: the hidden history* (Taylor 1999) and *A concise history of the University of Cambridge* (Leedham-Green 1996) for the archaeological and academic aspects respectively. I have also drawn on books and papers by Hesse (2007) on the East Fields, Hall & Ravensdale (1976) and Guillebaud (2005–2009) on the West Fields, Wright (1989) on Chesterton Fields, Bryan & Wise (2005) on the New Town, Roach (1959) on public health and Segal Quince Wicksteed (1985), Koepp (2002) and Kirk & Cotton (2016) on the 'Cambridge Phenomenon'. The account of the river and its riparian commons is taken from papers I wrote with John Sheail (Preston *et al.* 2003, Preston & Sheail 2007), the Hill of Health is dealt with by Preston (2018) and the two golf courses by Morrison (2015, 2016). For historic maps I have consulted the Cambridge Digital Library on the University Library website, Bendall (1998) and Lobel (1975).

Introduction

There is a long history of botanical recording in Cambridge, going back to the 16th century. The botanists, who were largely based in the city, and the urban botany of Cambridge, are admirably covered in the monumental *Flora of Cambridgeshire* by Alan Leslie (2019). Recording preferences have changed over the decades. Early botanists mostly made note of native species, often just describing a broad locality where the plants grew. There are some exceptions in Cambridge, particularly where an interesting plant grew in an unusual locality, for example **Tower Cress** *Pseudoturritis turrita* growing on the walls of Trinity and St John's Colleges in the eighteenth century. Recording alien species such as garden escapes has now become accepted practice, particularly with the availability of good identification guides, initially printed, but now often electronic.

Precision of recording has also improved. Prior to the introduction of gridded Ordnance Survey (OS) maps, plants were often recorded by parishes,

Figure 4.1 Jonathan Shanklin on a Cambridgeshire Flora Group visit to the Eddington site. (PJL).

which might cover tens of square kilometres. When the present OS grid system was introduced after the Second World War more precision was possible, though often the recorder could do no better than a few hundred metres. Today an average GPS unit will allow plants to be located within about ten metres and specialist units can record to even greater accuracy.

Another constraint is what is recorded. As an example it is usually acceptable to record a **Rowan** *Sorbus aucuparia* when it is a planted street tree, but not when it is planted in a domestic garden. In both cases it will produce fruits, which may get bird-sown in other locations and produce young saplings. Plants that seeded from a window box into a garden would not be recorded, but the same plant seeding onto a pavement would have its progeny counted. When recording in college gardens, churchyards and cemeteries it is often difficult to know where to draw the boundary.

In 2003 the Cambridge Natural History Society (CNHS) instituted intensive botanical recording in the city in an effort to resume field studies. The initial focus was to study phenology (the timing of occurrence of natural history events such as flowering) along the Coton Footpath between Adams Road and the M11. It turned out that this was in the 2 km square (tetrad) TL45J that had been selected by the Botanical Society of Britain & Ireland (BSBI) for its local change project (Braithwaite *et al.* 2006) and the focus switched to concentrate on botanical recording, but noting other taxa and events as well. In subsequent years other areas of the city were chosen, usually including significant 'wild' areas, and these visits are now established on a ten-year cycle with a view to monitoring long-term changes. Reports on the annual studies are published in *Nature in Cambridgeshire*.

Botanical records for the area used in this chapter cover the period from 2000, rather than just the main recording period for the NatHistCam project from 2010. The BSBI were running their Atlas 2020 project to record plants across Britain and Ireland between 2000 and 2019. An urban area takes far longer to record than open countryside, simply because of the greater amount of publicly accessible ground, and resources were not available to duplicate recording. Here we describe some interesting facets of the flora, covering species diversity, trees, rare plants and problem plants. Latin nomenclature follows Stace (2019).

Species diversity

In England the number of species ever seen per hectad (10-km square) has a median of around 950 with the most diverse square having 2871 species. For species seen since 2000 these values drop to 750 and 2412 respectively. The hectad that includes much of Cambridge (TL45) has 1947 species (1588 since 2000), ninth on the list but the highest outside the London area. This compares with the 2300 or so species recorded from the whole vice-county of Cambridgeshire (which excludes Huntingdonshire and Peterborough).

The much smaller 8×8 km area of the NatHistCam project has had some 1800 species recorded in it, with around 1630 seen since 2000. Species continue to be added, so recording is never finished. Some of the species are only casual – they appear for a year or two, but are then lost – so it is difficult to say how many species might be seen in any one year. As a lower estimate, the yearly totals

have a median of around 710 species, with a high of 874 in 2015.

The most intensively recorded tetrad (2-km square) in the vice-county is TL45J in West Cambridge, which has a wide variety of habitats, was a focus for BSBI and CNHS recording, and is where the author worked for the British Antarctic Survey. Between 2000 and 2019 an amazing 921 different species were recorded in the tetrad, and species are still being added.

Focussing in further to the monad (1-km square) level, the number of species ranges from 163 to 676, with a median of 295. The monad with the highest total, TL4458, encompasses the Backs and several Cambridge college gardens, and is boosted by the inclusion of some planted species. The four monads of tetrad TL45J (TL4258, TL4259, TL4358, TL4359) also do well, with all four now having over 500 species and TL4358 having over 600.

Even though the NHC area has been scoured to make sure that at least 150 plant species have been recorded in every monad, this does not make the survey complete. Not every street or open space has been walked at every time of year and the plant populations are always in a state of flux. In addition many areas are 'out of bounds' to casual visitors. There will therefore be much more to find and reports are always welcome. An estimate of completeness comes from recording during the Covid-19 lockdowns after the project closed. In just over sixteen months an average of over 30 new species per monad (an addition of roughly 10%) has been recorded.

The NHC project area is clearly one of high diversity and there are several factors leading to this. The urban area produces many garden escapes, which often appear on pavements or untended ground. A lot of new building takes place, which provides disturbed ground for ruderal species, and where areas to be grassed are often 'made good' by import of soil from elsewhere, along with the species that it contains. There is land still under arable cultivation, particularly farm land in the west of the area, and allotments within the city. Many of the Cambridge colleges retain unimproved areas of ground, which are increasingly being maintained for biodiversity. There are the commons, river and nature reserves which provide natural habitat. Finally there are the botanists – more reside in the city than elsewhere, making it inevitable that oddities are spotted that might be missed elsewhere.

Figure 4.2 Monad species counts 2000–2019. The outer fringe makes up a 10-km square, with 64 NatHistCam monads the centre. The squares outlined in green are visited by the CNHS during annual field studies. Monads are coloured according to their totals, with categories 93–197 grey, 204–295 blue, 305–388 pale biscuit 411–497 mid biscuit, 514–676 dark biscuit.

	41	42	43	44	45	46	47	48	49	50
62	158	220	128	180	137	226	459	278	197	118
61	184	291	191	328	225	363	368	216	180	224
60	136	272	261	251	260	241	549	255	163	131
59	204	497	555	344	305	514	459	365	256	250
58	336	522	601	676	469	388	563	191	246	113
57	339	189	261	618	481	295	366	370	256	147
56	169	207	252	355	340	274	274	484	245	161
55	189	230	448	263	411	355	253	422	170	106
54	153	216	421	313	347	329	268	288	265	93
53	117	122	375	193	162	163	144	217	484	196

The plants

With over 1600 species known from the NHC area it is not possible to discuss all of them. Some 70 common species are widespread in the area, with 28 of them found in every monad. Here we discuss some selected groups of plants.

Trees

There are only five named woods in the NHC area: the adjacent Eight Acre and Seven Acre Woods in the Trumpington Estate, the Old Mill Plantation by Byron's Pool, Pheasant Plantation in the north-west and the Beechwoods LNR in the south-east. The Trumpington woods are shown on the 1836 OS map, whilst the Beechwoods were planted in the 1840s. There are many more small copses, some planted and others naturally established. Trees are very good at planting themselves and much conservation work is carried out to remove unwanted trees that are damaging flower-rich grassland. It is surprising that so many groups want to plant trees, often of unsuitable species in unsuitable places, which then do not grow as well as self-sown seedlings. Trees grow quickly on abandoned land and the old Chesterton sidings are a good example, where after 30 years of neglect arose a forest of **Alder** *Alnus* spp., **Birch** mostly *Betula pendula* and **Sea-buckthorn** *Hippophae rhamnoides*, which is now being cut down for development. Sea-buckthorn is a Nationally Scarce plant in its native habitat, but is highly invasive where it is an alien.

There are some other alien trees that are invasive or better not to plant. **Tree-of-heaven** *Ailanthus altissima* is sometimes referred to as 'Tree-of-hell'

as it seeds very readily and there is soon a forest of suckers and saplings appearing. **False-acacia** *Robinia pseudoacacia* is often planted, but it is prone to suckering, and worse, its low sweeping young branches have large thorns that could easily injure passers-by. Conifers such as **Leyland Cypress** *Cupressus* × *leylandii* are frequently planted to provide a screen, but as with all trees, they grow and soon provide unwanted shade and obstruction. Climate change is probably helping the spread of **Walnut** *Juglans regia*, which is now present in all but 12 of the NatHistCam monads whereas it was recorded from only around 5 in 2000.

A City Council audit in 2013 suggested that there were around 240,000 trees in the city, however another survey five years later using different criteria suggested over 330,000. Of trees that were Council responsibility, some 14% were **Cherry** *Prunus* spp., 12% **Maples** and **Sycamores** *Acer* spp., 9% **Limes** *Tilia* spp., 8% **Birch** *Betula* spp., 8% **Rowans** and **Whitebeams** *Sorbus* spp. and 6% Ash *Fraxinus* spp. This contrasts with the botanical records, which have **Elder** *Sambucus nigra* and **Hawthorn** *Crataegus monogyna* as the most frequent woody species, present in all monads. The audit treated these as shrubs. Next are **Ash** *Fraxinus excelsior* and **Sycamore** *Acer pseudoplatanus*, present in 63 monads. The first Cherry family member on the botanical list is also a shrub, **Blackthorn** *Prunus spinosa*, recorded in all but 12 of the NHC monads.

The City Council has designated two 'Tree Trails' which show off some of the variety of city trees. One runs through Cherry Hinton Hall grounds and the other through the Accordia

Figure 4.3 Veteran Oak at the Eddington site. (JDS).

Figure 4.4 Veteran Black Poplar at Fen Ditton. (JDS).

Rediscovering Cambridge's Native Black Poplars

The **Native Black Poplar** *Populus nigra* subsp. *betulifolia* is described as Britain's rarest timber tree by Cambridgeshire and Peterborough Biological Records Centre (CPBRC 2006). It is a broad-crowned deciduous tree having down-curved branches with upturned tips and frequently a leaning, forked trunk with bosses on the bark. Unlike many other poplars it does not sucker but can regenerate from old stumps. Our native subspecies has sparsely hairy young leaves and stems which sets it apart from its European counterpart (subsp. *nigra*). The related fastigiate Lombardy Poplar which is strictly a very narrow variant 'Italica', is itself much less common than the wider hybrid 'Plantierensis'. Various hybrid poplars are much planted as garden specimens or where rapid growth is desired, such as wind breaks. Young examples of these can often be difficult to identify.

The Native Black Poplar's much changed natural habitat of river floodplains makes it doubtful whether it can now maintain a natural population. Being dioecious, it requires trees of both sexes to be in proximity, and for seed to fall on open ground which remains damp but not flooded.

The Cambridgeshire distribution of the tree was studied in detail by Graham Easy (1991), and his work has been updated by CPBRC, but the rapidly changing urban environment around Cambridge can make it difficult to trace the positions of recorded trees. As part of NatHistCam an effort was made to find trees in the survey area, which has a few old trees plus more recently planted specimens. Those wishing to examine labelled specimens can visit the Botanic Garden where male and female examples are present but none is fully mature.

Perhaps Cambridge's most striking examples of the tree are the two males visible over the River Cam at Fen Ditton (Figure 4.5). Two further males grow in the north of the Paradise LNR, with a young tree in the adjacent car park. A male tree which once flanked a drive to the University Field Laboratories, north Chesterton, now graces the front garden of a modern detached house. A fallen ancient tree adjacent to Hobson's Brook remains as a stump with regenerating shoots, while several trees known from around Cherry Hinton cement works are now represented by one example adjacent to Kathleen Elliott Way precariously close to a brownfield site. A male tree is known from the Adams Road reserve in west Cambridge, and there is a female tree hidden in the grounds of a hotel in Trumpington.

Some previously recorded trees could not be found again. There was no trace of one reported beside the Fen Causeway where, confusingly, several hybrid trees are present. Trees recorded around Newmarket Road Park and Ride were not found again.

Perhaps because of their rarity Native Black Poplars have been the subject of replanting. Such examples are present on Stourbridge Common where in the centre there is a male and a female, both small. Nearer the River Cam amongst young adult Limes and Willows there appear to be four well-grown female trees which have yet to develop all the characteristics of the subspecies. Although the City Council does an excellent job of mapping their trees, information shown in the Council's Cambridge Canopy Project website is often incomplete. The latter four trees are recorded only as '*Populus*' by the Project whereas the central pair are mapped in the company of five others, now lost. This emphasises the importance of constant vigilance in our recording of both old and newly planted examples of this rare tree species if it is to remain recognised as a feature of our landscape.

Figure 4.5 The two ancient Native Black Poplars at Fen Ditton viewed across the River Cam, January 2019. (RH)

Large Elms in Cambridge

Dutch Elm Disease (caused by the fungus *Ophiostoma novo-ulmi*) arrived in England in the 1960s and it spread during the following two decades to infect almost all of the **Elm** *Ulmus* species growing in Cambridge. Many parts of Cambridge had tall Elms that formed a significant feature of the city landscape. Parker's Piece had Elms around the edge, which were all felled in the 1970s. There were Elm trees behind the Catholic Church which carried a large rookery until they too were cut down. Along the Backs there were many tall Elms which formed the backdrop for the spectacular views of the colleges, before suffering the same fate. So it was with some surprise that we discovered during our discussions with the college head gardeners that some large Elm trees were still present and growing healthily.

The largest of these trees is to be found on the Queen's Road side of Queens' College in The Grove. This magnificent example is the tallest tree along the Backs and it has a second Elm tree beside it that is not quite as tall. The height has been measured to be 34.5 metres. This pair of trees are Chichester Elms, so named because they were first propagated at Chichester Hill near Danbury in Essex, which was the home of Gilbert White's brother Thomas White, a fellow of the Royal Society. The trees have recently been micropropagated and have produced several clones that have been distributed to other colleges in Cambridge. One of the clones was seen growing strongly in Queens' College and showing no signs of disease even though the Chichester Elm is known to be susceptible. Both of the larger trees have the disease to some degree but have not been killed by the infection. These trees and the suckers that continue to grow from the stumps of long felled giants along the Backs are the remnants of what was once a stately group of towering elms.

Leckhampton, which forms part of Corpus Christi College, also has a fine Elm tree, but the exact type and size has not been determined. It may be related to the Queens' Elms, but this is not yet confirmed. There are not many signs of disease on the tree.

The other pair of large Elm trees are on the Maids Causeway side of Midsummer Common. These trees are growing side by side on the edge of the Common and are also very tall (estimated at 24 metres). They flower each year and seem to be in good health. The leaves have been examined by Brian Eversham who has classified them as being **Huntingdon Elms** *Ulmus* × *vegeta*, based on morphological characteristics. It would be well worth having the genes sequenced for both the Leckhampton and Midsummer Common Elms to determine their genetic relationships.

It was particularly pleasing to find these last remaining remnants of the graceful trees that used to fill the Cambridge skyline. Perhaps some more specimens could be planted around the city, propagated from these trees that are at least partially resistant to Dutch Elm Disease.

Figure 4.6. Large Elms on Midsummer Common. (DJM).

development off Brooklands Avenue. The former has a smartphone app, whilst there is a printable map for the latter. Most of the trees on the trails have labels, which does make their identification much easier!

The city has a number of veteran trees, though the survey does not quantify how many. It does identify around 50 veteran trees, mostly Willows, on Coe Fen and Sheep's Green and a **Field Maple** *Acer campestre* in Cherry Hinton Recreation Ground. There are a few old **Black Poplar** *Populus nigra* subsp. *betulifolia*, notably two trees near Fen Ditton (see box on Black Poplar, page 43). The Eddington site in north-west Cambridge, a new development, has a veteran **Pedunculate Oak** *Quercus robur*, which has been made a feature of the new landscape. Most of the grand **Elms** *Ulmus* spp. have gone but a few remain (see box on Elms) and despite Dutch Elm Disease the tree is not threatened in England.

Having declared a biodiversity crisis, the City Council is keen to increase biodiversity and one way that they are doing this is by planting many different species of street trees. They note that variety also helps to minimise risks caused by plant pests and pathogens attacking particular tree species. The effects of one pest are particularly notable in the late summer. The larvae of the **Horse-chestnut Leaf-miner** moth *Cameraria ohridella* cause substantial browning and early loss of leaves, which occasionally leads to late flowering of the tree in autumn, but does not kill it. The tree is also affected by a bleeding canker or lesion caused by the bacterium *Pseudomonas syringae* pathovar *aesculi*, which may lead to its death. **Ash dieback** caused by the fungus *Hymenoscyphus fraxineus* is affecting many city **Ash** trees, but in some cases this may provide opportunity. For example West Pit has become heavily wooded over the last 70 years, but with trees dying, glades are appearing and chalk grassland species are beginning to reappear in some.

Because the diseases affecting them are causing a decline in their area of occupancy, **Wych Elm** *Ulmus glabra* is on the European Red List of Trees (Rivers *et al.* 2019) as Vulnerable and Ash is Near Threatened. The former has been retained in the county Register of Plants of Conservation Concern (RPCC) (Shanklin 2021) on account of this, although recent recording has shown that its distribution is stable.

Horse Chestnut is also listed as Vulnerable in Europe, but as this is not a native species in England, it cannot be included in the England Red Lists. At a more local level however, it is of cultural significance thanks to its 'candles' and conkers, so could be included in the county list if it is found to decline in future.

Halophytes

Halophytes are salt-loving plants. In Cambridgeshire they used to be largely confined to the tidal River Nene between Wisbech and Foul Anchor, but today are widespread along road verges thanks to winter road salting. The most frequently noticed are the white flowers of **Danish Scurvygrass** *Cochlearia danica*, which produce a white band along major road verges in the early spring. More subtle are the rosettes of **Buck's-horn Plantain** *Plantago coronopus* or the pale pink flowers of **Lesser Sea-spurrey** *Spergularia marina*. **Sea Barley** *Hordeum marinum* is an IUCN Vulnerable species in England in its normal coastal habitat, where in Cambridgeshire it was first recorded in 1831. Inland, however, it is expanding its population and there are four locations for it within the city. All are associated with the road network, an environment which only a few botanists are willing to explore. **Curved Hard-grass** *Parapholis incurva* is a very cryptic grass, often appearing as a short curved stem and so often overlooked. It was seen for the first time in the city area by Alan Leslie in 2020 near the Teversham roundabout on the Newmarket Road. Overall there are currently a dozen halophyte

Figure 4.7 Danish Scurvygrass in a crevice of paving on Long Road railway bridge. (MOH).

species within the survey area, but additions are likely to appear.

A fascinating account of the arrival of halophytes in Cambridgeshire is given by Coombe (1994). Apart from casual occurrences, the first to appear in Cambridge was **Reflexed Saltmarsh-grass** *Puccinellia distans*, found by Graham Easy at the Barton Road/M11 junction in 1987. In the 2020s, the richest site for halophytes is the north verge of Newmarket Road east of the P&R. The city centre and residential areas of the city are little salted and mostly unsuitable. Buck's-horn Plantain is now the commonest halophyte, known from 48 monads. It did not appear except as a casual until 1993. Unlike the other halophytes, it is widespread on roadsides across the city and is probably less dependent on salting.

Ferns

Cambridge is a hotspot for ferns in the county for several reasons. There is semi-natural habitat that suits them, there are plenty of old walls on which to grow, there are underground drains and leaking gutters, and many species are planted in gardens providing a local source of spores. As a result of this combination 28 fern species and hybrids are known from the city.

One of the oldest fern records from the city is of **Wall-rue** *Asplenium ruta-muraria* from Chesterton, where around 1650 John Pratt noted 'on ye churchyard wall. on ye side therof'. It is still in the churchyard, although now on the wall of the crypt steps. Another old record of Wall-rue is from the steps of the Senate House where it was seen by Charles Babington in 1860, and again is still present.

The banks of the deep, shaded drains that cross Cambridge provide ideal habitat on which ferns can grow. Two are particularly notable, the First Public Drain that crosses the Science Park, and the East Cambridge Main Drain that runs through Barnwell West LNR. The latter supports six species and a hybrid, with luxuriant growths of **Hart's-tongue** *Asplenium scolopendrium*.

Peering down drain covers can mark you as a bit of an eccentric or a council surveyor, but ferns are often lurking on the drain walls. Perhaps most frequent is Hart's-tongue, and **Male-fern** *Dryopteris filix-mas* is also common. Another sometimes found in this habitat is **Polypody** *Polypodium* sp., though it is not usually sufficiently well developed to determine to species. Sadly the spectacular fern growths along leaking gutters and down-pipes are

Figure 4.8 Adder's-tongue in Barnwell East LNR. (JDS).

becoming less frequent as they are being 'tidied', but a few remain.

Several species are most likely of garden origin and these include **Tender Brake** *Pteris tremula*, found on a wall in the Botanic Garden, although not grown there. Several other species of Brake have also been found, and **Bracken** *Pteridium aquilinum* is surprisingly frequent in the city. Species of **Holly-fern** *Cyrtomium* spp. appear from time to time, but rarely persist for very long.

There are several sites for **Adder's-tongue** *Ophioglossum vulgatum* in the city, mostly places where there is long-established grassland. It is a small fern, often only 5 cm high, so very easy to overlook. Barnwell East LNR and Trumpington Meadows are two places where it can be found. It was first reported in the county by John Ray (Ray 1660), who found it in 'Grantcester meadow abundantly', but it has not been seen there for over 150 years.

One fern that you might notice, though not as a fern, is the **Water Fern** *Azolla filiculoides*, which grows on the surface of some of the ditches, streams and rivers. In most years it is abundant in the central ditch across Coe Fen, and colours the surface brown, green and orange. It is an introduced species from tropical America and was first seen in the city in 1913 in Jesus Ditch.

Rare and notable species

An axiophyte is a plant species that is neither very common nor very rare and generally indicates a good habitat. There have been nearly 400 such species in the NHC area, though only around 350 are still extant. There are 370 species featured in the RPCC that have been found in the NHC area, with around 300 that are extant. Typical axiophytes are plants like **Kidney Vetch** *Anthyllis vulneraria* and **Wild Thyme** *Thymus drucei* found in Cherry Hinton chalk pits, or **Marsh Foxtail** *Alopecurus geniculatus* and **Skullcap** *Scutellaria galericulata* which are on Stourbridge Common.

The commons and nature reserves are good for the axiophytes, and also support several species that are rare in the county. The older city walls and drains support many species of fern, several of which are rare. Cambridge is something of a hotspot for orchids (see Chapter 5). Quite a few rare species are relatively shortly-persisting plants that have come in through imported soil, or have accidentally arrived with municipal planting. Some rare species are not associated with any particularly notable habitat. There are also interesting plants of historical interest.

Monk's-hood *Aconitum napellus* is named for the cowl-like upper 'petal', and is one of our poisonous plants. Symptoms can be provoked by simple contact with the leaves. It is grown in the Botanic Garden and St John's College Fellows' Garden and occasionally escapes, so that it has been seen in the drain at Garret Hostel Lane.

Marsh-mallow *Althaea officinalis* as its name suggests was traditionally a plant of fens and marshes in Fenland but it has not been seen in those haunts for many years. Recent records probably arise from seeding of garden plants and the one Cambridge record comes from near the Jesus Lock footbridge on Chesterton Road, where a plant appeared in scrub.

Birthwort *Aristolochia clematitis* has a long association with what is now Jesus College, but which was formerly a nunnery. Although first recorded here in the late 19th century it was probably planted by the nuns, who were not known for their celibacy. The plant was traditionally used as an abortifacient; however it is also toxic, causing kidney damage. It also grows on the Eddington site and there are specimens in the Botanic Garden.

Caucasian Beet *Beta trigyna* comes from south-eastern Europe and south-western Asia and has one location in the county, along the Babraham Road out of Cambridge. It was originally grown as a vegetable, both for the roots and the leaves which can be eaten raw or cooked. It was first cultivated in England in 1796. New plants came up from seed when the footpath along the road was widened to create a cycle path and it can be found from the roundabout to the lower slopes of the Gog Magog Hills.

Interrupted Brome *Bromus interruptus* is an endemic annual species of grass, often associated with **Sainfoin** *Onobrychis viciifolia*. It became extinct in the wild, but material was grown on in botanic gardens, first in Cambridge where it died out. Fortunately stock had been maintained in Edinburgh, which allowed seed to be returned to Cambridge where it was propagated and then re-introduced to a farm near Whittlesford. A visit to the Botanic Garden may reveal the plant in the experimental beds.

Figure 4.9 Birthwort on the Eddington site. (JDS).

Whorl-grass *Catabrosa aquatica* is a plant of stream and pond sides, which is in substantial decline across England. All three of the known extant Cambridgeshire locations are in the NHC area. Those along the central ditch of Coe Fen and on Coldham's Brook across Coldham's Common have been known since 1901 and 1934 respectively, whilst the third site, on Ditton Meadows, was only found in 2020. It may be present elsewhere, but cattle love it and it is quickly grazed down.

Spear-leaved Willowherb *Epilobium lanceolatum* is relatively common in the south-west and south-east of England. It is rare in Cambridgeshire, with the only recent records being in Cambridge, perhaps associated with the old railway sidings at Chesterton, where it might have come in by rail.

Field Eryngo *Eryngium campestre* is regarded as an alien species in Cambridgeshire, though it has a very scattered, possibly native distribution in the south of England. It only has one location in the county, the traffic island on Barton Road, where it was first seen in 2007. Although seen there the following year, it was not seen again until 2018.

Longleaf *Falcaria vulgaris* was known from West Pit LNR since 1949, where it was something of a pilgrimage plant for botanists. It is however known from scattered other locations, mostly across England, although it originates from Europe to western Asia. Access to see it is now difficult as it was lost from the LNR but persists along the margin of the adjacent school playing field.

Martin's Ramping-fumitory *Fumaria reuteri* has been known for nearly a decade from a location by the Guided Busway, with another site recently found nearby on the Cambridge Science Park. We do not know how it got here, as historically the plant was mostly found in southern England. Recent records concentrate around Hampshire, and there is a novel cluster north of Dundee. It is a plant listed in Schedule 8 of the Wildlife & Countryside Act 1981, so it is an offence to interfere with it in any way.

Purple Toothwort *Lathraea clandestina* was originally planted in the Botanic Garden, probably in the nineteenth century. It is a parasitic plant, usually on willow, and only the purple flowers are likely to be seen, in the spring. It was considered to have been introduced onto willow on Coe Fen before 1908 and has spread a little, now being found on Sheep's Green and along Hobson's Conduit. It is an alien species, coming from western Europe.

Figure 4.10 Purple Toothwort on Coe Fen. (JDS).

Figure 4.11 Field Gromwell at Magog Down. (JDS).

Arable weeds such as **Field Gromwell** *Buglossoides arvensis* are becoming very scarce with the widespread sterilisation of arable fields. There is only one recent record for it in our area, at Great Shelford in 2007, though it may be seen in the arable weeds plot at Wandlebury. It is occasionally grown as a crop for the oil which contains stearidonic acid, an omega-3 fatty acid.

Toothed Medick *Medicago polymorpha* is generally found on rough ground, with two of the three recent county records in Cambridge. It is one of three medicks that have coiled fruits that look a bit like tyres of quad bikes, but this one has spotless leaves without hairs.

Yellow Bartsia *Parentucellia viscosa* has only two records in the county, both from Cambridge. It is a hemiparasite and in both cases was probably introduced with sown meadow seeds.

Four-leaved Allseed *Polycarpon tetraphyllum* has recently become a widespread weed of Cambridge streets, coincidently often being found in streets where botanists live. It is a small, rare native of south-west England, growing in open sandy and waste ground near the sea. Here plants are often first noticed on brick-paving setts fixed in sand and this perhaps resembles the native habitat.

Tower Cress *Pseudoturritis turrita* has a long history in Cambridge, first recorded in 1722 when it grew on the garden walls of Trinity College. A few years later it was on the walls of St John's College. In the 20th century it was only known from the wall on the western side of the Fellows' Garden at St John's, and whilst this was cleaned in 2017, it has returned and it is also a persistent weed in the Master's Garden.

Orchard Park is the only location for **Hairy Buttercup** *Ranunculus sardous* in the city and there is only one other recent location for it in the county. It is an annual of damp coastal pastures and the Cambridgeshire plants are likely to have been introduced with grass-seed mix.

Field Woundwort *Stachys arvensis* is another of many rapidly declining arable weeds and all bar one of the recent records come from the Fens. The exception was from 2013 when it was found in disturbed ground of the Babraham Road Park & Ride.

Bog Stitchwort *Stellaria alsine* was first recorded in Cambridge in 1833 on 'Sheep's Green, opposite the osier island'. It was last seen here in 1950 and was thought to be lost. In 2017, 'The Rush', the stream that crosses Sheep's Green, was re-engineered to increase its flow and this changed the deposition around several meanders. The coronavirus lockdown in 2020 provided an excuse to make recording visits to local sites, and on one summer visit a decision to brave a bank of nettles revealed a patch of the plant on a shallow meander bend.

It is fairly certain that **Navelwort** *Umbilicus rupestris* was never a native species in Cambridgeshire as the damp rocky ledges on which it thrives in the west of England do not exist here. It was only ever an introduced plant and may be extinct in the city. It is reputed to have been grown

Figure 4.12 Four-leaved Allseed on a Cambridge street. (JDS).

Figure 4.13 Small flower of Bog Stitchwort on Sheep's Green. (JDS).

on the Zoology Department roof (though never actually seen there) but young plants were seen by the old steps to the Museum of Zoology for a couple of years around 2010.

Nobody would have expected to find **Tower Mustard** *Turritis glabra* in Cambridge as its only other site in the county was at Gamlingay, where it has not been seen since 1995. It was therefore something of a surprise to find the plant growing in a new shrubbery on the West Cambridge Site in 2015. Despite asking the gardeners not to weed it out, they did just that and it has not been seen since. Most likely it was introduced with bark chippings from the Brecks.

A group of rarer species favours the arable fields of west Cambridge. These are **Stinking Chamomile** *Anthemis cotula*, **Slender Tare** *Ervum gracile*, **Dwarf**

Spurge *Euphorbia exigua*, **Broad-leaved Spurge** *Euphorbia platyphyllos* and **Spreading Hedge-parsley** *Torilis arvensis*. Most survive on the field margins, but are more likely to be found when the crop is beans rather than wheat due to the differing spraying regimes. At one time a low growing member of the Umbellifer family, **Shepherd's-needle** *Scandix pecten-veneris*, which has long pointed seeds like coarse sewing needles, could have been added to these, but it has not been seen wild in the city since 2004. Another plant in this group is **Yellow Vetchling** *Lathyrus aphaca*, which used to grow along the Coton Footpath, but the only recent site for it is near Junction 12 of the M11.

A different group of rare plants can be found in the chalk pits of Cherry Hinton. They are **Great Pignut** *Bunium bulbocastanum*, **Moon Carrot** *Seseli libanotis*, **Wild Candytuft** *Iberis amara* and **Autumn Gentian** *Gentianella amarella*. Today they are found both in East Pit and at the very top of West Pit, one of the steepest climbs in Cambridge. The Great Pignut has been known from the area since 1839, but has steadily decreased and now only a few plants are seen each year. The Moon Carrot has a longer history at the site, being known there since at least the 18th century. It is quite similar in appearance to **Wild Carrot** *Daucus carota* but with practice the subtle differences can be discerned. One feature is the flowering time, with the Moon Carrot usually flowering later than Wild Carrot. Autumn Gentian has been known from Cherry Hinton since the 18th century, but today's plants are perhaps of more recent origin, arising when green hay was spread over a newly scraped chalk surface at the top of West Pit. They were first reported in 2001. The story of Wild Candytuft is very uncertain. The habitat for the plant has been suitable for a long time, but it was last seen in Cherry Hinton in 1879. Then suddenly from 2014 onwards it began to be found in new locations on the chalk of the county. These included West Pit, where it was found in 2016, and in East Pit the following year. Whilst this could possibly be a response to climate change, there is a suspicion that seeds have been sown in suitable locations.

There are several county rare species of normally wet habitats that seem to have been accidentally introduced with ornamental plantings in newly designed habitats. The two main areas where this has happened are Hobson's Park and the West Cambridge site. **Common Cottongrass** *Eriophorum*

Figure 4.14 Yellow Vetchling on the Coton Footpath in 2003. (JDS).

Figure 4.15 Autumn Gentian at West Pit. (JDS).

Figure 4.16 Common Cottongrass at Hobson's Park. (MOH).

Figure 4.17 Rough Clover, seen here at RSPB Lakenheath. (JDS).

angustifolium and **Cut-grass** *Leersia oryzoides* have been found at the former, with **Wood Club-rush** *Scirpus sylvaticus* and **Small Water-pepper** *Persicaria minor* at the latter. Other sites may appear as Cambridge development proceeds and it is worth keeping an eye out for the unusual or unexpected.

A final habitat for rare plants in the city is that created by import of material from elsewhere. The majority are specialists of sandy ground and have probably originated with the use of Breckland sand for ballast or 'making good' areas destined to be lawns for new housing. This group includes: **Silver Hair-grass** *Aira caryophyllea*, **Sand Sedge** *Carex arenaria*, **Mossy Stonecrop** *Crassula tillaea*, **Smooth Rupturewort** *Herniaria glabra*, **Smooth Cat's-ear** *Hypochaeris glabra*, **Bird's-foot** *Ornithopus perpusillus*, **Hoary Cinquefoil** *Potentilla argentea*, **Greater Chickweed** *Stellaria neglecta*, **Bird's-foot Clover** *Trifolium ornithopodioides*, **Rough Clover** *Trifolium scabrum* and **Spring Vetch** *Vicia lathyroides*. This type of ground is rare in Cambridgeshire, with large areas only in the west on the Greensands and in the east at the Breckland margin.

Problem plants

Cambridge is home to many species that can escape from gardens and become invaders in the wider countryside. Some of these are recent problems (see box on **Floating Pennywort** *Hydrocotyle ranunculoides*) whilst others such as **Himalayan Balsam** *Impatiens glandulifera* and **Japanese Knotweed** *Reynoutria japonica* have

long-standing notoriety. Somewhat surprisingly the latter does not do that well in Cambridgeshire, perhaps not liking the climate. **Butterfly-bush** *Buddleja davidii* is probably one of the more economically damaging species, readily seeding into crevices on walls, and then steadily weakening them as the plant grows.

There are signs that several species of garden origin are beginning to make their presence felt outside Cambridge. These are listed in the Register of Plants of Conservation Concern (RPCC) (Shanklin, updated annually) as posing a potential or actual threat to native species. The list is a relatively long one, so here are a few examples, showing the risk of growing ornamental plants in gardens or introducing them to road verges.

Italian Lords-and-Ladies *Arum italicum* starts to produce its leaves in winter and is therefore planted to provide some early foliage and an exotic spathe. There are two subspecies, one is a native, though normally from the south and south-west of England. The other, the one favoured by gardeners, comes from southern Europe. It was first recorded from a hedgerow just outside the city in 1984, with the first city record not coming until 2007, when it was found in Barnwell East LNR. It is spreading rapidly and is now in 20 of the 64 monads of the NHC area. Outside the city, its spread around Fenland is particularly noticeable.

Druce's Cranesbill *Geranium × oxonianum* is also often planted in gardens as an ornamental species, but quickly spreads to neighbouring gardens. It is of garden origin, being the hybrid between **French Crane's-bill** *G. endressii* (from the Pyrenees) and **Pencilled Crane's-bill** *G. versicolor* (from southern Italy and the Balkans). First recorded in the county in 1995 at the base of a wall on Midsummer Common, it is now found in 11 of the city monads and is starting to crop up in scattered locations across the county. It seems that it has been rather slow to get going here, as its distribution is much more extensive around London.

Stinking Iris *Iris foetidissima* is widely planted in gardens for its flowers and seed heads. The name comes from the smell of the bruised leaves, which some liken to roast beef. First noted in Teversham by Ray in 1660, it is a native species but thanks to gardeners and birds is now found in 55 of the city monads. It is a plant that is nationally spreading northwards, presumably in response to climate change.

Spotted Medick *Medicago arabica* was first recorded by Ray in 1660 'In the field on the right hand of the lane which leads from Barnwell to the Pesthouses, or the Common called Coldhams, on the green by the lanes side.' It is quite an attractive plant with small dark-spotted leaves and golden yellow flowers. The spotting of the leaves is quite variable with plants in some areas showing only weak brown spotting and in other places the spots are a prominent black. It is possible that different varieties from the continent have been included in wild-flower mixes, but it is clear that in recent decades there has been a substantial increase in its distribution so that it is now in 60 city monads. It had seemed to be a relatively harmless plant, but it is increasingly being found to dominate patches in meadows.

Green Alkanet *Pentaglottis sempervirens* lives up to its name as the leaves keep growing through the winter. It has a long tap-root and once established in a garden it is difficult to eradicate, much to the regret of those gardeners who introduce it. It seeds readily and quickly establishes a dense thatch if allowed to, thus obliterating all other plants. It was first recorded in the county in the grounds of Emmanuel College in 1730, but is a native of south-west Europe. It is now nearly ubiquitous in the city, having been recorded from 56 of the 64 monads. In the wider countryside it is steadily colonising new locations, particularly in Fenland.

White Comfrey *Symphytum orientale* has been widely planted in gardens and was first recorded as being established in the wild in a hedgebank near the Observatory in 1849. It originally came

Floating Pennywort

Floating Pennywort *Hydrocotyle ranunculoides* is a most undesirable addition to the flora of Cambridge. First reported in the county in 2003, and in the NHC area in 2004, it was widespread by 2007, becoming dominant in some slow-moving ditches and also colonising parts of the Cam. By 2016 huge, floating rafts of this invasive non-native species from the Americas, which has no natural enemies in Britain, engulfed the river at Grantchester Meadows. It impacted on local recreational activities, particularly angling, canoeing and punting. It was sparsely distributed or absent in central Cambridge where smooth bank revetments prevent establishment. Studies have shown tetraploidy (2n=96) within some British clones with possible hybrid vigour. It is, unfortunately, frost tolerant and survives during ice cover. Rhizomatous stems are capable of growing into soft bank sides from which new plants can emerge. Plants can regenerate from single nodes on stem fragments and these are easily carried downstream. Seed production and germination can occur under British conditions, but we have no evidence that this has any significance in the establishment of new colonies in Cambridge. It is a nutrient scavenger but also thrives in eutrophic conditions, achieving high linear growth rates up to 23 cm/day.

For an account of its removal from the upper River Cam, see Chapter 16.

Figure 4.18 Floating Pennywort. (MFPF).

from western Russia and the Caucasus region. It is now present in 36 of the city monads.The county distribution is concentrated around towns and villages, but it is beginning to crop up in the wider countryside.

Looking to the future, there are other plants on the radar, which whilst not yet widely 'out there', could become more widespread or create problems. **Mexican Fleabane** *Erigeron karvinskianus*, originally from Mexico, is an attractive flower largely confined to towns and villages, preferring the walls and pavements of the built environment. There are only a few natural habitats in the county which might be to its liking. For this reason it is not listed in the RPCC, although from its first city record in the Botanic Garden in 1987 it has spread to 17 monads.

Atlas Poppy *Papaver atlanticum* is an orange flowered poppy, which the RHS Encyclopedia of plants & flowers (Brickell 2006) says 'Is good for a rock garden'. It doesn't stay there however, and is frequently found on verges and other grasslands. Its original home was the high Atlas Mountains of Morocco. In Cambridge it was first noted from a wall in Malting Lane in 1940 and is now in 24 city monads. One site where it is becoming a problem is the churchyard of St Andrew's Chesterton, which is a City Wildlife Site, though it has been known from here since at least 1991. Elsewhere it is widely scattered across the county, mostly confined to urban locations.

With little control on the import of garden plants there will be new species that become pests. In order to get something of an early warning, the BSBI and Coventry University are running a citizen science project called Plant Alert. This asks gardeners to report plants which are becoming invasive in their gardens. Do let them know if you have something new to report.

Stoneworts

Stoneworts Characeae are complex green algae that look a little like **Horsetails** *Equisetum* and are traditionally included with vascular plant recording. They are usually found in ponds with good water quality, and occasionally in slow flowing rivers. When fresh they have a sulphurous smell, and are often encrusted with calcium carbonate. Seven species have been recorded in the NHC area since 2000, compared to 16 for the county as a whole. By far the most frequent is **Common Stonewort** *Chara vulgaris* which can appear in virtually any pond that is suitable for it. Several rare species used to occur in Coldham's Brook near the football ground, but this chalk stream has had its flow interrupted and they have not been seen for some time. **Pointed Stonewort** *Nitella mucronata* was an unexpected find in slack water of the River Cam, showing that often it is a case of looking carefully rather than quickly walking past.

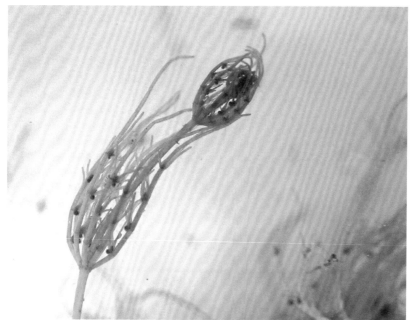

Figure 4.19 Common Stonewort at Adams Bird Sanctuary. (JDS).

We turn now from the flora to the distributions of plants and their habitats, comparing their frequency in the NHC area with that in the wider countryside. We report on orchids and Mistletoe, and on three important urban habitats, domestic gardens, roadsides and walls.

Cambridge plants in a Cambridgeshire context

In the following comparison, we consider a narrower range of taxa than in chapter 4, where 1630 taxa were noted from the NHC area since 2000. The criteria for selecting them are explained fully in an account of the distribution of plants in the vice-county of Cambridgeshire (Hill *et al.* 2020). In that paper we analysed 1245 taxa of which 1016 have been recorded since 2000 in the NHC area. The 1016 taxa comprise 983 species, 2 subspecies, 25 hybrids and 6 aggregates. In the following account they are all loosely termed

'species'. Some of them are trees that have been planted in public spaces, such as **Atlantic Cedar** *Cedrus atlantica*, **Leyland Cypress** *Cupressus × leylandii* and **Hybrid Balsam-poplar** *Populus × hastata*, and are therefore not wild. These are a small minority and their presence hardly affects the conclusions.

Of the 1630 taxa in the NHC area, 614 were excluded from our comparison with Cambridgeshire. Of these, only 184 were found in more than one Cambridge monad. The excluded taxa are neophytes, cultivars, hybrids and also some planted trees. None of them is a British native species. Some of them are interesting and are listed as rare and notable plants in Chapter 4. Four of the more frequent ones can be considered as an example here. **Tulip Tree** *Liriodendron tulipifera* is always planted. **Mock-orange** *Philadelphus* spp. is mostly planted but one sapling may have been self-sown. **Chinese Pokeweed** *Phytolacca polyandra*

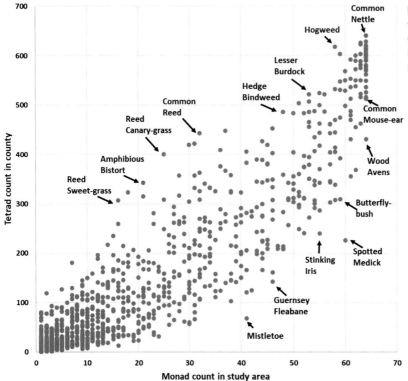

Figure 5.1 Frequency of vascular plant species in Cambridgeshire tetrads in relation to counts of monads in the NHC area.

is planted and marked with a label in the Botanic Garden, and has escaped to some private gardens in Chaucer Road and Latham Road. It is also known from Midsummer Common and St Edward's churchyard. Chinese Pokeweed fruits abundantly and is potentially quite invasive. **Dappled Hawkweed** *Hieracium scotosticum* is uncommon in public places but is a persistent weed in some private gardens. It too fruits abundantly.

Common and rare species

Twenty-nine species occur in all 64 monads of the study area; 74 species are found in at least 90% of monads. Many of the most frequent are plants of roadsides, such as **Nettle** *Urtica dioica*, **Cleavers** *Galium aparine*, **Yarrow** *Achillea millefolium* and **Daisy** *Bellis perennis*, and occur in every single monad. Others such as **Shepherd's Purse** *Capsella bursa-pastoris* are plants of disturbed ground. There are a few trees that seem to grow everywhere, notably **Field Maple** *Acer campestre* and **Ash** *Fraxinus excelsior*.

Compared to Cambridgeshire as a whole the only species from the county top ten that is significantly less frequent in Cambridge is **Hogweed** *Heracleum sphondylium*. It is a plant of rough or disturbed ground and so is missing from intensively built parts of the city such as Chesterton. Some of the commonest Cambridge species are less frequent outside the city. As its English name suggests, **Wood Avens** *Geum urbanum* is found in the Cambridgeshire woods, and as its scientific name suggests, it is also an urban plant. It is absent from large parts of Fenland and so it appears at 74th in the county list. **Common Mouse-ear** *Cerastium fontanum* and Daisy are also plants that avoid Fenland, often only being found in the mown lawns of isolated houses. The relative frequency in fenland and Cambridge shows up clearly in Figure 5.1. Species such as Hogweed and **Common Reed** *Phragmites australis* that are commoner in fenland are ranged along the top of the scatter diagram, and species such as **Mistletoe** *Viscum album* that are commoner in Cambridge are ranged along the bottom.

In the NHC area, as almost everywhere, there are more rare species than common ones (Figure 5.2). What is perhaps surprising about the curve is that the number of species is more or less level between 22 and 63 monads. Then it jumps up to 29 for 64 out of 64. There are 229 species which are present in the county but absent in

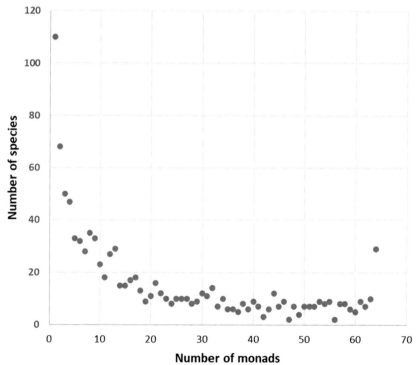

Figure 5.2 Numbers of species in relation to frequency in the NHC area.

Cambridge. Most are aquatic or wetland plants, including **Marsh Thistle** *Cirsium palustre*, **Frogbit** *Hydrocharis morsus-ranae*, **Fine-leaved Water-dropwort** *Oenanthe aquatica*, and **Fan-leaved Water-crowfoot** *Ranunculus circinatus*. A few of the absentees grow on dry land, notably **Common Gromwell** *Lithospermum officinale*, **Common Rock-rose** *Helianthemum nummularium* and **Sulphur Clover** *Trifolium ochroleucon*. All of these have occurred in the NHC area in the past.

Orchid distributions

Nine species of orchid were recorded in the NHC area. This compares with twenty species in the whole county, of which twelve are found in five or fewer tetrads. Fenland in the north of the county, defined as land below 5 m altitude, is very poor in orchids, with only 0.3 species per tetrad. In the NHC area there are 2.8 orchid species per tetrad, while in non-fenland tetrads outside the study area there are 1.4 species. The higher count in Cambridge may in part reflect the intensity of observation, with quite small areas, such as domestic gardens, being studied carefully.

Table 5.1 shows that by far the commonest species both in the study area and the county as a whole is **Bee Orchid** *Ophrys apifera* which was found in all the tetrads of the NHC area, and in about a half of the non-fenland tetrads in the rest of Cambridgeshire.

Common Spotted-orchid *Dactylorhiza fuchsii* was in about half the tetrads in the NHC area and a quarter of non-fenland tetrads elsewhere. As well as the two **Marsh-orchids** *D. incarnata* and *D. praetermissa* the hybrid between the two was recorded in two locations.

Pyramidal Orchid *Anacamptis pyramidalis* is the next most frequent in the NHC area, present

Figure 5.3 Bee orchid growing in Longworth Avenue. (RJJ).

in almost 38% of 16 tetrads. **Common Twayblade** *Neottia ovata* is in 19% of tetrads in the NHC area, compared with 14% in the rest of the non-fenland area. The relatively low frequency of Common Twayblade in the NHC area reflects the scarcity of woodland.

White Helleborine *Cephalanthera damasonium* has long been known from the Beechwoods LNR on the southern edge of the city (in monad TL4854) and also occurs on the edge of Gog Magog Golf

Table 5.1. Frequency of orchid species in the NHC area compared with non-fenland tetrads elsewhere in Cambridgeshire. Excluding tetrads that are either in the NHC area or partly in other counties, there are 205 non-fenland (i.e. >5 m altitude) tetrads in the county.

Species	NHC Monads	NHC Tetrads	NHC Tetrads %	Non-fenland tetrads	Non-fenland %
Bee Orchid	33	16	100%	97	48%
Common Spotted-orchid	10	8	50%	54	26%
Pyramidal Orchid	6	6	38%	49	24%
Common Twayblade	3	3	19%	29	14%
White Helleborine	3	3	19%	3	1%
Early Marsh-orchid	3	3	19%	8	4%
Southern Marsh-orchid	3	3	19%	10	5%
Broad-leaved Helleborine	1	1	6%	5	2%
Green-flowered Helleborine	1	1	6%	1	0%

Course in the same monad. It grows not far away along the edge of Nightingale Avenue Recreation Ground (in TL4755) and has been found in a suburban street nearby (Topcliffe Way). In these sites it grows in its preferred habitat (Stace 2019) of bare chalky ground under Beech *Fagus sylvatica*. However, its habitat on the other side of Cambridge, in monad TL4359 was unexpected. Here it was growing in grassland under Lime trees at the back entrance to Fitzwilliam College and nearby on a lawn under Pines. Nationally this species has a southern distribution with only a few records further north than Cambridge.

Green-flowered Helleborine *Epipactis phyllanthes* has been known from one location near the centre of Cambridge for over a century. The first record of it on Robinson Crusoe Island, in the River Cam, was in 1896 and it has been recorded there in small quantities intermittently ever since. The plants however are very small and the site is now overgrown and has been disturbed by Council work. Of the orchids recorded in the NHC area this is the rarest nationally with a rather scattered distribution, concentrated in southern England.

Broad-leaved Helleborine *Epipactis helleborine* was found in 2019 by the Cherry Hinton lakes, but had not been seen anywhere near Cambridge for over a century. Nationally it is widespread but with few records from Cambridgeshire.

Unlike Bee Orchid the distribution of the other orchid species found in the NHC area is patchy (Figure 5.5). The richest site is the Barnwell East LNR with Common Spotted-orchid, Southern Marsh-orchid, Common Twayblade and Pyramidal Orchid, as well as Bee Orchid.

Figure 5.4 White Helleborine growing near the children's play area on Nightingale Avenue. (MEF).

The picture of Cambridge orchids obtained during the project is unlikely to be a static one. Climate change is already playing a part in a changing orchid distribution, with species such as Pyramidal Orchid becoming more common.

Habitats of Cambridge plants

The rich variety of Cambridge habitats was noted in chapter 1. Here we compare some Cambridge plant habitats with those in the wider county.

Water and wetland

Although water plants are commoner in the fens, Cambridge is also a moderately good locality for them. The most frequent are **Bulrush** *Typha latifolia*, **Common Duckweed** *Lemna minor*, **Common Reed** *Phragmites australis*, **Fool's-water-cress** *Helosciadium nodiflorum* and **Water-cress** *Nasturtium officinale* agg. These can be found in many ponds and streamlets. Species that are found mainly in the deeper water of the River Cam include **Yellow Water-lily** *Nuphar lutea*, **Arrowhead** *Sagittaria sagittifolia*, **Unbranched Bur-reed** *Sparganium emersum*, **Flowering-rush** *Butomus umbellatus* and **Perfoliate Pondweed** *Potamogeton perfoliatus*.

Wetland plants are found abundantly in grassland and ditches along the Cam, as well as by low-lying ditches and ponds elsewhere. The best locality is Coe Fen and its associated nature reserve, Paradise LNR. On the banks of the Cam are many planted **White Willows** *Salix alba*, which were traditionally pollarded but now mostly allowed to grow tall. By the Cam and elsewhere, the most frequent wetland species are **Grey Willow** *Salix cinerea*, **Hairy Sedge** *Carex hirta*, **Hard Rush** *Juncus inflexus*, **Hedge Bindweed** *Calystegia sepium* and **Water Figwort** *Scrophularia auriculata*. There are many other common species, all of them characteristic of eutrophic wet grasslands and watersides.

There are also a few species that occur outside Cambridge mainly in traditionally managed fens and wet meadows. They avoid eutrophic conditions and are rare in Cambridge. Examples are **Common Sedge** *Carex nigra*, **Greater Bird's-foot-trefoil** *Lotus pedunculatus*, **Marsh Horsetail** *Equisetum palustre*, **Skullcap** *Scutellaria galericulata* and **Tufted-sedge** *Carex elata*. These persist mainly in sites along the river, notably Skaters' Meadow, Paradise LNR and Ditton Meadows.

Woodland and hedges

The NHC area has only one woodland of note, the Beechwoods LNR, planted in the 1840s (chapter 1). Most other woodland is more recent, consisting of planted tree-lines, scrubbed-up vacant land and edges of parks and gardens. The plants that colonise new woodland are almost all species that can be found in hedges and gardens, from which they emerge to occupy ground under trees. Small undisturbed patches of woodland are often almost

Figure 5.5 Distribution of orchid species, excluding Bee Orchid (left) and of Bee Orchid (right); small dots are one other species, large dots are two to four.

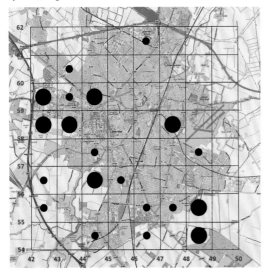
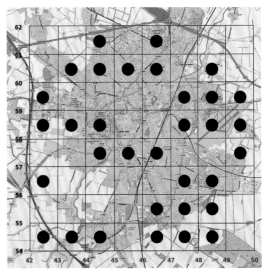

Figure 5.6 Herb-robert, here seen in St Clement's churchyard, is a woodland plant that has adapted to many urban habitats, including gardens. (MOH).

completely covered in **Ivy** *Hedera helix*, which carpets the ground and swarms up trees.

Typical herbs of hedges and woodland edges are **False Brome** *Brachypodium sylvaticum*, **Garlic Mustard** *Alliaria petiolata*, **Herb-Robert** *Geranium robertianum*, **Lesser Celandine** *Ficaria verna*, **Lords-and-Ladies** *Arum maculatum*, **Wood Avens** *Geum urbanum* and **Wood Dock** *Rumex sanguineus*. These spread without any help from gardeners. However, gardeners also cultivate plants that are more typical of ancient woodland, notably **Bluebell** *Hyacinthoides non-scripta*, **Bugle** *Ajuga reptans*, **Common Dog-violet** *Viola riviniana* and **Wood Anemone** *Anemone nemorosa*, which then escape into Cambridge's wider environment though rarely into new woods. **Goldilocks Buttercup** *Ranunculus auricomus* is a woodland plant that thrives, presumably unplanted, in lawns of Trinity and Magdalene colleges, but in general the NHC area is lacking in species that are characteristic of ancient woodland elsewhere in Cambridgeshire.

Grassland

There are large areas of grassland in our area, of which the airport is perhaps the poorest and the Gog Magog Golf Course is the most notable for rare species. College lawns and sports grounds account for a substantial area. Churchyards and cemeteries have many interesting plants, which are described in chapter 15. The really common grassland species are found in lawns, on road verges, in parks and in

gardens. They are tolerant of eutrophic soils. The 'top ten', with most records in the NHC study, are species of coarse grassland and waysides (Table 5.2).

English name	Scientific name	Records
Grasses		
Cock's-foot	*Dactylis glomerata*	263
False Oat-grass	*Arrhenatherum elatius*	257
Daisy family		
Creeping Thistle	*Cirsium arvense*	262
Spear Thistle	*Cirsium vulgare*	241
Common Ragwort	*Jacobaea vulgaris*	234
Dandelion	*Taraxacum* agg.	253
Others		
Cow Parsley	*Anthriscus sylvestris*	251
Ribwort Plantain	*Plantago lanceolata*	241
Creeping Buttercup	*Ranunculus repens*	238
Common Nettle	*Urtica dioica*	329

Table 5.2 The top ten grassland and wayside species, with number of records

Slightly less frequent, particularly in the arable fringe, are plants of grazed or managed grassland. Those of garden lawns and mown verges are described below under Domestic gardens and Urban and suburban roadsides.

Agriculturally unimproved grassland is infrequent in our area, especially in densely urban areas and the arable fringes. Characteristic species are the grasses **Crested Dog's-tail** *Cynosurus cristatus* and **Yellow Oat-grass** *Trisetum flavescens*, together with **Common Bird's-foot-trefoil** *Lotus corniculatus*, **Common Sorrel** *Rumex acetosa*,

Figure 5.7 Common Bird's-foot-trefoil is a plant of unimproved grassland and unfertilised lawns. It is absent from eutrophic grassland. (PAR).

Cowslip *Primula veris*, **Lady's Bedstraw** *Galium verum*, **Hedge Bedstraw** *Galium album* and **Perforate St John's-wort** *Hypericum perforatum*. These species avoid eutrophic soils and are absent where the grass is rank or heavily fertilised. They are still frequent on Coldham's Common but totally absent in Grantchester Meadows. Some sites with unimproved grassland are public open spaces with extensive managed grass, for example the Science Park in the north and the Babraham Road Park and Ride car park in the south.

Arable land

Arable fields near Cambridge differ widely depending on the soil. We saw in chapter 4 that several rare arable weeds occur on the claylands to the west. **Dwarf Spurge** *Euphorbia exigua* is found not only on the clay but also on the chalk in the south-east. On the chalk, several members of the poppy family were formerly present as arable weeds – **Dense-flowered Fumitory** *Fumaria densiflora*, **Fine-leaved Fumitory** *F. parviflora*, **Few-flowered Fumitory** *F. vaillantii*, **Prickly Poppy** *Roemeria argemone* and **Rough Poppy** *R. hispida*. These are now rare plants of field margins, but some of them still occasionally appear in uncultivated fields along with **Common Poppy** *Papaver rhoeas*.

As arable fields have become less weedy, so many plants that used to grow there have become relatively more frequent on disturbed ground in the urban environment. **Sun Spurge** *Euphorbia helioscopia*, **Fat-hen** *Chenopodium album*, **Knotgrass** *Polygonum aviculare*, **Redshank** *Persicaria maculosa*, **Perennial Sowthistle** *Sonchus arvensis* and **Annual Mercury** *Mercurialis annua* are common arable weeds in the fens, but in Cambridge are mainly in the town.

Figure 5.8 Sun Spurge is a common arable weed in the fens, but is mainly in ruderal habitats in our area. (PAR).

Chalk pits and other post-industrial sites

East Pit and West Pit are two of the best sites for chalk plants in our area. Several rare plants are mentioned in chapter 4. East Pit is notable not only for its native flora such as **Basil Thyme** *Clinopodium acinos*, **Common Milkwort** *Polygala vulgaris*, **Large Thyme** *Thymus pulegioides* and **Wild Thyme** *Thymus drucei*, but also for a bewildering variety of shrubby **Cotoneaster** species, which have escaped from gardens. Shrubs, especially **Butterfly-bush** *Buddleja davidii*, would rapidly cover the site without the intervention of conservation volunteers, whose work is described in chapter 16.

Several smaller chalk pits are managed by the volunteers and retain interesting native plants. Other post-industrial sites are more transient and are often blockaded to prevent public access. The best of them is the area of former railway sidings in Chesterton, which were effectively open to the public by tolerated trespass and are now rapidly being developed. The Chesterton sidings (see photos in chapter 7) were colonised by a wide range of interesting plants and lichens. Prior to development they were rapidly reverting to woodland, but remaining open spaces were notable for their abundance of ruderals, including **Fleabanes** *Erigeron* spp., **Fumitories** *Fumaria* spp., **Mulleins** *Verbascum* spp., **Ragworts** *Senecio* spp. and **Willowherbs** *Epilobium* spp., together with many unusual plants such as **Common Calamint** *Clinopodium ascendens*, **Pampas-grass** *Cortaderia selloana* and **Slender Thistle** *Carduus tenuiflorus*.

Building sites, car parks and business parks

The hectic pace of development in Cambridge has provided many other opportunities for ruderal plants. The vast Cambridge Biomedical Campus, workplace of 20,000 people, already covers 70 ha and is rapidly expanding southwards. In the north, the Cambridge Science Park covers 60 ha, with new developments planned to the east of it. Both of these sites are noted for their interesting plants, especially ruderals. Sand for building has been brought from the Breckland, introducing **Bur Medick** *Medicago minima*, **Early Forget-me-not** *Myosotis ramosissima*, **Hairy Rockcress** *Arabis hirsuta*, **Hare's-foot Clover** *Trifolium arvense* and **Viper's-bugloss** *Echium vulgare*. Sandy soils also occur naturally at the Observatory, which is located between Churchill College and Eddington. Natural gravels have been disturbed during building works, allowing sandy-soil specialists to thrive.

Figure 5.9 Viper's-bugloss on sparsely vegetated sandy ground, with Common Restharrow *Ononis repens* in the background. Small plants of Hare's-foot Clover and Buck's-horn Plantain *Plantago coronopus* are also visible. (JDS).

Slightly smaller but between them occupying several tens of hectares, are the 'Park and Ride' car parks at the edge of the city. In these, constant disturbance and the import of building materials have also favoured ruderals, as well as many other annuals and biennials such as **Great Brome** *Anisantha diandra*, **Small-flowered Buttercup** *Ranunculus parviflorus*, **Venus's-looking-glass** *Legousia hybrida* and **Wall Bedstraw** *Galium parisiense*.

Numerous other building sites and business parks ensure that Cambridge has a far richer ruderal flora than anywhere else in the county.

Urban and suburban habitats
The plants of domestic gardens, roadsides and walls are described below. Garden escapes account for a large part of the richness of Cambridge's flora. Some of the commonest are **Canadian Goldenrod** *Solidago canadensis*, **Feverfew** *Tanacetum parthenium*, 'Himalayan Giant' **Blackberry** *Rubus armeniacus*, **Oregon-grape** *Mahonia aquifolium,* **Purple Toadflax** *Linaria purpurea*, **Red Valerian** *Centranthus ruber* and **Yellow Corydalis** *Pseudofumaria lutea*. All of these are still cultivated in some gardens. Other species are relicts of former cultivation. Nobody now cultivates **Pellitory-of-the-wall** *Parietaria judaica*, but according to Leslie (2019) it may formerly have been cultivated by

herbalists. **Wall Lettuce** *Mycelis muralis* is a British native, but not native to our area. It is thought to have been introduced to Cambridge from the Botanic Garden around 1900.

Several other British natives such as **Early Meadow-grass** *Poa infirma*, **Jersey Cudweed** *Laphangium luteoalbum*, **Shining Crane's-bill** *Geranium lucidum* and **Wavy Bitter-cress** *Cardamine flexuosa* have strongly urban distributions in Cambridgeshire. Also strongly urban and rapidly increasing is **Mistletoe** *Viscum album*, to which we turn next.

The NatHistCam Mistletoe survey
Early on in the NatHistCam project it was decided to survey the current status of Mistletoe *Viscum album* in the city. This was partly because it was felt that this might be a good way of engaging the general public in collecting data, as the plant is quite recognisable, but also because according to a report in 2009, there had been an explosive increase of Mistletoe in Cambridge (Cadbury & Oswald 2009). One of our committee members, Duncan Mackay, was interviewed on BBC Radio Cambridgeshire and wrote a blog for the NatHistCam website about this. We followed this up with a press release in January 2017, which resulted in some coverage in a local paper.

Over the next few months records of Mistletoe in Cambridge trickled into the Cambridgeshire and Peterborough Environmental Records Centre. By the end of May 2017 we had had 122 reports of Mistletoe. Further data were collected in subsequent years and by the end of 2019, 211 records of Mistletoe had been gathered from within the NHC area. Jonathan Shanklin systematically visited every monad to try and find at least one plant in each.

Plotting the data on a map (Figure 5.10) shows that Mistletoe is not evenly distributed across Cambridge – there are some monads where none has been recorded and others where there are large quantities. The monads without Mistletoe are mostly peripheral and half the Mistletoe records are in more central monads. Mistletoe is found more in the north and west of the NHC area, with fewer locations in the south and east. It is an urban plant, not recorded in the more rural areas. The highest number of records of Mistletoe in a single monad was 23. There were 23 monads (out of 64) where no Mistletoe was reported.

Cadbury and Oswald (2009) surveyed Mistletoe in the winters 2007/8 and 2008/9 and found it on 206 trees and shrubs in 15 monads, all but one (TL4762 Milton Country Park) within the NHC area. Their survey was systematic and attempted to be complete within the city, but they counted trees rather than making locational records. Table 5.3 provides a comparison with their data. In the NHC survey there was a notable concentration of records in Chesterton and Arbury, where Cadbury and Oswald had found no Mistletoe (Figure 5.11). There has undoubtedly been an enormous increase in this area. Chris Preston acted as a scout for Cadbury and Oswald and did not see it in West Chesterton. He tells us that there has been continued expansion

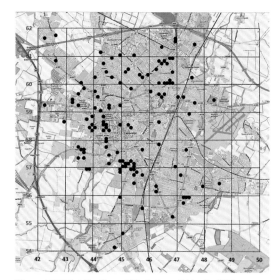

Figure 5.10 Distribution of Mistletoe within the NHC survey area.

during 2016–2019, the period of his street transects (see Urban and suburban roadsides below). He thinks that it mostly spread in from outside the area, though there may have been concealed colonies in gardens in Chesterton and Arbury. Mistletoe has also increased in other parts of Cambridge, with 41 monads in the NHC survey compared with the 15 reported by Cadbury and Oswald. There may have been decreases in areas A and F but in the absence of tree counts from the NHC survey it is hard to know.

Traditionally, Mistletoe is associated with Apple trees but this is not the case in Cambridge. Although the identity of the host tree was not recorded for about half the records, a wide variety of hosts was noted, with over a dozen different genera. Lime trees were the hosts in about 40 instances

Table 5.3 Records of Mistletoe 2016–2019 compared with the number of host trees recorded by Cadbury & Oswald in the winters 2007–2008 and 2009–2010. In addition to trees, hedges were noted by Cadbury & Oswald in areas B and E.

Area	Cadbury & Oswald location	Monad	Trees	Records
A	Newnham, including Barton Road, Gough Way and Downing College sports ground	TL4357	25	7
B	Queen's Road to Wilberforce Road	TL4358, 4458	31	26
C	Jesus Green and Chesterton Lane to Madingley Road, Churchill College	TL4359, 4459	52	15
D	Coe Fen, Trumpington Road, Brooklands Avenue	TL4456, 4457, 4556, 4557	38	36
E	Botanic Garden	TL4557	22	10
F	Hills Road area	TL4655, 4656	26	12
G	Christ's Pieces	TL4558	2	4
H	Tredegar Close, Arbury	TL4561	1	3
I	Barnwell Junction	TL4759	1	5

Monad	42	43	44	45	46	47	48	49
61	2		3	3	5	2		
60	1	1	8	10	21	2		
59	2	5	10	3	8	5	1	
58	2	11	15	4	3	1		
57		7	10	23	2	2		
56		2	2	11	8	3	1	
55			1	1	4	4		
54			1	1				

Figure 5.11 Distribution of Mistletoe in the NHC area by monad. Values are the number of records of Mistletoe 2016–2019. Shaded monads are those where Cadbury and Oswald had recorded Mistletoe.

20–25% according to a study in Sheffield (Gaston *et al.* 2007). They are a notable resource for wildlife and full of interesting animals and plants. In summer 2016 we developed a protocol for recording species in gardens and tried it out in four. We went on to bring the total to 60 at the end of 2019. We tried to space them out by requiring that not more than two gardens were sampled in any one monad. However, monads TL4459 and TL4656 contain three.

In each garden we listed the weeds in flower beds and all species in the lawn. We asked the householder to tell us of the vertebrates that they had seen in the past two years. We enquired about management, in particular pest control and activities to encourage wildlife. We made records of (1) vascular plants (summer and early autumn, including a separate list for the road verge outside the property) and (2) mosses and liverworts (autumn and winter). The last garden was recorded on 31 October 2019. In late October there should be fully developed rosettes of **Bee Orchid** *Ophrys apifera* in lawns (only three gardens were found to

(almost 20% of records). **False-acacia** *Robinia pseudoacacia* was the host for 8 records. Apples, including Crab Apples, were the host species for 23 records with Hawthorns host for another 7. Apples are not a common street tree but are more frequent in gardens. However, trees in gardens are often visible from the street and the NatHistCam survey of gardens found that few contained Mistletoe. Cadbury and Oswald (2009) identified at least 21 tree or shrub species, plus 7 hybrids, as known to have supported Mistletoe in Cambridge. Limes, Poplars, Apples, False-acacia and Hawthorns were the most frequent.

It is clear from the two surveys that Mistletoe has increased in frequency in Cambridge, now being found in 41 monads compared to 15 in the earlier survey, especially in the north of the city. What is driving the increase is not clear. Climate change and increased planting of susceptible trees are likely factors. Increased **Mistle Thrushes** and overwintering **Blackcaps** (Chapter 13) are another likely cause. Some Mistletoe is deliberately introduced as people can be enthusiastic about encouraging it, and there are detailed instructions and 'Mistletoe grow kits' available online.

Domestic gardens

Urban domestic gardens occupy a substantial proportion of the area of British towns – about

Figure 5.12 Lime tree (*Tilia* × *europaea*) heavily infested with Mistletoe near the Botanic Garden. (PAR).

have Bee Orchids). The earliest recorded garden was on 25 May, with the result that two early bloomers **Lesser Celandine** *Ficaria verna* and **Ivy-leaved Speedwell** *Veronica hederifolia* were not recorded. **Common Whitlowgrass** *Erophila verna* was occasionally identified from dead husks. **Bluebells** *Hyacinthoides* spp. were regularly recorded, if only as dead stems, but could not be identified to species. We also listed the weeds in two sample quadrats of size 1 m² placed in flower beds, and took soil samples to measure the pH.

One garden of particular note belongs to Paul Rule. This is described in Chapter 15 as a site of special interest, for its marvellous range of species. We recorded its plants in October 2016, and were interviewed for Cambridge TV. This garden has no flower beds but many bushes and trees with berries.

Garden survey results

The total area surveyed was 2.8 ha. We enumerated 395 plant species, of which 54 were planted trees or bushes. Of the unplanted species, 204 were native, 48 were ancient (pre-1500) introductions and 89 were recent introductions to Britain. The natives were twice as frequent as the recent introductions (averaging 11.2 species per garden, as against 5.5), with the ancient introductions intermediate (7.4).

Figure 5.14 Rosie Earwaker interviewed by Jamie Wyver in Paul Rule's garden for Cambridge TV. (PAR).

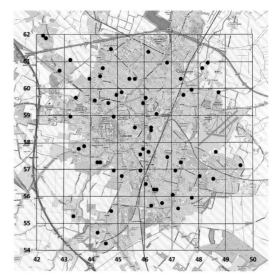

Figure 5.13 Location of the 60 gardens surveyed 2016–2019.

Species found in gardens are considered below, but it is also interesting to know which plants were not found in the gardens (Table 5.4). The commonest of these are **Hedge Mustard** *Sisymbrium officinale*, **Charlock** *Sinapis arvensis* and **Curled Dock** *Rumex crispus*. Most of these absent plants are coarse species of waysides, which would immediately attract the attention of diligent gardeners and be removed. However, the three annual arable weeds are relatively small. **Scentless Mayweed** *Tripleurospermum inodorum* was in a fairly new garden with no vegetable plot. **Swine-cress** *Lepidium coronopus* was not found in any garden. **Small Nettle** *Urtica urens* has a nasty sting; it was found only in the large vegetable plot of our biggest garden.

As well as noting garden weeds, we recorded the three (or fewer) main trees in each garden. **Apples** *Malus domestica* were in 21 gardens with ornamental species of *Malus* in four more. **Cypresses** *Cupressus lawsoniana*, *C. × leylandii*, *C. macrocarpa*, *C. nootkatensis*, *C. sempervirens* were in 13 gardens. **Plums** *Prunus domestica*, **Pears** *Pyrus communis* and **Silver Birches** *Betula pendula* were also in 8 gardens as planted trees, with birches in six more as seedlings or self-sown saplings.

Gardeners have enormously differing aspirations and energy. We tried to avoid having too many gardeners with a green agenda, and for that reason did not advertise to members of the Cambridge Natural History Society. Our most extreme wildlife garden was not big, 130 m² in area. It had a pond,

Table 5.4 Common Cambridge species that were found in 0 or 1 gardens, together with the count of Cambridge monads where they occur. Only species present in more than 48 (75%) of Cambridge's 64 monads are listed.

Common name	Scientific name	Type of plant	Monad count	Garden count
Scentless Mayweed	*Tripleurospermum inodorum*	Annual arable	55	1
Small Nettle	*Urtica urens*	Annual arable	49	1
Swine-cress	*Lepidium coronopus*	Annual arable	52	0
Charlock	*Sinapis arvensis*	Annual wayside	59	0
Hedge Mustard	*Sisymbrium officinale*	Annual wayside	61	1
Soft-brome	*Bromus hordeaceus*	Annual wayside	54	0
Hemlock	*Conium maculatum*	Biennial wayside	51	0
Hogweed	*Heracleum sphondylium*	Biennial wayside	58	1
Lesser Burdock	*Arctium minus*	Biennial wayside	53	0
Common Knapweed	*Centaurea nigra*	Perennial grassland	55	0
Hedge Bedstraw	*Galium album*	Perennial grassland	51	0
Blackthorn	*Prunus spinosa*	Perennial hedge	50	0
Colt's-foot	*Tussilago farfara*	Perennial wayside	52	1
Curled Dock	*Rumex crispus*	Perennial wayside	59	0
Mugwort	*Artemisia vulgaris*	Perennial wayside	58	1

long grass, pollinator-friendly bushes, a bird bath, a log pile, a hedgehog home and space under the fence for hedgehogs to move between gardens. There was a bird box and the gardener fed birds and hedgehogs. Herbicides and pesticides were not used. This intense wildlife regime had only been running for

Figure 5.15 Charlock is often found on disturbed land in new housing developments, but does not thrive once gardens are established. It was not observed in any of our sample of 60 gardens. (PAR).

two years, so with 45 plant species the garden was not especially rich for a garden of that size.

Some gardens were run down and neglected. One had a 50 m² bramble thicket and was largely uncultivated except for a vegetable patch. Another, in central Cambridge, had only a small tilled area, and the rest of it was covered with **False Brome** *Brachypodium sylvaticum*, which is normally a plant of woodland and scrub.

There seems to be little correlation between lawn care and bird feeders. One large lawn was so intensely managed that the only dicot present was a single tuft of **Dandelion**. The garden had three bird feeders.

In our sample, average garden size varied with age of house (Table 5.5). Many of the oldest houses are in densely-built urban areas, so the average size was not as large as that for the interwar period 1920–1939. The period since 1970 has seen steadily increasing land prices and smaller gardens. Indeed, many modern housing developments do not have any private gardens.

Other statistics of Cambridge gardens are given in Table 5.6. Note that although bird boxes

Table 5.5 Average area of gardens in relation to date of house build.

Date of house	N=	Average garden area (m²)
1799–1910	18	456
1920–1939	17	579
1950–1967	15	465
1970–2013	10	296
All houses	60	466

Table 5.6 Proportions of Cambridge gardens with particular features or attributes.

Feature	%	Feature	%
Flower beds	93%	Bird box	52%
Lawn	90%	Herbicide use	44%
Separate front garden	85%	Vegetable patch	43%
Compost heap	57%	Pond	40%
Bird feeder	57%	Metaldehyde use	38%
Climber on house	52%	Inorganic fertilizer	35%

were present in 52% of gardens, they were only occupied in 35% of them. The pH of soil samples varied from 5.2 to 8.1 but was mostly greater than 7. It was generally higher in the chalky south east of the city, averaging 7.54 there as opposed to 7.15 elsewhere. Two gardens had notably low pH. One, in Trumpington, had a mean pH of 5.6, but did not seem otherwise remarkable. The other, in Girton, had a mean pH of 6.0 and also did not seem different from the others. Soil texture of Cambridge gardens was mostly sandy or gritty, but it was clayey in the north-west and chalky in the south-east.

Nice weeds and nasty weeds

The Botanical Society of Britain and Ireland does not advise its recorders to list plants in private gardens although gardens are full of wild plants thriving as weeds. In vegetable plots, the distinction between weeds and crops is clear. In flower beds and shrubberies, the distinction may not be obvious. Gardeners are capricious. Sometimes they may cherish a particular plant but then decide later that it is a nuisance and must go. For this reason we recorded some plants as 'semi-cultivated', meaning that they were spreading round the garden but the gardener's attitude towards them was unclear. These are the nice weeds.

Top of the list for 'semi-cultivated' species were **Wood Forget-me-not** *Myosotis sylvatica*, **Common Dog-violet** *Viola riviniana*, **Balm** *Melissa officinalis*, **Sweet Violet** *Viola odorata*, **Purple Toadflax** *Linaria purpurea*, **Stinking Iris** *Iris foetidissima* and **Wild Strawberry** *Fragaria vesca*.

At the other end of the scale are weeds that are really detested by gardeners. We asked gardeners to name their worst weeds. These are the nasty weeds. Top of the list were **Large Bindweed** *Calystegia silvatica*, **Ground Elder** *Aegopodium podagraria* and **Green Alkanet** *Pentaglottis sempervirens*. Large Bindweed was particularly unpopular, present in 34 gardens and worst weed in 15. Green Alkanet on the other hand is sometimes valued as a garden plant; it occurred in 38 gardens and was worst weed in six. Lawn-lovers listed **Dandelion** *Taraxacum* agg. as worst weed in four gardens, and moss as worst weed in two. In four gardens the worst weed was a cultivated plant that had got out of control: **Russian-vine** *Fallopia baldschuanica*, **Stephan Jasmine** *Jasminum* × *stephanense*, **Variegated Yellow Archangel** *Lamiastrum galeobdolon* subsp. *argentatum* and **Soapwort** *Saponaria officinalis*.

In between the good and the bad weeds are the majority, which may be a nuisance or may be completely harmless. **Cleavers** *Galium aparine* is present in 31 gardens and is uniformly unloved, but **Herb-Robert** *Geranium robertianum*, in 42, is quite pretty and usually easy to control.

Figure 5.16 Wood Forget-me-not and Common Dog-violet were present in more than half the gardens. It was often unclear whether or not they were cultivated. (MOH & PAR).

Figure 5.17 Large Bindweed – such a beautiful plant but the worst weed in 25% of Cambridge gardens. (MOH).

It would have been nice to report back to home owners that there were rare weeds. In fact there were none. **Small Balsam** *Impatiens parviflora* was present as one large plant in a single garden; it is known from three sites in West Cambridge and the Botanic Garden. **Least Yellow-sorrel** *Oxalis exilis* and **Wood Meadow-grass** *Poa nemoralis* were each found in two gardens, and were each otherwise recorded in 8 of the NatHistCam monads. These were the rarest. In 2.8 ha, rarity was not to be expected, and was not found.

Larger gardens have more weeds

It is hardly surprising that bigger gardens have more weeds than smaller ones. On average there were 53 unplanted species per garden, with a range from 15 in a 26 m² back yard with no lawn to 96 in the 1500 m² grounds of a Victorian mansion. The largest garden sampled was 2,600 m² in Grantchester. If you double the garden size, you add about 9 unplanted species. Technically, the species-area curve is characterised by index z = 0.28 for the slope of the log number of species against log area. This is very close to the typical index for vascular plants z = 0.27 (Williamson *et al.* 2001).

Two large gardens stand out from the trend. That of the Victorian mansion was rather run down, with much Ground Elder, large trees, a rockery and an old wall. The garden noted for exceptional weed control was truly remarkable. There were no Buttercups or Daisies even in the lawn, almost no weeds in the flower beds, and only a single plant of Green Alkanet in the whole garden. The main lawn weeds were **Slender Speedwell** *Veronica filiformis* and **Field Bindweed** *Convolvulus arvensis*, both of which were absent from the flower beds. The enthusiastic gardener of this exceptional garden followed our plant recorder while he searched for weeds. Every time he found one, she zapped it!

Plants of garden lawns

Fifty-four of the 60 gardens had lawns. Most Cambridge lawns have been seeded with **Ryegrass** *Lolium perenne* and many with **Red Fescue** *Festuca rubra*. **White Clover** *Trifolium repens* has also been included in some seed mixes. Most of the other grasses and herbs have colonised naturally. It is probable that some older lawns were seeded

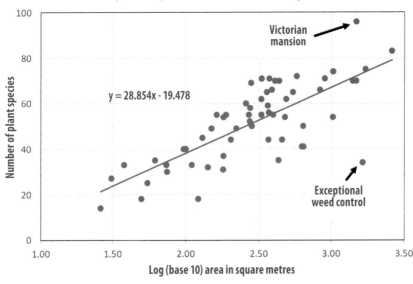

Figure 5.18 Number of plant species in relation to garden area. Larger Cambridge gardens have about 8.7 more species for a doubling in area.

y = 28.854x - 19.478

with **Creeping Bent** *Agrostis stolonifera* and three lawns had **Common Bent** *Agrostis capillaris*, which is not really suitable for calcareous soils but was regularly included in seed mixtures in the past. Creeping Bent thrives in wet weather, but dies back when there is a drought. It is an unreliable lawn component.

The other grasses that are regularly present in lawns are **Annual, Smooth** and **Rough Meadow-grass** *Poa annua, P. pratensis, P. trivialis,* Cock's-foot *Dactylis glomerata* and **Yorkshire-fog** *Holcus lanatus.* The first three blend into the green turf, but Cock's-foot is coarse and Yorkshire-fog looks out of place because of its silky grey leaves. Apart from White Clover, the three most frequent lawn weeds are **Daisy** *Bellis perennis,* **Yarrow** *Achillea millefolium* and **Dandelion** *Taraxacum* agg. Daisy and Yarrow are true lawn plants, but Dandelions can crop up almost anywhere in the garden and constantly reinvade. Daisy must be quite easy to eliminate from lawns by herbicides; indeed, several lawn-tidy gardens were without it. Then there are the lesser lawn weeds, the perennials **Selfheal** *Prunella vulgaris* and **Ribwort Plantain** *Plantago lanceolata,* and the annual legumes **Lesser Trefoil** *Trifolium dubium* and **Black Medick** *Medicago lupulina.* **Common Ragwort** *Jacobaea vulgaris,* is also frequent, but does not thrive in mown lawns, persisting as rather unsightly small tufts.

Plants of garden beds

The difference between garden beds and other garden ground is that the soil is tilled, not necessarily every year, but often enough to maintain an intermittently open community. In smaller or bushier gardens, there is usually not much sun on the flower beds, so shade plants predominate, and in many neglected beds, these gradually take over as ecological succession takes place.

There were 17 different kinds of weeds in one of our weediest 1 m² quadrats. These included **Ivy** *Hedera helix,* **Bramble** *Rubus fruticosus,* **Nettle** *Urtica dioica,* **Rough Meadow-grass** *Poa trivialis,*

Figure 5.19 Ryegrass and Cock's-foot in a Cambridge garden lawn. Ryegrass makes a good turf and is sown both in private lawns and on council verges. Cock's-foot is drought-tolerant and readily invades lawns. In the garden context it is coarse and ugly, and tends to suppress smaller and more attractive plants. (MOH).

Figure 5.20 Daisies and Ribwort Plantain are the perfect lawn-compatible weeds. When closely mown, their leaves lie flat on the ground, and Daisies steadily spread by short underground stems. (MOH).

Figure 5.21 Petty Spurge is by far the most frequent weed of garden beds in Cambridge and was present in 95% of Cambridge gardens. It germinates rapidly when the soil is disturbed but if undisturbed its seeds can reputedly survive for a century. (PAR)

Black Horehound *Ballota nigra* and **Stinking Iris** *Iris foetidissima*, which are typical of newish woodland in Cambridge, but there were also some light-loving annuals such as **Chickweed** *Stellaria media*, **Smooth Sow-thistle** *Sonchus oleraceus*, **Groundsel** *Senecio vulgaris* and **Shepherd's-purse** *Capsella bursa-pastoris*.

By chance, **Petty Spurge** *Euphorbia peplus*, which was present in 51% of our quadrats, was absent in this one. Petty Spurge can tolerate partial shade, provided that the soil is disturbed at

intervals. Other frequent weeds, present in more than 20% of our quadrats were Dandelion, **Wood Avens** *Geum urbanum* and Wood Forget-me-not.

It is interesting that most of the more frequent weeds in Cambridge garden beds are either native to Britain or ancient introductions. Only three are recent introductions, but Cambridge plants of Wood Forget-me-not are of a large-flowered form, var. *culta*, which is not native to the county. Two of the three worst weeds are recent introductions, and **Procumbent Yellow-sorrel** *Oxalis corniculata* was

Figure 5.22 Procumbent Yellow-sorrel has two leaf-colour forms, both of which are common in Cambridge gardens. The purple-leaved var. *atropurpurea* is illustrated here. (PAR)

Table 5.7 The most frequent weeds in 97 Cambridge garden beds, with native status and counts of the monads in Cambridge and Cambridgeshire where they have been recorded. Key to Native status: N – native, Arch – ancient introduction (archaeophyte), Neo – post-1500 introduction (neophyte).

Species	Scientific name	Native status	Garden beds	Cambridge monads	Cambs monads
Petty Spurge	*Euphorbia peplus*	Arch	49	57	495
Dandelion	*Taraxacum* agg.	N	28	63	1209
Ivy	*Hedera helix*	N	23	64	871
Wood Avens	*Geum urbanum*	N	23	64	709
Wood Forget-me-not	*Myosotis sylvatica*	N	22	43	264
Herb-Robert	*Geranium robertianum*	N	18	58	627
Nipplewort	*Lapsana communis*	N	14	61	871
Smooth Sow-thistle	*Sonchus oleraceus*	N	13	64	956
Green Alkanet	*Pentaglottis sempervirens*	Neo	12	55	393
Groundsel	*Senecio vulgaris*	N	12	64	1048
Creeping Bent	*Agrostis stolonifera*	N	11	56	882
Procumbent Yellow-sorrel	*Oxalis corniculata*	Neo	11	38	187
Rough Meadow-grass	*Poa trivialis*	N	11	60	841
Annual Meadow-grass	*Poa annua*	N	10	64	1042
Barren Brome	*Anisantha sterilis*	Arch	8	64	1070
Sweet Violet	*Viola odorata*	N	8	57	499
Large Bindweed	*Calystegia silvatica*	Neo	8	51	338
Broad-leaved Willowherb	*Epilobium montanum*	N	8	39	185
Field Bindweed	*Convolvulus arvensis*	N	8	62	1036

also deemed to be the worst weed in two of the gardens. This plant is deplored by Alan Leslie in his *Flora of Cambridgeshire* as a pernicious weed. It is especially difficult to eliminate from potted perennials such as cacti. It is not particularly frequent in public spaces in the NHC area (38 out of 64 monads) but was present in 65% of gardens. It is relatively scarce in the wider county. It increased strongly in Cambridge in the late 20th century.

The other frequent weed that stands out as being scarce in the wider countryside is **Broad-leaved Willowherb** *Epilobium montanum*, which was present in 52% of Cambridge gardens. It is native to Britain and its natural habitat is woodland, but it has clearly also found a happy home in sheltered garden beds, where it is notably shade-tolerant.

Urban and suburban roadsides

The environment of the street is a more rigorous one than that of the garden. Plants colonising the most frequent habitats, roadsides, pavements and walls, must be able to grow in sites with little or no soil, although deeper soil is available on grass verges, gravel-covered areas and around the bases of street trees. The streetscape is drought-prone (no-one goes along the road with a watering-can or a hose) and it is intensively managed. The City Council treats the streets of Cambridge with herbicide in late spring or early summer to kill pavement weeds, and it makes a particular point of ensuring that the ground at bases of trees is thoroughly sprayed. In some years the annual spraying is followed up a few weeks later by a 'hit squad' which physically removes any surviving plants. However much botanists might regret it, 'cleaning' the streets in this way probably has public support. The local Liberal Democrats must certainly have thought so when they distributed a leaflet a few years ago which promised that they would use a herbicide which killed weeds without harming wildlife. Corporate owners (including colleges and large commercial landlords) also keep their frontages clear of pavement weeds, as do some private householders. However, plants survive not only in areas which happen to be protected temporarily from the sprayer by parked cars and bikes, but also by the complex pattern of interdigitating public and private spaces which provides many refuges in forecourts and passageways, as well as on walls, in hanging baskets, window boxes and other streetside plantings and in private gardens. Species quickly recolonise from these sources, or regenerate from buried seed.

Figure 5.23 Barren Brome, Buddleia *Buddleja davidii* and other pavement weeds dead or dying after the City Council's herbicide application, Green's Road, June 2016. (CDP).

Figure 5.24 Despite this careful mechanical clearing of street weeds in Green's Road, Cambridge (March 2020), some plants such as the Pellitory-of-the-wall at the start of a passageway (arrowed) are protected by their position. Seven months later there was once again a vigorous stand of 11 weed species at the foot of this 3-m stretch of wall, six of which had already flowered. (CDP).

The common street weeds

For four years (2016–19) I recorded the plants flowering in eight streets in North Cambridge at the start of each month. There were 11 species recorded in all streets every year, and a further six were almost as frequent (Table 5.8).

Ten of the 17 species listed in Table 5.8 are annuals. **American Willowherb**, though potentially perennial, probably behaves as an annual in many sites. The true perennials are either tolerant of heavy trampling, as is famously the case with **Greater Plantain**, or escape it by growing on walls and on pavements at the very base of walls (**Pellitory-of-the-wall, Yellow Corydalis**).

The most numerous annuals on the streets, such as **Common Chickweed**, **Groundsel** and **Hairy Bitter-cress**, can germinate at any time of year and it takes only a few weeks for the seedlings

Table 5.8 The most frequent plants recorded in flower in 8 Cambridge streets over 4 years, with native status, plant type and the street total. Plants recorded in all streets in all years attain a maximum street total of 32. Records of Guernsey Fleabane in streets may include some of Bilbao Fleabane *Erigeron floribundus*. Key to Native status: N – native, Arch – ancient introduction, Neo – post-1500 introduction (neophyte).

Species	Scientific name	Native status	Type of plant	Street total
Shepherd's-purse	*Capsella bursa-pastoris*	Arch	Annual	31
Hairy Bitter-cress	*Cardamine hirsuta*	N	Annual	32
American Willowherb	*Epilobium ciliatum*	Neo	Perennial	30
Guernsey Fleabane	*Erigeron sumatrensis*	Neo	Annual	32
Petty Spurge	*Euphorbia peplus*	Arch	Annual	32
Procumbent Yellow-sorrel	*Oxalis corniculata*	Neo	Perennial	31
Pellitory-of-the-wall	*Parietaria judaica*	N	Perennial	32
Greater Plantain	*Plantago major*	N	Perennial	32
Annual Meadow-grass	*Poa annua*	N	Annual	32
Knotgrass	*Polygonum aviculare*	N	Annual	32
Yellow Corydalis	*Pseudofumaria lutea*	Neo	Perennial	31
Procumbent Pearlwort	*Sagina procumbens*	N	Perennial	30
Groundsel	*Senecio vulgaris*	N	Annual	32
Hedge Mustard	*Sisymbrium officinale*	Arch	Annual	31
Smooth Sow-thistle	*Sonchus oleraceus*	N	Annual	32
Common Chickweed	*Stellaria media*	N	Annual	32
Dandelion	*Taraxacum* agg.	N	Perennial	32

Figure 5.25 Knotgrass flourishing in the drought of the 2018 summer. (CDP).

to flower, self-pollinate and set seed. Populations therefore recover rapidly even if all growing plants are killed, although the number of plants on the streets falls in hot summers when the spring herbicide treatment is followed by a drought that temporarily retards re-establishment from seed. **Knotgrass** is unusual as it germinates only in spring, but it is intensely drought-resistant and so it is able to flower and fruit even in the hottest and driest summers.

One intriguing possibility is that some of the common street weeds have evolved herbicide-resistant genotypes. Herbicide resistance has been demonstrated experimentally in populations of **American Willowherb** and several of the common street annuals in places where they grow as agricultural or horticultural weeds. It is also known, or strongly suspected, in **Pellitory-of-the-wall**, which became abundant in citrus orchards in Crete following the introduction of glyphosate weedkillers. In the absence of experimental studies of the street flora we can only speculate, but the subject would repay further research.

Rare and transient species

Although the species listed in Table 5.8 provide the most constant and prominent members of the street flora, there are many other established species, ranging from those that are only slightly less frequent to others that persist as rare but surprisingly persistent populations. Two rather restricted colonies of **Mediterranean Nettle** *Urtica membranacea* were discovered by Alan Leslie in Cambridge in 2009 and they have persisted for the last 10 years in just these localities. It is rather remarkable that an annual plant has spread from southern Europe to Cambridge but apparently lacks the ability to spread from one Cambridge street to the next. At a more local level, the native **Toad Rush** *Juncus bufonius*, though not uncommon in Cambridgeshire, has persisted since 2016 around a single manhole cover in Castle Street, but has not been seen anywhere else in the eight streets in the North Cambridge study area. In some years it is accompanied by tiny plants of **Marsh Yellow-cress** *Rorippa palustris*, which can sometimes also be found on the nearby

Figure 5.26 Mediterranean Nettle flowering in Castle Street, April 2021, and Toad Rush in full fruit by a manhole cover in Castle Street, June 2020. (CDP).

pavement but again has been seen nowhere else in these streets.

In addition, there is an ever-varying cast of transients, plants which may persist for only one season (sometimes as only a single individual). The botanist needing to identify these species, or wanting to photograph them, soon learns not to procrastinate as in some cases they are literally here today and gone tomorrow. In the eight North Cambridge streets 46 species were recorded just once between 2016 and 2019, and over half of these were present as just a single flowering individual. The latter included crop plants such as **Garden Radish** *Raphanus sativus* and **Broad Bean** *Vicia faba*, garden perennials, e.g. **Japanese**

Anemone *Anemone hupehensis* and **Argentine Needle-grass** *Nassella tenuissima*, plants grown in hanging baskets and window boxes, including **Bacopa** *Chaenostoma cordatum* and **Busy Lizzie** *Impatiens walleriana*, and ruderals such as **Mugwort** *Artemisia vulgaris* and **Oxford Ragwort** *Senecio squalidus*. Alan Leslie's *Flora of Cambridgeshire* expatiates lovingly on the pleasures of hunting for rare alien plants in the streets of Cambridge.

Cambridge garden plants compared with roadsides

Our survey of 60 domestic gardens included a systematic survey of 10-m lengths of adjacent road

Table 5.9 The most frequent plants in Cambridge gardens, compared with their frequency on adjacent roadsides.

Species	Scientific name	Garden (n = 60)	Roadside (n = 60)	Cambridge monads (n =64)	Cambs monads (n = 2224)
Petty Spurge	*Euphorbia peplus*	57	14	57	495
Dandelion	*Taraxacum* agg.	57	43	63	1209
Perennial Rye-grass	*Lolium perenne*	55	23	64	1107
Red Fescue	*Festuca rubra*	55	10	64	932
Wood Avens	*Geum urbanum*	53	8	64	709
Annual Meadow-grass	*Poa annua*	53	49	64	1042
Ivy	*Hedera helix*	53	15	64	919
Creeping Bent	*Agrostis stolonifera*	50	15	56	882
Nipplewort	*Lapsana communis*	47	7	61	871
White Clover	*Trifolium repens*	43	14	63	960
Herb-Robert	*Geranium robertianum*	42	10	58	629
Wood Forget-me-not	*Myosotis sylvatica*	39	0	43	264
Procumbent Yellow-sorrel	*Oxalis corniculata*	39	10	38	187
Green Alkanet	*Pentaglottis sempervirens*	38	8	55	393
Smooth Sow-thistle	*Sonchus oleraceus*	37	21	64	956

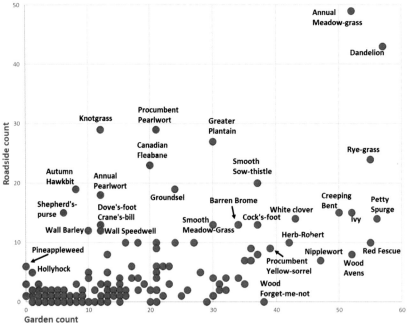

Figure 5.27 Species frequency on roadsides compared with that in gardens. Red symbols show species that were at least as frequent by roads as in gardens. The dot labelled Canadian Fleabane includes two closely related species that were not distinguished in the survey *Erigeron canadensis, E. sumatrensis.* Hollyhock *Alcea rosea* would not normally have been counted as a weed in gardens so would not have been listed.

Chart labels (y-axis: Roadside count; x-axis: Garden count):
Annual Meadow-grass, Dandelion, Knotgrass, Procumbent Pearlwort, Greater Plantain, Canadian Fleabane, Rye-grass, Autumn Hawkbit, Annual Pearlwort, Smooth Sow-thistle, Groundsel, Barren Brome, Creeping Bent, Petty Spurge, Shepherd's-purse, Dove's-foot Crane's-bill, White clover, Smooth Meadow-Grass, Cock's-foot, Ivy, Wall Barley, Wall Speedwell, Herb-Robert, Pineappleweed, Nipplewort, Red Fescue, Hollyhock, Procumbent Yellow-sorrel, Wood Avens, Wood Forget-me-not

Figure 5.28 Annual Meadow-grass is tolerant of trampling and was found on 81% of our roadsides. Here it is seen with a tiny plant of Procumbent Pearlwort in a crevice of block paving. Both Procumbent Pearlwort and Annual Pearlwort are particularly frequent in block paving, but occur also on asphalt and in gutters. (MOH).

to the right of each property facing the door. All species on the pavement or verge and to the middle of the carriageway were counted. Twenty of the roadsides had mown grass verges and six of these had trees. Of the remainder 27 were pure asphalt (3 with trees), 7 were block paving and 6 were soil banks or gravel.

Roadsides had many fewer plant species than gardens, averaging 14 as compared with 53 for the gardens. Table 5.9 lists the most frequent species in gardens, with the roadside count for comparison. Only **Dandelion** and **Annual Meadow-grass** were really frequent by roads. The least frequent were **Wood Avens**, **Nipplewort**, **Wood Forget-me-not** and **Green Alkanet**. These are plants that like shade, which is often absent on urban roadsides.

Although there were fewer plant species on roadsides, there were several roadside specialists (Figure 5.27). Notable among these are **Knotgrass** *Polygonum aviculare* agg., **Fleabane** *Erigeron* spp., **Procumbent Pearlwort** *Sagina procumbens* and **Annual Pearlwort** *S. apetala agg.* **Pineappleweed** *Matricaria discoidea*, present on six roadsides, was never seen in a garden.

Figure 5.29 The delightful Autumn Hawkbit is a characteristic plant of mown grass verges. Here it is seen in a lawn beside Addenbrooke's Hospital, where it is abundant. It is much less frequent in domestic garden lawns than in those beside roads. (MOH).

Figure 5.30 Wall Barley, seen here growing among Ryegrass, is a common roadside plant. It is not frequent in gardens, where if it is present at all, it grows near the road in the front garden. (MOH).

Ryegrass was always present where there was a grass verge, no doubt because it had been sown there. White Clover, Smooth Meadow-grass, Daisy, Creeping Bent, **Autumn Hawkbit** *Scorzoneroides autumnalis* and **Wall Barley** *Hordeum murinum* were also characteristic of grass verges but were mostly absent where there was only asphalt or block paving.

Walls

Walls share with pavements the absence of any depth of soil and a susceptibility to drought.

They are less likely to be treated with herbicide, except along the base, but careful property owners attempt, sometimes unsuccessfully, to remove potentially destructive woody plants. A few owners value their mossy or flowery walls, most are probably indifferent to them and only the excessively tidy try to keep their walls clear of all vegetation. However, all plants may be eliminated periodically by repointing or more drastic restoration. Walls offer a range of microclimate from south-facing to north-facing sides, although in narrow streets even the south-facing walls are

Figure 5.31 A north-facing wall off Tennis Court Road, Cambridge, on which we recorded 17 species in a 10 m length. (CDP).

shaded by the buildings opposite. Colonisation by seeds is less straightforward than for habitats on the ground. Riparian walls provide a special habitat with no equivalent on the street.

Walls are perhaps less prominent as a feature of Cambridge's historic cityscape than they are in Oxford. Whereas the Jurassic limestones near Oxford have always provided a ready supply of beautiful construction materials, Cambridge builders had to bring their stone from afar (or to scavenge supplies from disused buildings such as the medieval abbeys and friaries). Although many of the grand buildings of the city are built of stone, the walls around them tend to be made of brick and to be functional rather than monumental. Nevertheless Cambridge was the site of one of the pioneer studies of wall vegetation in Britain, a paper in the *Journal of Ecology* by John Rishbeth (Rishbeth 1948).

In May and June 2020 we (CDP and JDS) recorded the species growing on 85 walls in the NHC area. We selected for study lengths of walls up to 10 m long with five or more vascular plants growing on them, listing the species and counting the number of individuals of each on the top of the wall and on one side. We noted additional species occurring on the wall nearby but not represented in the sample. We were recording during an exceptionally sunny and warm start to the summer, and spoke to one owner who was watering the wilting **Snapdragons** *Antirrhinum*

majus on her wall. Late-flowering species of **Willowherb** *Epilobium* spp. and **Fleabane** *Erigeron* spp. were usually only present as rosettes and thus had to be recorded simply as the genus. We originally aimed to select a sample of walls distributed evenly across the study area but it proved impossible to do this. Suitable walls were not difficult to find in the historic city centre and the centres of the nearby villages, and were also scattered in areas of Victorian terrace housing, but the suburbs built in the interwar period tend to have fences or hedges rather than walls as

Figure 5.32 Location of the 85 walls studied in 2020.

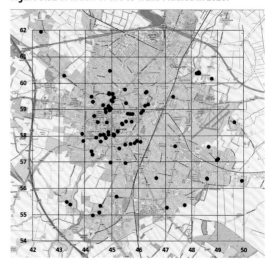

Figure 5.33 Rue-leaved Saxifrage in the large population on a wall top by Queens' College. (PAR).

boundaries and even these may be absent from some later open-plan developments. Our sample excluded walls inside college grounds, as these were firmly closed at the time of recording.

Of the 85 walls studied, 75 were built mainly or entirely of brick, though some of these were capped with stone or metal. The other construction materials were flint with a cap of brick or stone (4 walls), stone (4) and concrete (1) with one wall built of stone in the lower half and brick above. The stone walls were alongside a church, a master's lodge, a large farm and the University's Senate House, a clear indication of the use of stone for walls only in high-status sites.

We recorded 177 species on the walls we studied, with a total of 876 species records on the 10-m lengths plus 25 records of additional species just outside the sampled length. Seven walls had the bare minimum of five species needed to qualify for inclusion in the study. The four richest walls, with 26–29 species, were all alongside the River Cam or nearby brooks and ditches. **Rue-leaved Saxifrage** *Saxifraga tridactylites* was the species with the largest single population, over 500 plants on the top of a 10 m length of wall alongside Queens' College. At the other extreme, 356 of the 876 species occurrences were of single individuals. **Ivy-leaved Speedwell** *Veronica hederifolia* grew on six walls but never as more than one plant.

Different types of wall have different species. An analysis of our wall data revealed three ecologically distinct species groups. The first group consisted of annuals: **Thale Cress** *Arabidopsis thaliana*, **Hairy Bitter-cress** *Cardamine hirsuta*, **Sticky Mouse-ear** *Cerastium glomeratum*, **Common Whitlowgrass** *Erophila*

verna, **Annual Pearlworts** *Sagina apetala* agg., **Groundsel** *Senecio vulgaris* and **Wall Speedwell** *Veronica arvensis*. **Annual Meadow-grass** *Poa annua* is also an annual when it grows on walls. The annuals are characteristically found on dry wall tops where numerous individuals of several species often grow intermixed in an open community which is at its best in spring. By midsummer most plants have usually set seed and died, and in the exceptional heat of the 2020 season quite a few shrivelled before flowering or setting seed. **Procumbent Pearlwort** *Sagina procumbens*, although a perennial, is clearly very drought-tolerant and is very much a member of the same community. Rue-leaved Saxifrage also belongs with this group, though we recorded it on only three walls.

The second group consists of winter-green perennials, including **Wall-rue** *Asplenium ruta-muraria*, **Red Valerian** *Centranthus ruber*, **Mexican Fleabane** *Erigeron karvinskianus*, **Common Ivy** *Hedera helix*, **Green Alkanet** *Pentaglottis sempervirens* and **Yellow Corydalis** *Pseudofumaria lutea*, plus the robust annual **Barren Brome** *Anisantha sterilis*. These are found, often (but not always) in small numbers, on the tops and sides of dry walls (with Wall-rue and Yellow Corydalis showing a marked preference for the sides). **Ivy-leaved Toadflax** *Cymbalaria muralis* and **Pellitory-of-the-wall** *Parietaria judaica*, also winter-green perennials, link these species to the third ecological group. These are perennials with a preference for walls by water, including **Wood Avens** *Geum urbanum*, **Wood Dock** *Rumex sanguineus*, **Common Nettle** *Urtica dioica* and especially **Gypsywort** *Lycopus europaeus*. Only eight riparian walls were included in the survey and there were several infrequent waterside plants including **Hemp-agrimony** *Eupatorium cannabinum*, **Meadowsweet** *Filipendula ulmaria* and **Purple-loosestrife** *Lythrum salicaria*.

The commonest wall species

The twelve commonest species in our samples are listed in Table 5.10. Ron Payne studied 608 walls in the Isle of Ely between 1999 and 2004 and listed his top ten species; the percentage of walls on which he found those species that also occur on our list is given in the table. There is clearly much in common between our walls and those in the Isle of Ely. Ron Payne recorded walls with just one species and some of his sites were examined with

Table 5.10 The most frequent plants recorded on 85 Cambridge walls, with a comparison with published data from Ely. Records of *Erigeron* include *E. canadensis*, *E. sumatrensis* and perhaps *E. floribundus*. Key to Native status: N – native, Arch – ancient introduction (archaeophyte), Neo – post-1500 introduction (neophyte).

Species	Scientific name	Native status	Type of plant	% samples	% Isle of Ely (rank)
Annual Meadow-grass	*Poa annua*	N	Annual	39	29 (3)
Smooth Sow-thistle	*Sonchus oleraceus*	N	Annual	36	21 (8)
Dandelion	*Taraxacum* agg.	N	Perennial	34	29 (2)
Ivy-leaved Toadflax	*Cymbalaria muralis*	Neo	Perennial	31	25 (5)
Fleabanes	*Erigeron* (*Conyza*) spp.	Neo	Annual	30	
Hairy Bitter-cress	*Cardamine hirsuta*	N	Annual	26	23 (6)
Wall Speedwell	*Veronica arvensis*	N	Annual	25	
Willowherbs	*Epilobium* spp.	N, Neo	Perennial	24	
Annual Pearlworts	*Sagina apetala* agg.	N	Annual	23	
Common Ivy	*Hedera helix*	N	Perennial (climber)	23	18 (9)
Procumbent Pearlwort	*Sagina procumbens*	N	Perennial	22	
Groundsel	*Senecio vulgaris*	N	Annual	22	18 (9)

binoculars from a distance; he suggested that for this reason his most frequent species, **Buddleia** *Buddleja davidii*, was over-represented in his list. It does not appear in our top twelve though we did record it on 20% of our walls. The other species in his top ten are Nettle, on 25% of his walls but only 8% of ours, and **Elder** *Sambucus nigra*, which he had on 21% of his walls but we recorded in just a single site. **Fleabanes** have increased on walls in Cambridgeshire since Payne's survey because of the spread of **Guernsey Fleabane** *Erigeron sumatrensis*, which was not recorded in the county until 1997.

Changes in the wall flora since the 1940s

John Rishbeth also listed the top 12 species in his survey of walls in Cambridge (mainly 1939–40) and in Ely and Cambridgeshire villages (mainly 1945–46). His top twelve are listed in Table 5.11, with the number of their sites. He does not give the total number of walls surveyed, so these numbers cannot be converted to percentages, and he said nothing about his sampling strategy.

Annual Meadow-grass appears at the top of both Rishbeth's list and ours, and **Dandelion**, second on Rishbeth's list, is third on ours. **Groundsel** and **Ivy-leaved Toadflax** are the other species on both lists. Otherwise the differences are very substantial, and it is striking that several of the top twelve Rishbeth species were scarcely recorded in our survey. Robust perennials dominate Rishbeth's list, including one tree, one shrub, tall herbs (**Feverfew** and **Rosebay Willowherb**) and a rhizomatous grass (**Red Fescue**). The only woody species on our list is **Ivy**, a species which it is difficult to know when to record as it often invades walls from plants rooted at the base but may persist

Table 5.11 The most frequent plants recorded on Cambridgeshire walls by John Rishbeth, 1939–1946. The percentage of sites in our survey is given for comparison, with rank order for the species in our top 40 (so many of the rarer species occur in the same number of sites that lower rank orders are uninformative). Key to Native status: N – native, Arch – ancient introduction (archaeophyte), Neo – post-1500 introduction (neophyte).

Species	Scientific name	Native status	Type of plant	No. samples	% our samples (rank)
Annual Meadow-grass	*Poa annua*	N	Annual	83	39 (1)
Dandelion	*Taraxacum* agg.	N	Perennial	54	34 (3)
Red Fescue	*Festuca rubra* agg.	N	Perennial	54	7 (39)
Snapdragon	*Antirrhinum majus*	Neo	Perennial	47	6
Ivy-leaved Toadflax	*Cymbalaria muralis*	Neo	Perennial	46	31 (4)
Thyme-leaved Sandwort	*Arenaria serpyllifolia* agg.	N	Annual	38	5
Elder	*Sambucus nigra*	N	Perennial (shrub)	32	1
Groundsel	*Senecio vulgaris*	N	Annual	30	22 (11)
Feverfew	*Tanacetum parthenium*	Arch	Perennial	29	0
Sycamore	*Acer pseudoplatanus*	Neo	Perennial (tree)	25	7
Shepherd's-purse	*Capsella bursa-pastoris*	N	Annual	25	1
Rosebay Willowherb	*Chamaenerion angustifolium*	N	Perennial	24	2

Figure 5.34 This Birch sapling has probably survived on a wall top on Shelly Row, Cambridge by hiding amongst the branches of a vigorous Pyracantha growing in the garden. (CDP).

(and therefore be recorded) when the basal plants are cleared away.

According to Rishbeth, 15% of the species he recorded on walls were trees and shrubs and these comprised 13% of his site records, if riparian species are excluded. For annuals (therophytes), the figures were 27% of species and 31% of site records. We recorded a higher proportion of trees and shrubs (19%) but a lower percentage of site records (11%), again excluding specialised waterside species for the sake of comparison (although this actually makes little difference to the proportions). Conversely, we had a slightly smaller proportion of annual species (25%) but more site records (38%) than Rishbeth. Rishbeth commented on the number of garden escapes amongst his woody species and the range is even greater now, but even so the decrease in the proportion of site records of woody species, and the increasing proportion of annual records, again suggests that the wall vegetation has become more open.

A direct comparison of Rishbeth's records with ours is complicated by the fact that he recorded walls over a wider area, extending as far as Ely, and also within college grounds. However, it seems unlikely that this is the sole reason for the substantial change in the top twelve species. What might have caused the changes in Cambridge's walls since 1940? There are several possibilities – changes in the surrounding land in the city, which is the 'catchment area' from which the wall flora is derived; warmer summers and milder winters; a higher standard of maintenance of the walls themselves, with less tolerance of woody species; and reduced air pollution from coal-burning fires. **Elder** must have decreased in Cambridge but remains frequent in the Isle of Ely, suggesting that climatic factors are less likely to be involved than a general tidying up or development of waste places in Cambridge. This might also explain the decrease in **Rosebay Willowherb**. The increasing proportion of annuals might result from a combination of the clearance of woody species, the repair or replacement of derelict walls, climatic changes and perhaps reduced 'acid rain'. We can conclude that there have probably been major changes in the wall flora, but the reasons are uncertain.

6. Mosses and liverworts

Mosses and liverworts, together with the hornworts, are collectively known as bryophytes. Traditionally, they were regarded as 'primitive plants' from which the 'higher plants' evolved. Modern research has turned this theory on its head, implying that bryophytes are small plants which are descended from larger plants that had stomata (breathing pores) on their surface, as vascular plants do today. There is nothing particularly primitive about them except that they lack pollen and have to be fertilised by sperm cells swimming in water. In this they resemble ferns.

Cambridgeshire is not a rich county for mosses and especially not for liverworts, but with assiduous recording we have found 175 species in the NHC area between 2010 and 2019 (Table 6.1). This compares with 908 vascular plant taxa (counting only those that were in a list of plant attributes called PLANTATT (Hill *et al.* 2004)). The number of liverworts is a very small proportion of the national total, whereas for dicots it is half the total. The number of gymnosperms is inflated by records of planted trees; only a few conifer species establish from seed in the city.

Survey of Cambridge monads

As with the vascular plants, we made a systematic survey of Cambridge monads, concentrating entirely on the 64 monads of our area. We aimed to visit each monad at least twice. Mosses and liverworts are mostly shrivelled and dried up in the summer, and we generally ignored them from May to September. We made 6018 records. In addition to our systematic monad records, bryophytes were surveyed in some of the gardens in our garden survey (see Chapter 5). Gardens that were visited from September onwards could have their bryophytes recorded at the same time as the vascular plants. In the end we got bryophyte records in only 30 of the 60 gardens.

Rather to our surprise we found at least 40 species in every monad except for the one with the airport, where most of the land is both inaccessible and covered by mown grass, which is a very poor bryophyte habitat (Figure 6.1). There is a clear but rather weak correlation between bryophyte species richness and that of the vascular plants (Figure 6.2). Monads with more than 300 vascular plants had on average 57 bryophyte species, while those with less than 300 vascular plant species had on average 46. Here again, vascular plants were counted only if they were listed in PLANTATT. Apart from the airport, there is a group of peripheral monads

Table 6.1 Number of species of bryophytes and vascular plants compared with totals for Cambridgeshire and the British Isles. Percentages show the proportion of species in the NHC area compared with Cambridgeshire as a whole and with Great Britain and Ireland.

	NHC	%Cambs	%Br Isles	Cambs	Br Isles
Liverworts	21	66%	7%	32	303
Mosses	154	52%	19%	298	795
Total bryophyte	175	53%	16%	330	1098
Ferns etc.	23	88%	29%	26	78
Gymnosperms	9	69%	64%	13	14
Dicots	682	83%	52%	822	1322
Monocots	194	72%	41%	269	473
Total vascular	908	80%	48%	1130	1887

Figure 6.1 Bryophyte species totals in NHC monads. Monads are coloured according to their totals, with categories 40–49 shown in blue, 50–59 in pale biscuit, and 60–79 in mid biscuit. The airport monad is white and the Botanic Garden monad is dark biscuit.

	42	43	44	45	46	47	48	49
61	47	41	45	43	58	46	42	46
60	54	41	43	41	45	49	47	45
59	58	48	52	55	50	50	42	55
58	54	72	75	56	43	65	34	54
57	42	49	63	92	43	48	43	45
56	44	40	54	42	49	52	61	44
55	45	56	42	41	42	47	73	44
54	43	45	51	43	43	41	64	46

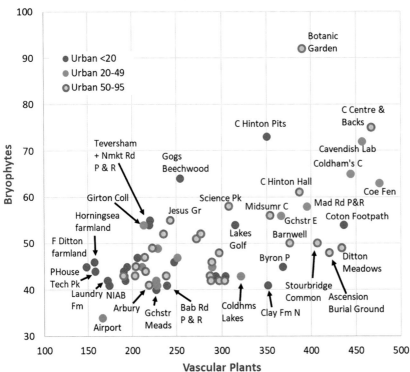

Figure 6.2 Monad counts of bryophyte species in comparison with those of vascular plants. Monad symbols are coloured according to the percentage of urban (including suburban) land cover.

(including the urban King's Hedges) with fewer than 200 vascular plant species. These are all rather poor in bryophytes.

If a monad has few houses, it will probably be rather poor in bryophytes because it lacks the characteristic urban species. For example, the Grantchester Meadows monad is poor, with 40 bryophyte species, because it has only one house. Arable fields are also poor in bryophytes. Copses, tree lines and ditches are more productive. At the other end of the scale are the well-known hotspots of the Cherry Hinton chalk pits and the Beechwoods LNR. However, the two richest monads are the city centre (including the Backs, with 40% green space) and the Botanic Garden. The Botanic Garden monad has 92 bryophyte species, of which 88 were found in the garden and just 4 extra in the adjacent area. In the Botanic Garden, there were 8 species that occurred nowhere else in our study area and 17 species that occurred in 1–3 other monads. Of these 25 species, 8 were on imported Carboniferous limestone, 5 on other imported rocks, and 6 on mud by the streams or the lake. Of the remaining six species, two were on buildings, two on lawns, one in a flowerbed and one on a tree. The great richness of the site is due to imported rock combined with the presence of water.

The discovery that even apparently featureless monads had at least 40 species suggests that there is in fact rather little difference between Cambridge and its surroundings. In the NHC area the richest monads are characterised by permanent features such as woodland, parkland and grand gardens. Several such sites exist in the near neighbourhood of Cambridge, notably Madingley Wood, Madingley Hall, Milton Country Park and Wandlebury Country Park. These are good bryophyte sites, and there are also many nearby villages which are surely richer than Grantchester Meadows. As explained below, there is indeed a concentration of rare species in Cambridge but these are in a small number of sites. The average Cambridge monad is no richer than the surrounding villages.

Composition of Cambridge bryophyte flora
A recent book (Preston & Hill 2019) gives a comprehensive account of the county's bryophytes. According to this account, there are ten habitat categories in the county (Table 6.2). Here we do not go into detail about the habitat categories, but note that the cluster 'Common' is not a habitat but includes those species that are so common that they are found on almost all excursions. The cluster

Table 6.2 Bryophytes of Cambridge compared with the county; only records from the period 2000–2019 are included. Monad counts for clusters are the sum of monad counts for the species in that cluster, and the ratio is that between counts for the NHC area and that for the rest of the county.

Habitat cluster	Cluster name	Monads NHC	Monads county	Ratio	Species city	Species county
1	Arable	188	1568	12%	11	21
2	Ruderal	656	3759	17%	22	21
3	Calcicole	141	761	19%	24	41
4	Built	761	3517	22%	29	30
5	Water	123	832	15%	16	28
6	Shade	200	1441	14%	11	12
7	Common	710	5254	14%	16	15
8	Epiphyte	332	2460	13%	23	34
9	Acid & Fen	16	262	6%	9	42
10	Woodland	46	1156	4%	14	34
	Total	3173	21010	15%	175	278

'Acid and Fen' includes species that grow on acid substrates as well as those that occur in fenland.

It is immediately clear that the woodland specialists and those of Acid & Fen are much less common in Cambridge than elsewhere in the county. The woodland species are those that are more characteristic of ancient woodland than of shaded ground in secondary woodland, which are included in the 'Shade' cluster. Their scarcity in Cambridge is because there is no ancient woodland. Likewise there is almost no acid ground, so that plants of acid substrates are confined to a few restricted habitats. Among the small number of woodland species in the NHC area, **Common Striated Feather-moss** *Eurhynchium striatum* can colonise secondary woodland fairly rapidly. It was found in seven of our monads, and was present in two woods that had been planted in the past 30 years. The beautiful **Common Tamarisk-moss** *Thuidium tamariscinum* is a slower colonist and was found in only three monads.

These plants have colonised naturally from the surrounding countryside, as indeed have all but three members of the Woodland cluster. Two of the three were introduced with Carboniferous Limestone to the Botanic Garden.

The third, **Pale Glaucous Thread-moss** *Pohlia wahlenbergii*, was in a garden pot, and was doubtless a transient occurrence which would disappear when the pot was emptied.

Only three members of the Acid & Fen cluster were fenland plants. **Marsh Bryum**

Figure 6.3 Common Tamarisk-moss *Thuidium tamariscinum* is a woodland plant that has spread to three localities in our study area. Here it is seen on a shaded bank in the wooded former chalk pit at Limekiln Close. (MOH).

Figure 6.4 Fringed Heartwort *Ricciocarpos natans* is a floating liverwort that resembles Duckweed. It occurred naturally in Chesterton in 1942, but died out in the Cambridge area until its reintroduction by Jonathan Shanklin in 2013. The plants shown here are in Wicken Fen. (CRS).

Bryum pseudotriquetrum was found on the margin of four artificial ponds, where it was clearly a natural colonist. **Jagged Germanderwort** *Riccardia chamedryfolia* by the Botanic Garden lake could also have colonised naturally. However **Fringed Heartwort** *Ricciocarpos natans* was deliberately introduced from Denbighshire to a pond at the British Antarctic Survey by Jonathan Shanklin in 2013. It was still present in 2020. As far as we know, no other bryophytes have been deliberately introduced, although several have been unintentionally introduced with their substrate.

Of the six acid-loving species in the Acid & Fen cluster, several were presumably introduced with their substrate – two on sandstone rock by the Botanic Garden lake, two on railway cess of the Chesterton sidings, two on granite hoggin in the University West Residences car park and two on granite hoggin in the Sidgwick site.

Bryophytes are rather rarely introduced with their substrate, and when they are, the introduced colonies tend not to persist for long. A notable exception to this is the limestone and sandstone rock of the Botanic Garden. Most bryophytes are highly effective colonists. As a result, they have been able to reach Cambridge naturally, and only a few are not native to Britain. Indeed, only six non-native bryophytes have been found in Cambridgeshire, of which five have been found in the NHC area and one just outside it, in Madingley (Table 6.3).

The first of the non-natives to be found in Cambridge was **Shady Beard-moss** *Didymodon umbrosus*. It had previously been overlooked and was well established in the city at that time. One of us (MOH) found it on two of the houses that he lived in as an undergraduate in 1965 and 1966. It typically grows on shaded brickwork, and was present in two of the 30 domestic gardens that were surveyed for bryophytes. The next to appear was **Cape Thread-moss** *Orthodontium lineare*, which was found in the Beechwoods LNR in 1968 and 1983. It is a strong calcifuge and disappeared along with the native **Nodding Thread-moss** *Pohlia nutans* as the Cambridge rainfall became less acid. It normally grows on rotting wood, and can still be found in the vicinity of the city, both in ancient woods and in long-established secondary woods.

Heath Star Moss *Campylopus introflexus* is also a strong calcifuge and a highly effective colonist,

Figure 6.5 Urn Haircap *Pogonatum urnigerum* introduced with granite hoggin to a car park in the West Cambridge Site. (PGL).

Table 6.3 Non-native bryophytes of Cambridgeshire with dates of first discovery in the county and in our study area. Monad counts are for the period 2010–2019 and those for Cambs exclude monads in our study area.

Common name	Scientific name	Cambs 1st	Cambridge 1st	Cambridge monads	Cambs monads
Heath Star Moss	*Campylopus introflexus*	1965	1990	11	104
Shady Beard-moss	*Didymodon umbrosus*	1965	1965	14	15
Short Pottia	*Hennediella macrophylla*	2003	2005	13	5
Stanford Screw-moss	*Hennediella stanfordensis*	1977	2006	2	1
Cape Thread-moss	*Orthodontium lineare*	1947	1968	0	55
Pond Crystalwort	*Riccia rhenana*	1959	-	0	0

appearing rather randomly on suitably acid substrates. It has persisted or perhaps recolonised in the Gogs beechwood on the base of a beech tree. Other substrates are cracks between acid roof tiles, rotting wood chips and rotting fences.

Short Pottia *Hennediella macrophylla* has spread rapidly in Cambridge since 2005, and is more frequent here than in the rest of the county. It favours trampled ground along the Backs and in parks and college gardens, and many have arrived here on the shoes of tourists. The last non-native to appear in Cambridge was the enigmatic **Stanford Screw-moss** *Hennediella stanfordensis*. This was discovered near the River Cam in Duxford long before Short Pottia, but has spread very little. The two records from NHC area are from Girton

College and a roadside in Cherry Hinton, both on trampled ground under trees.

In addition to the non-native species that grow outdoors are a few that occur in the Botanic Garden glasshouse. These have not been studied in detail but Robin Stevenson identified the liverworts *Heteroscyphus coalitus* and *Lophocolea muricata*.

Commonest bryophytes in Cambridge

All the top 20 commonest bryophytes in Cambridge were mosses (Table 6.4). One of these **Wood Bristle-moss** *Orthotrichum affine* is almost exclusively an epiphyte, although several of the others also grow commonly on the trunks and branches of trees and bushes. The other common mosses belong to the Common, Built and Ruderal

Table 6.4 Mosses found in at least 90% of the 64 NHC monads. The number of records from the 30 surveyed gardens is given for comparison.

Common name	Scientific name	Cluster	NHC	Garden
Creeping Feather-moss	*Amblystegium serpens*	Common	64	25
Lesser Bird's-claw Beard-moss	*Barbula convoluta*	Ruderal	62	21
Bird's-claw Beard-moss	*Barbula unguiculata*	Ruderal	64	17
Rough-stalked Feather-moss	*Brachythecium rutabulum*	Common	64	25
Silver-moss	*Bryum argenteum*	Ruderal	64	17
Capillary Thread-moss	*Bryum capillare*	Common	64	25
Bicoloured Bryum	*Bryum dichotomum*	Ruderal	64	14
Pointed Spear-moss	*Calliergonella cuspidata*	Common	60	21
Redshank	*Ceratodon purpureus*	Common	60	13
Grey-cushioned Grimmia	*Grimmia pulvinata*	Built	63	21
Cypress-leaved Plait-moss	*Hypnum cupressiforme*	Common	62	17
Common Feather-moss	*Kindbergia praelonga*	Common	64	22
Wood Bristle-moss	*Orthotrichum affine*	Epiphyte	63	13
White-tipped Bristle-moss	*Orthotrichum diaphanum*	Common	64	15
Swartz's Feather-moss	*Oxyrrhynchium hians*	Common	64	16
Hornschuch's Beard-moss	*Pseudocrossidium hornschuchianum*	Ruderal	64	9
Clustered Feather-moss	*Rhynchostegium confertum*	Common	58	23
Intermediate Screw-moss	*Syntrichia montana*	Built	63	18
Great Hairy Screw-moss	*Syntrichia ruralis*	Built	62	15
Wall Screw-moss	*Tortula muralis*	Built	64	27

Figure 6.7 Rough-stalked Feather-moss *Brachythecium rutabulum* is the commonest moss in our area, relishing the eutrophic Cambridgeshire environment. It is particularly abundant in patches of Nettles among Elders, but can be found in sheltered woods, lawns, wall-bases, streamsides and gardens. (MOH).

clusters in Table 6.2. Much the commonest is **Rough-stalked Feather-moss** *Brachythecium rutabulum*, which is the commonest species in the county as well as the city.

For many citizens mosses are a nuisance, and moss surveyors are routinely asked 'How can I get rid of moss from my lawn?'. Mosses tend to thrive in lawns where the grass does not grow well, especially in dry shade under trees. Assiduous gardeners can eliminate lawn moss by application of ferrous sulphate, either as a component of lawn sand or directly as a spray. Several of the very tidy lawns observed in our garden survey had been treated in this way.

Figure 6.8 Springy Turf-moss *Rhytidiadelphus squarrosus* in a Cambridge lawn. It is mixed with a few shoots of Pointed Spear-moss *Calliergonella cuspidata*, which often grows in the same habitat. (MOH).

Although Rough-stalked Feather-moss is very common in lawns it is often not the most abundant species. Two notable lawn mosses are **Common Feather-moss** *Kindbergia praelonga* and **Springy Turf-moss** *Rhytidiadelphus squarrosus*. These are very different in their prevalence. Common Feather-moss will rapidly invade almost any lawn where the grass is shaded or disturbed, and is often abundant in municipal parks and gardens. If there is bare ground, it will appear rapidly. Springy Turf-moss, on the other hand, takes its time, and does not thrive in the highly fertilised grass maintained by the City Council. However, in private gardens where lawns are regularly mown and not much fertilised, Springy Turf-moss comes into its own. It forms a dense mat which can choke the lawn mower and compete with the grass even in the absence of shade or disturbance. It is a true lawn moss, and has almost no other habitat in the NHC area. It is much less frequent in the Cambridgeshire countryside than in towns and villages.

Fortunately, most mosses do not cause annoyance to anybody, but **Capillary Thread-moss** *Bryum capillare* and **Intermediate Screw-moss** *Syntrichia montana* form large tufts on roofs, and have a tendency to block gutters when they become detached after frost or drought. Their growth habit is quite different from that of the lawn mosses, which are crawlers, known technically as pleurocarps. The non-crawling mosses are known as acrocarps, and may either be tufted or form extended carpets of shoots growing upwards from

Figure 6.9 Wall Screw-moss *Tortula muralis* is the most characteristic urban moss, producing miniature forests of erect capsules. Its vast spore production ensures that it colonises almost all suitable substrates. The capsules all ripen together in early summer, having been fertilised in the autumn. (CDP).

the ground or outwards from a wall or branch. The most notable of these is **Wall Screw-moss** *Tortula muralis*, which is the most successful of all urban mosses and was found in 27 out of the 30 gardens surveyed. It rapidly colonises new mortar and is present on almost all older buildings in Cambridge. It is a strong calcicole and is the most characteristic species of the built environment, recorded from all 64 of the Cambridge monads. However, a special search had to be made for it in the newly built-up West Cambridge Site. This has impressive new laboratories and residences, but there was no

Wall Screw-moss except on the concrete base of a former shed.

Liverworts in Cambridge

Liverworts are much rarer than mosses in Cambridge (Table 6.5). However, **Common Liverwort** *Marchantia polymorpha* is indeed common in built-up areas. It was found in 14 of the 30 gardens. It can be abundant on concrete patios, where householders attack it with power-hoses and brushes. **Crescent-cup Liverwort** *Lunularia cruciata* is nearly as frequent in the city but much less so in gardens. It is more often in shady spots than on patios. The next most frequent liverworts in the

Figure 6.10 Common Liverwort *Marchantia polymorpha* in St Clement's churchyard, Cambridge. Both females (fingered receptacles) and males (lobed receptacles) are present and are so thick on the ground that the underlying thalli are almost invisible. (MOH).

Table 6.5 Liverworts found in at least 10% of the 64 NHC monads. The number of records from the 30 surveyed gardens is given for comparison.

Common name	Scientific name	Cluster	NHC	Garden
Thalloid liverworts				
Greasewort	*Aneura pinguis*	Calcicole	17	1
Crescent-cup Liverwort	*Lunularia cruciata*	Built	45	5
Common Liverwort	*Marchantia polymorpha*	Ruderal	54	14
Forked Veilwort	*Metzgeria furcata*	Epiphyte	33	0
Bluish Veilwort	*Metzgeria violacea*	Epiphyte	7	0
Endive Pellia	*Pellia endiviifolia*	Shade	18	0
Leafy liverworts				
Minute Pouncewort	*Cololejeunea minutissima*	Epiphyte	9	0
Dilated Scalewort	*Frullania dilatata*	Epiphyte	40	3
Bifid Crestwort	*Lophocolea bidentata*	Shade	33	5
Variable-leaved Crestwort	*Lophocolea heterophylla*	Wood	12	0
Even Scalewort	*Radula complanata*	Epiphyte	21	0

city are two epiphytes, **Dilated Scalewort** *Frullania dilatata* and **Forked Veilwort** *Metzgeria furcata*, together with **Bifid Crestwort** *Lophocolea bidentata*, which normally grows at the edges of shaded lawns. Like Wood Bristle-moss, the epiphytic liverworts have increased enormously as the rainfall became less acid. Dilated Scalewort was found at Byron's Pool in 1951 and was not seen again in our area till 2000. It did not become frequent until 2009. Forked Veilwort was seen once or twice in a decade until it also became frequent in 2009. Bifid Crestwort, on the other hand, is in no way a calcicole and was present in Cambridge lawns and spinneys throughout this period.

A notable new arrival since 2010 is the tiny epiphyte **Minute Pouncewort** *Cololejeunea minutissima*. It first appeared in Cambridgeshire in 2007 and was found in Cambridge in 2011. You have to be very sharp-eyed and diligent to find it; almost all our records were made by Jonathan Shanklin.

Greasewort *Aneura pinguis* and **Endive Pellia** *Pellia endiviifolia* are thalloid liverworts which are frequent in wet places by ponds and streams, as well as on bare chalk in East Pit LNR. Extraordinarily, Greasewort was also seen in a Cambridge garden, where it grew on a damp coir mat by the back door of a house.

Rare bryophytes in Cambridge

Rarity depends on the scale at which it is assessed. At the European scale **Scarce Redshank** *Ceratodon conicus* and **Strap-leaved Earth-moss** *Ephemerum recurvifolium* are judged to be near-threatened (Hodgetts & Lockhart, 2020). However, Scarce Redshank is very similar to **Redshank** *Ceratodon purpureus*, which is common on Cambridge pavements. Our specimen of Scarce Redshank grew on soil by a concrete manhole cover in Milton Road, and was confirmed by matching its DNA. Strap-leaved Earth-moss is cryptic for a different reason, namely that it is very small and grows on bare chalky soil in the autumn. During the NatHistCam project, Chris Preston got his eye in for it and found it in 23 separate places (admittedly three of them were in Wulfstan Way). It is not signified as near-threatened in Britain and we suspect that other Europeans have overlooked it.

At the scale of Great Britain the Cherry Hinton chalk pits were in the past outstanding, with **Short-beaked Aloe-moss** *Aloina brevirostris*, **Rigid Aloe-moss** *Aloina rigida*, **Spiral Chalk-moss**

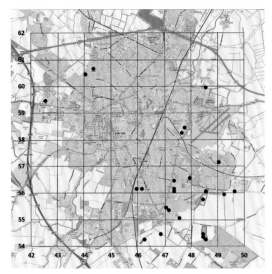

Figure 6.11 Distribution of Strap-leaved Earth-moss *Ephemerum recurvifolium* in Cambridge. It is found on disturbed calcareous soil, especially in the chalky south-east of the city. (CDP).

Pterygoneurum lamellatum and **Chalk Screw-moss** *Tortula vahliana*. Three of these are signified by Hodgetts & Lockhart (2020) as endangered in Britain, and Spiral Chalk-moss is now extinct, having been last seen in East Pit in 1970. Chalk Screw-moss was refound in very small quantity in 2017 but the others have not been seen since 2009, in spite of careful searching.

At the scale of Cambridgeshire, we found 17 species that occur outside our study area in two or fewer monads (Table 6.6). Four of them were in Beechwoods LNR, which is a fairly stable habitat. The two from the Sidgwick and West Cambridge sites were imported with granite hoggin and are clearly transient. Also transient is **Schimper's Bristle-moss** *Orthotrichum schimperi*, which was found as a single tuft on hawthorn by the railway on Coldham's Common. It is likely that this resulted from a wind-borne spore coming from a more southerly part of Europe, where it is common. The Impington plants were from a gravel pit whose margin was still sufficiently open to support ruderals. The site will no doubt shortly become unsuitable because of ecological succession. **Frizzled Crisp-moss** *Tortella tortuosa* has persisted since 1955 on imported limestone of the rock garden in the Botanic Garden. However **Common Haircap** *Polytrichum commune* was in a gutter and was removed as soon as it was discovered. The St John's College Feather-mosses (*Rhynchostegiella* species)

Table 6.6 Bryophytes that are present in Cambridge but are found in fewer than three monads elsewhere in Cambridgeshire. Liverworts are marked (L). NHC is the number of monads in which species has been found in the NatHistCam area.

English name	Scientific name	Locality	NHC	Cambs
Lesser Featherwort (L)	*Plagiochila porelloides*	Beechwoods LNR	1	0
Chalk Feather-moss	*Campylophyllum calcareum*	Beechwoods LNR	1	0
Spiral Extinguisher-moss	*Encalypta streptocarpa*	Beechwoods LNR	1	1
Woodsy Thyme-moss	*Plagiomnium cuspidatum*	Beechwoods LNR	1	0
Common Haircap	*Polytrichum commune*	Botanic Garden	1	1
Frizzled Crisp-moss	*Tortella tortuosa*	Botanic Garden	1	0
Schimper's Bristle-moss	*Orthotrichum schimperi*	Coldham's Common	1	0
Chalk Notchwort (L)	*Lophozia perssonii*	East Pit	1	2
Slender Beard-moss	*Didymodon icmadophilus*	East Pit	1	2
Stanford Screw-moss	*Hennediella stanfordensis*	Girton, Cherry Hinton	2	1
Archangelic Thread-moss	*Bryum archangelicum*	Impington	1	0
Heim's Pottia	*Hennediella heimii*	Impington	1	1
Scarce Redshank	*Ceratodon conicus*	Milton Road	1	0
Common Threadwort (L)	*Cephaloziella divaricata*	Sidgwick site	1	1
Urn Haircap	*Pogonatum urnigerum*	Sidgwick Site, West Cambridge Site	2	0
Curve-stalked Feather-moss	*Rhynchostegiella curviseta*	St John's College	1	1
Scabrous Feather-moss	*Rhynchostegiella litorea*	St John's College, Lime Kiln Close	2	2

grew on the banks of the Bin Brook, which is likely to be a fairly stable habitat. In conclusion, we may say that about half our rare species are not expected to persist, although others, especially in the beechwood, have persisted for decades.

Change in the bryophyte flora

As noted by Preston & Hill (2019), Cambridgeshire's bryophyte flora is dynamic, with rapid losses and gains.

Of the 40 species that have not been found in Cambridge since 2009, perhaps the most remarkable is **Claw-leaved Hook-moss** *Palustriella falcata*, a plant of calcareous marshes, which was found in 1883 by H.N. Dixon in the area now known as Empty Common. There was once a species-rich marsh there, but it was destroyed by coprolite digging. The site is now occupied by allotment gardens. However, the biggest loss of species has not been of marsh plants but of calcicoles. In the 1950s, the golf course and sides of the Roman Road were home to the chalk grassland specialists **Fir Tamarisk-moss** *Abietinella abietina* and **Montagne's Cylinder-moss** *Entodon concinnus*. The habitat deteriorated as a result of eutrophication and loss of grazing. There are no records of either after 1979. More numerous were the calcicole specialists of disturbed open ground. These thrived in East Pit while the quarry was working. After its closure in 1984 they gradually succumbed to ecological succession and had mostly disappeared by the end of the 20th century. Only the Beechwoods LNR retained its calcicole flora. The combination of shallow soil, sloping terrain and heavy shade cast by the beech trees has kept the ground relatively open so that it remains favourable to chalk specialists.

A particularly large change has resulted from the changing acidity of the rainfall. Since the 1970s, UK emissions of sulphur dioxide (SO_2) have fallen by about 98% and the effect on the bryophyte flora of Cambridge has been remarkable. In urban Cambridge there were in addition many coal fires, which coloured our Cambridge brick a nasty greyish tint and filled the tufts of mosses on roofs with smuts. The great gainers from acid air pollution in the 1960s and 1970s were **Redshank** *Ceratodon purpureus* and **Common Pincushion** *Dicranoweisia cirrata*. Redshank was abundant on roofs and pavements, and Common Pincushion was abundant on tree trunks. Both are calcifuges and Common Pincushion has very dense chloroplasts which protect it from bleaching by SO_2. At the present time Redshank remains common, especially on asphalt, which must have a sufficiently acid surface to retain this calcifuge moss. It has decreased enormously on other substrates. Common Pincushion has become much rarer and was found in only 21 of our 64 monads, mostly on rotting wood but with five occurrences on living trees.

As the rainfall became less acidic, the pH of concrete surfaces and tiled roofs increased, and they developed a calcicole flora. **Thickpoint Grimmia** *Schistidium crassipilum* and **Intermediate Screw-moss** *Syntrichia montana* increased massively. Between 1950 and 1989, Thickpoint Grimmia was recorded in our area only from Trumpington churchyard, Grantchester churchyard, Fen Causeway bridge and a house in Chaucer Road. Intermediate Screw-moss was slightly commoner (or perhaps more conspicuous). It was found in the two churchyards, the Botanic Garden and about four places near the river. In our 2010–2019 survey, these species were found in 57 and 63 monads respectively.

The effect on epiphytes was even more marked. We have noted that the liverworts **Dilated Scalewort** *Frullania dilatata* and **Forked Veilwort** *Metzgeria furcata* did not become frequent until 2009. **Wood Bristle-moss** *Orthotrichum affine* was seen in just three localities in our area between 1960 and 1999. It became frequent in 2001. **Lateral Cryphaea** *Cryphaea heteromalla* was not seen at all until 2009, and became frequent in our area from 2015. **Small Hairy Screw-moss** *Syntrichia laevipila* was repeatedly found in East Pit from 1960 to 2009, but only in two other localities. No doubt the dust from the working chalk pit made the bark less acid before quarrying ceased in 1984. After 2018 it became moderately frequent. Examples could be multiplied, but the clear picture emerges that epiphytes became frequent in our study area between 2001 and 2018 and are now well established. The one exception is the calcifuge Common Pincushion which was rarely seen on tree bark after 2005.

Figure 6.12 Lateral Cryphaea *Cryphaea heteromalla* on *Sycopsis sinensis* in the Botanic Garden. (CDP).

Figure 6.13 A sheet of Marble Screw-moss *Syntrichia papillosa* on the bark of an Ash alongside Histon Road, Cambridge. (CDP).

Although rainfall has become less acidic, levels of nitrogen oxides (NO_x) have not decreased to the same extent and may even have increased along major roads. **Marble Screw-moss** *Syntrichia papillosa* was very uncommon in Cambridge until recently, but is now increasing. It can be seen, for example, covering the bark of some roadside ash trees along Histon Road. It is a plant that thrives in nitrogen-rich conditions. It has never been found fruiting in Britain but spreads by spherical gemmae which are clustered on the leaf surface.

Sand-hill Screw-moss *Syntrichia ruraliformis* is another moss that has much increased in Cambridge. As its name suggests, its main natural habitat is on dunes, where it forms extensive carpets on mobile sand. It is locally abundant also on sands in the Breckland. Other sandy areas are frequently colonised, especially in eastern England. It first appeared in the NHC area on the Gog Magog Golf Course in 1960, introduced with sand for a bunker. It was regularly seen there in subsequent years. The next appearance was at Cambridge Airport in 1999 and it was found in three other places in central and north Cambridge up to 2009. From 2010 it was frequent, not mainly on sand, but rather on gritty flat surfaces of aging concrete, asphalt and gravel. When growing in wide carpets, it is a handsome moss.

Finally we should mention the remarkable invasion of **Nicholson's Beard-moss** *Didymodon nicholsonii*. Until 1980 this was an uncommon species found mainly by streams and canals. There were two records from brick walls in Gamlingay. Then from 1980 onwards it was increasingly found on asphalt pavements in the south and west of Britain. It reached Cambridge in 2001 and rapidly became frequent in this habitat. Presumably this was a new genotype, spreading by gemmae on the protonema, as it almost never fruits.

Figure 6.14 Nicholson's Beard-moss *Didymodon nicholsonii* on asphalt at Wandlebury. At the bottom left of the picture is a small tuft of Intermediate Screw-moss *Syntrichia montana*, with characteristic hair-points at the apex of each leaf. Nicholson's Beard-moss, although a new arrival, is now an established component of the pavement flora in Cambridge. (PGL).

Macrofungi

Macrofungi are those fungi that give rise to readily visible fruiting bodies such as mushrooms. No systematic survey of macrofungi in the city has been carried out, however the CNHS has made casual records during field studies visits and has also made specific 'fungal forays' during an autumn visit. Autumn forays to the Botanic Garden have taken place annually since 2001, and a report was published in *Nature in Cambridgeshire* (Shanklin & Tribe 2017). This report found that three-quarters of the species were seen only once or twice and only 10% were recorded on six or more forays. This picture is likely to be replicated across the city and elsewhere in eastern England. Oliver Rackham recorded fungi in Brandon Park, Suffolk, almost every autumn for over 50 years but he nevertheless found six new species there on his last visit, in 2014, as many rarely fruit (Rackham 2015). Most exist as a mycelium either underground, or hidden within wood and it is not until the fruiting body emerges that they become obvious.

In general more species of fungi are seen during the autumn and in woodlands than at other times of year, so that can be the best time and place to start looking for them. There are however species around from spring to autumn and they can be found in a wide variety of habitats. A few even emerge during the winter, with the unusual **Winter Stalkball** *Tulostoma brumale* found just outside the NHC area at Magog Down.

Fungi can be difficult to identify, so it is generally only the readily identifiable species that are recorded. Many more are found, but often remain unidentified, even to genus, especially 'small brown jobs' and resupinate fungi. Because of these difficulties, this chapter only describes some of the more distinctive species found across the city.

Some fungi are edible, but there are often very similar species that are poisonous. In addition, some fungi can be eaten without harm by some people, but cause other people to become sick. For this reason it is usually best to buy your fungi from the grocer unless you are an expert! The species listed here are given in the order in the Collins Fungi Guide (Buczacki *et al.* 2012), which is a useful field guide to most of the common fungi.

Figure 7.1 A fungal foray in the Botanic Garden. (JDS).

Agaricus species include the familiar and edible **Field Mushroom** *Agaricus campestris* and **Horse Mushroom** *Agaricus arvensis*, but also include poisonous species such as **Yellow Stainer** *Agaricus xanthodermus*. All have a ring on the stem and smell of mushrooms!

Dapperling species such as **Freckled Dapperling** *Lepiota aspera* and **Stinking Dapperling** *Lepiota cristata* have a distinctive unpleasant rubbery smell which helps with identification.

Shaggy Parasol *Chlorophyllum rhacodes* and **Parasol** *Macrolepiota procera* have the largest caps of the commonly found mushrooms, often 15 cm or more across. They typically grow on woodland edges or in pasture.

Magpie Inkcap *Coprinopsis picacea* is an attractive black and white/pink coloured large fungus, often found in the Botanic Garden growing under conifers near Hobson's Conduit by Brooklands Avenue. Other Inkcaps are quite frequent with **Lawyer's Wig** or **Shaggy Inkcap** *Coprinus comatus*, **Glistening Inkcap** *Coprinellus micaceus* and **Pleated Inkcap** *Parasola plicatilis* amongst those regularly recorded.

Yellow Fieldcap *Bolbitius titubans* is usually found in pasture, often on cow-pats. It is a small

Figure 7.2 Magpie Inkcap in the Botanic Garden. (JDS).

Figure 7.3 Redlead Roundhead in the Botanic Garden. (JDS).

fungus, but the yellow patch at the top of the cap is distinctive, though it sometimes washes off after rain.

Specimens of *Stropharia* showing the typical slimy, bluish cap of the common native species are often found during forays. Although frequently identified as **Verdigris Roundhead** *S. aeruginosa*, it can be confused with **Blue Roundhead** *S. caerulea*, which looks very similar. The alien **Redlead Roundhead** *Leratiomyces ceres*, formerly *Stropharia aurantiaca*, with a striking reddish cap, is now sometimes found on woodchip piles.

Sulphur Tuft *Hypholoma fasciculare* is named in English after the colour of the gills, which is similar to that of sulphur powder. It is a very common fungus, mostly growing on tree stumps.

Funnel species are often gregarious and **Trooping Funnel** *Clitocybe geotropa* is typical. Growing in soil or grass at woodland or scrub edges it can form lines or rings of fungi.

St George's Mushroom *Calocybe gambosa* was sometimes found in grassland during April field studies, as might be expected from the English name; St George's day being April 23. It is edible, however beware that late fruiting specimens may be mixed with similar looking poisonous species.

Honey Fungus *Armillaria mellea* will be familiar to gardeners as it often kills trees. As the bark falls off the dead trunk it reveals the bootlace-like strands of the fungal mycelium.

Wood Blewit *Lepista nuda* and **Field Blewit** *Lepista saeva* are two commonly found Blewits. Wood Blewit has lilac gills and a faint sweet smell; for some it is good to eat. Field Blewit has paler gills and less of a smell; it is more widely edible.

The distinctive **Fly Agaric** *Amanita muscaria* has not been recorded on any of the CNHS forays.

Figure 7.4 Field Bird's Nest *Cyathus olla*. (JDS).

It is a species that most often grows under Birch on acid ground, a habitat that is almost non-existent in Cambridge.

Waxcap fungi are sometimes found on grassland, particularly in churchyards, as it is often a long time before a new grassland habitat becomes suitable for them. One of the first to arrive is **Snowy Waxcap** *Hygrocybe virginea*. Several species are present in East Pit including **Blackening Waxcap** *Hygrocybe conica*.

Boletes are uncommon fungi in Cambridge as many species prefer more acidic ground, but do turn up from time to time. Although looking like mushrooms they have pores rather than gills below the cap. In 2019 both **Brown Birch Bolete** *Laccinum scabrum* and **Slippery Jack** *Suillus luteus* appeared at the British Antarctic Survey site.

Puffballs are sometimes encountered, with **Stump Puffball** *Lycoperdon pyriforme* living up to its name and **Giant Puffball** *Calvatia gigantea* occasionally appearing on grassland, though it then gets used as a football. This may help the fungus as each kick generates a cloud of spores!

Earthstars *Geastrum* spp. are another group that lives up to the English name, with a spherical fruiting body supported by star-like rays. At least four species are known from across the city and all have been found in the Botanic Garden: **Sessile Earthstar** *G. fimbriatum* in the New Pinetum, **Beaked Earthstar** *G. pectinatum* under **Black Pine** *Pinus nigra* also in the New Pinetum, **Striate Earthstar** *G. striatum* under the **Caucasian Wingnut** *Pterocarya fraxinifolia* by the Stream Garden and **Collared Earthstar** *G. triplex*. In some years they can be frequent, but in others cannot be found despite diligent searching.

Field Bird's Nest *Cyathus olla* and **Fluted Bird's Nest** *Cyathus striatus* are often found on bark chippings and have been noted at several locations across the city. These small fungi, about a centimetre across, live up to their English name, complete with small 'eggs' in the nest. The 'eggs' are in fact peridioles, which are specialised spore-bearing tissues.

Club and Coral fungi are quite distinctive, though often overlooked as they can be quite small. Some are grassland specialists, whilst others may be found on bark chippings. **Meadow Coral** *Clavulinopsis corniculata* and **Yellow Club** *Clavulinopsis helvola* are yellow, the latter for example found on Coldham's Common. **Upright Coral** *Ramaria stricta* is one that grows on wood chippings, for example in the Botanic Garden; it is somewhat grey in colour.

Turkeytail *Trametes versicolor*, **Lumpy Bracket** *Trametes gibbosa*, **Smoky Bracket** *Bjerkandera adusta* and **Southern Bracket** *Ganoderma australe* are all bracket fungi, which project horizontally from a tree or log and deposit spores from the lower surface. The first three are all smaller species, usually less than 10 cm across and quite thin and flexible. The last is often much larger, sometimes 50 cm across and rigid. It is extensively present on a **Horse Chestnut** *Aesculus hippocastanum* in the Botanic Garden near Hobson's Conduit, coating the tree with rusty spores. It can be confused with the close relative **Artist's Bracket** *Ganoderma applanatum*, which has white spots in its flesh and may have small cone-shaped galls (Bacon 2015).

Chicken-of-the-Woods *Laetiporus sulphureus* often grows on Willow, and when freshly emerged shows a golden yellow colour and is then worth eating, though can cause an allergic reaction in some people.

Dryad's Saddle *Polyporus squamosus* is another large fungus that grows on trees, particularly Horse Chestnut and Sycamore. The upper surface is covered in concentric scales and it is fairly soft and fleshy, unlike the large bracket fungi. It gets its English name from the belief that it formed a seat for a dryad or woodland fairy.

Elder Whitewash *Hyphodontia sambuci* is one of the few resupinate fungi that are easy to identify. It grows around the base of **Elder** *Sambucus nigra* shrubs and often looks as if someone has painted around the base of the tree.

Jelly Ear, formerly Jew's Ear *Auricularia auricula-judae* is a brownish fungus that often grows on Elder. It is edible, but not worth the bother.

Coral Spot *Nectria cinnabarina* puts pink-to-orange spots on dead twigs and thin branches of broad-leaved trees. It is very easy to recognise.

King Alfred's Cakes or Cramp Balls *Daldinia concentrica* often grow on decaying Ash trunks. When the crispy black fungi are cut open they show concentric black and white growth bands, which gives the species its Latin name.

Candlesnuff Fungus *Xylaria hypoxylon* and Dead Man's Fingers *Xylaria polymorpha* are often seen on dead wood. The former has a white top to the antler-like fungus growing a few centimetres high, whilst the latter has black 'fingers' pushing up from dead wood near the soil surface.

Orange Peel Fungus *Aleuria aurantia* usually grows on bare ground and a cluster by the car park at Cherry Hinton Hall was initially mistaken for its namesake.

Ash Dieback *Chalara fraxinea*, which is more of a microfungus, has become increasingly common across the city since 2014. Ash *Fraxinus excelsior* saplings are particularly badly affected, with mature trees taking longer to succumb. Some trees are apparently unaffected and there have been suggestions that isolated trees do better. Locations with Ash woodland, such as West Pit, Cherry Hinton have many dying trees but this may open up the site, allowing some regeneration of chalk grassland. Sycamore Tarspot *Rhytisma acerinum* is another readily identifiable microfungus. It is another species that lives up to its name, forming black spots on the leaves of Sycamore. The fungal spores are released in the spring from fallen leaf debris and are distributed by the wind to fall on fresh leaves.

Figure 7.5 Candlesnuff Fungus. (JDS).

Figure 7.6 Orange Peel Fungus at Cherry Hinton. (JDS)..

Although belonging to a completely different phylum, myxomycetes are often encountered during fungal excursions. *Mucilago crustacea* is one of the more common species and is colloquially known as Dog's Vomit. It appears as a creamy-white mass binding grass stems together and becomes darker and more crusty with age.

Rusts, smuts and mildews

Alongside the obvious wildlife of Cambridge, the birds, plants and butterflies, there are of course many more species that we scarcely notice. The rusts, smuts and mildews considered in this section are part of this disregarded world. They are plant parasites, and have evolved to live on vascular plants. They may reduce their vigour or their output of seeds, or even distort their growth, but they do not actually kill them. A few are fairly conspicuous and may therefore be seen, and combated, by gardeners, but most are easily overlooked. It is only once you start to study them that you realise how frequent they are, and wonder why you never noticed them before.

The species considered here are biotrophic parasites, as opposed to necrotrophic parasites such as Potato Blight *Phytophthora infestans* and Dutch Elm Disease *Ophiostoma ulmi sens. lat.* which kill their hosts. Biotrophic parasites are able to integrate their metabolism with that of their host to a remarkable extent. One consequence of this is that they are highly specialised – the species are adapted to a narrow range of hosts and they cannot easily be cultivated in their absence. Like so many biological categories the distinction between biotrophic and necrotrophic parasites is useful but not absolute, and some parasites ('hemibiotrophic') have intermediate characteristics.

A range of completely different organisms have cotton on to the biotrophic lifestyle. Many are fungi. Only four groups are considered here. Both **rusts** and **smuts** are basidiomycetes, members of one of the two major groups of fungi along with the familiar mushrooms and toadstools. **Powdery mildews** belong to the other big fungal group, the ascomycetes, which also includes larger if somewhat oddball fungi such as the cup fungi, earth tongues, morels and truffles. **Downy mildews** are fungoids rather than fungi, members of a totally unrelated group (oomycetes) which have evolved in parallel a fungus-like appearance and lifestyle. Oomycetes are chromists, members of a major evolutionary group which also includes the brown algae, diatoms and the coccoliths whose exoskeletons make up our chalk rocks.

Plant pathology was a major research interest of scientists in Cambridge University from the appointment of Harry Marshall Ward as Professor of Botany in 1895 for almost a century. Before the First World War mycologists in the Department of Botany joined students of flowering plants and bryophytes in investigating species in the wild, as well as those of agricultural importance. However there was little subsequent interest in plant parasites in the wild, and few amateur naturalists have taken an interest in them. Unlike many groups, these and other fungi have been studied less intensively in Cambridgeshire than in several neighbouring counties. This section is based on species seen in the NHC area and in Cambridgeshire (v.c.29) as a whole between 2017 and 2020.

The number of species found in the county is given in Table 7.1, with the native status of their vascular plant hosts; the details of those in the NHC area are included in Table 7.2.

Downy mildews

The downy mildews invade the tissues of the plants they parasitise. Some cause symptoms such as yellowing or distortion of their leaves and stems, or stunt their growth, a reminder of the relationship of the downy mildews to their fellow oomycetes, the notoriously destructive blights. However, the effects of other species are much less obvious and symptoms may just be some rather inconspicuous leaf spots. The colonies of the mildew emerge through the stomata in the leaf as tiny groups of dichotomously or irregularly branched hyphae like miniature trees which bear asexual spores on their branches. The tree-like branching of the hyphae is diagnostic of the downy mildews. Sexual oospores develop within the tissues of the host.

Many species have only been recorded once or twice in Cambridgeshire in recent years, even if they parasitise widespread hosts. This rare or sporadic appearance seems to be typical of the

Table 7.1 Vascular plant hosts of the species in four biotrophic fungus and fungoid groups in Cambridgeshire (v.c. 29), 2017–2020. Species appear in more than one column if they have hosts in more than one category.

Group	Species	Native hosts	Archaeophyte hosts	Neophyte hosts	Neophyte hosts only	Mean number hosts per species
Downy mildews	52	39	14	4	4	1.2
Powdery mildews	89	62	20	57	22	3.3
Rusts	102	84	12	28	13	2.0
Smuts	18	9	4	7	5	1.3

Table 7.2 Number of species recorded in four biotrophic fungus and fungoid groups in the NHC area and in Cambridgeshire (v.c. 29) as a whole.

Group	Species in NHC area	Species in Cambs	NHC area only	NHC area and wider county	Wider county only	Mean no. records per species
Downy mildews	27	52	9	18	25	4.2
Powdery mildews	84	89	15	69	5	16.1
Rusts	67	102	10	57	35	9.9
Smuts	13	18	3	10	5	6.2
Total	191	261	37	154	70	10.6

Figure 7.7 (left) Chickweed stems infected by *Peronospora alsinearum*, next to uninfected flowering stems, (right) *Perofascia lepidii* on Swine-cress. (CDP).

group in other parts of Britain, raising questions about the population dynamics of the species which cannot currently be answered. Many species seem to be more apparent during periods of wet weather, and spring is perhaps the best season to look for them. They are largely parasites of annuals or herbaceous perennials, and the species recorded in Cambridgeshire are predominantly associated with native hosts. For this reason only 52% of the county's species have been recorded in the NHC area, even though this has been surveyed much more intensively than the other areas of the county.

Peronospora alsinearum is one of the more frequent downy mildews in Cambridge. In late winter and early spring infected plants of its host, **Common Chickweed** *Stellaria media*, can be spotted by their yellow stems, stout pedicels and swollen flower buds, which remain closed. The fungoid hyphae are less conspicuous. By contrast *Perofascia lepidii* can be seen throughout the summer. The leaves of the host, **Swine-cress** *Lepidium coronopus*, are yellow and distorted and they become covered by a conspicuous white mass of spore-bearing hyphae. This downy mildew has the remarkable ability to make one of the ugliest plants in the British flora even uglier.

Powdery mildews

The powdery mildews are the most obvious of the plant parasites, and many gardeners will at least know the mildew *Podosphaera pannosa* on their roses. They are unusual in that most species have their fungal threads or mycelium on the surface of their leaf, hence their visibility, rather than embedded in the leaf tissues. From the outside they penetrate the leaf to tap it for water and nutrients. There is a general belief that mildews are favoured by moist conditions, a completely mistaken notion that presumably arises from an association of these parasites with other fungi which colonise inert substrates in such conditions. In fact the powdery mildews are xerophytic, adapted to the dry conditions on the leaf surface. Not only do they do well in dry summers, but casual observation suggests that they are often more frequent on droughted plants than on nearby specimens of the same host growing in moister soils. Unlike the smuts and downy mildews, powdery mildews can be found on trees as well as shrubs and herbs. The introduced **Oak Mildew** *Erysiphe alphitoides* is one common tree-dwelling species.

Unlike vascular plants, but like many other cryptogams, the powdery mildews tend to combine copious asexual reproduction with a degree of sexual reproduction that varies from species to species. The mycelium on the leaf surface produces small asexual spores (conidia) budding off the branches and these give actively growing patches a glistening or dewlike appearance. The sexual spores are borne in ascocarps, fruiting bodies like small black golf balls embedded in the mycelial layer. Powdery mildews can be found throughout the year

Figure 7.8 (left) *Podosphaera filipendulae* on the native Meadowsweet *Filipendula ulmaria*, (right) *Arthrocladiella mougeotii* on the garden escape Chinese Teaplant *Lycium chinense*. (CDP).

on evergreen hosts, but are certainly most frequent (or at least most conspicuous) in the autumn.

Powdery mildews are much more predictable in their occurrence than the downy mildews; sometimes they may infect a high proportion of the plants in the host population but sometimes just a single infected plant is encountered. In the Cambridge area they are the most numerous of the plant parasites considered here. They are almost as frequent on garden plants as in the wild, and a very high proportion of the county's species (94%) has been recorded in Cambridge.

Rusts

Rust fungi are famous for the complexity of their life-cycles, although the details vary greatly from species to species. Some are able to persist from year to year on a single host, or group of related hosts, and these include several common species in Cambridgeshire. Others have alternate hosts, reproducing on one in the early season and another later in the year. The name refers to the masses of dark spores which often develop on leaf surfaces, so that they may look like rusted metal. As with the downy mildews, there is a high proportion of native hosts and consequently a relatively low proportion (66%) of the county's species in the well-recorded Cambridge area.

One rust attracted much attention during the NatHistCam project, the **European Pear Rust** *Gymnosporangium sabinae*. This has increased markedly in southern England in recent years and in late summer the characteristic bright red leaf spots are easily spotted by gardeners on their **Pear trees** *Pyrus communis*. It also infects other pear species, including **Callery Pear** *Pyrus calleryana*,

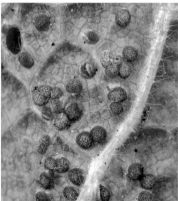

Figure 7.9 (left) Leaves of Pyrus communis 'Pitmaston Duchess' infected with European Pear Rust. (CDP). **(right) Lower side of a leaf of Hollyhock infected with** *Puccinia malvacearum*. (PAR).

now frequently planted as a street tree. Closer inspection of the leaf spots reveals brown lumps on the lower side which at maturity bear conical, tent-like structures of fibres which are united at the top. The spores produced by this stage of the life cycle infect a group of **Juniper** species, *Juniperus sabina* and its relatives, but these are not especially frequent as cultivated plants so it is not entirely clear how the flourishing populations of the rust on pear trees are maintained.

The most frequent rust in the county infects a wide range of plants in the mallow family Malvaceae, including the garden **Hollyhock** *Alcea rosea* and the **Wild Mallow** *Malva sylvestris*. This has only a single stage in the life cycle, which overwinters on the leaves of the host. It was introduced to Europe in the middle of the 19th century and spread extremely rapidly. When it first appeared it had a much more devastating effect on Hollyhocks than it does today.

Smuts

The authors of the New Naturalist volume on plant disease (Ingram & Robertson 1999) refer to the 'dark and secretive smuts'. Although a few species are conspicuous, many are very difficult to detect, especially if you are not already familiar with their appearance. Only 18 species are recorded in Cambridgeshire, with 13 (72%) in the Cambridge area. This shamefully low total suggests that many are currently being overlooked. By contrast over 60 species are known from Cardiganshire, one of Britain's best recorded counties.

The smuts colonise the tissues of their hosts and their spores are produced in different places. Several spring bulbs including **Grape-hyacinths** *Muscari* and **Squills** *Scilla* may be infected by species of *Antherospora*, and as a result the pollen which would normally be produced in their anthers is replaced by a dark mass of spores. Later in the year *Microbotryum lychnidis-dioicae* infects **White Campion** *Silene latifolia* in a similar manner, and the fungal spores produce a conspicuous mess when released onto the white petals.

An even more remarkable but less conspicuous smut fungus infects **Bindweeds** *Calystegia* species. Under the influence of *Thecaphora seminis-convolvuli* the anthers of the host produce asexual fungal spores, which are small and colourless so much less conspicuous than *Antherospora* and *Microbotryum* spores. Later in the season the fruits of the Bindweed produce not seed but a sooty mass of dark sexual fungal spores.

Other smuts infect the vegetative parts of the plant. The commonest species in the Cambridge area is *Entyloma ficariae*, which is recognisable by the leaf spotting on its host, **Lesser Celandine** *Ficaria verna*. These spots are easily confused with the pale leaf markings which are often found naturally on this species, but the asymmetrical distribution of the spots on a leaf provides an initial indication that they might be fungal in

Figure 7.10 (left) flowers of Glory-of-the-snow *Scilla forbesii* infected by *Antherospora scillae*, (right) flowers of White Campion infected by *Microbotryum lychnidis-dioicae*. (CDP).

Figure 7.11 Leaves of Lesser Celandine spotted by *Entyloma ficariae*. (CDP).

Figure 7.12 Spores of *Urocystis eranthidis* bursting out of the stems and bracts of Winter Aconite. (CDP).

origin. Another spring-flowering species which is often infected by a smut fungus is **Winter Aconite** *Eranthis hyemalis*, where the dark masses of the spores of **Urocystis eranthidis** break out of the stems and bracts.

Lichens

Lichens are curious dual organisms, a close association between a fungus and a photosynthetic partner, usually a green alga (Figures 7.13, 7.14). This association is so intimate that Victorian biologists argued about whether lichens were a single organism or a partnership. One school of thought

maintained that the microscopic green cells within them were organelles produced by the fungus while others argued that the green cells were algae that had been entrapped by the fungus. We now know that the latter is correct but the degree to which the algae are exploited is still a matter for debate.

Though lichens were long regarded as plants, there is no long and continuous history of study

Figure 7.13 A cross section through a lobe of *Xanthoria parietina* (an extremely common lichen) as seen through a microscope. The algal cells (looking rather like peas but only one thousandth of the size) are seen in a layer towards the upper part. The glassy structures forming the bulk of the lichen are the fungal hyphae. (MP).

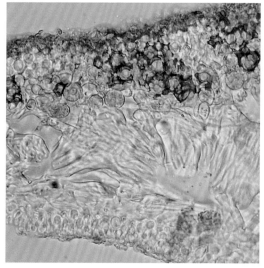

Figure 7.14 *Xanthoria parietina* on the bark of Chinese Mastic *Pistachia chinensis* in the Botanic Garden. (CDP).

in Cambridge comparable to that for flowering plants. They were neglected even in the second half of the 20th century, when there was a great revival of interest in lichens nationally and when both vascular plants and bryophytes received detailed study in Cambridge. However the situation has been transformed in the last ten years with the work of the Cambridge Lichen Group, whose field meetings have usually been led by the expert lichenologist Mark Powell of Bedfordshire. In recent years many of these meetings have taken place in the NHC area. It is a great pity that Mark has been prevented by ill-health from writing this account, but we have been able to draw on his detailed reports of the Lichen Group excursions.

The recent fieldwork has taken place against the background of massive and continuing change in the distribution of lichens in eastern England. The growth of most lichens, like that of epiphytic bryophytes, was greatly restricted by the high levels of atmospheric sulphur dioxide (SO_2) which prevailed in the area until the 1980s. Sulphur dioxide was produced mainly by the domestic and industrial burning of coal, although brick-pits in Bedfordshire and Peterborough added significantly to air pollution locally. Levels of SO_2 have now fallen to such low levels that they no longer limit the growth of most species, although pollution by nitrogen oxides (NO_x) is still thought to have an important influence. Many lichens have in consequence colonised, or recolonised, formerly polluted areas in recent years.

Fortunately a brief account of the lichens of Cambridge walls was published by a visiting lichenologist, the schoolmaster Frank Brightman, in 1965. On the limestone parapets of the Silver Street bridge, he found three species which together covered rather less than 50% of the stonework. When the Lichen Group resurveyed the same parapets in 2011 they recorded 23 species with a total cover of about 90%. Similarly Brightman found just one species on the sandstone parapets of King's College bridge, the then ubiquitous *Lecanora conizaeoides*. This species flourished in the age of 'acid rain' but is now found only on the most acidic substrates. It had disappeared from King's bridge by 2011, replaced by a mixed community of 18 other species (Powell & Cambridge Lichen Group 2012). The only other documented lichen excursion in the city in modern times was a British Lichen Society field meeting in 1974.

A further on-going change is the increase in our understanding of lichen taxonomy. This has affected the species listed even during the relatively brief period that the Lichen Group have been at work in the city. St Andrew's Church, Chesterton, was first visited in 2010 when over 60 species were found in three hours' recording. On the next visit in 2018 several species were added to the list simply because they had not been understood eight years previously; these included *Caloplaca dichroa*, described new to science in 2006 but now known to be one of the dominant lichens on limestone memorials in England, *C. limonia*, not added to the British list until 2011, and *Verrucaria calciseda*, which was confused with another British species, *V. baldensis* until about 2012. On many excursions specimens have been found that defied all attempts to identify them, and there are clearly genera and species requiring further study.

There are three main growth forms of lichens, crustose (crusts, spots, etc.), foliose (with leafy lobes) or fruticose (like miniature shrubs). Examples include the crustose *Xanthoria parietina* (Figure 7.14), the foliose *Parmotrema perlatum* (Figure 7.27) and the fruticose *Cladonia rangiformis* (Figure 7.29). Lichens tend to occur in communities of species which prefer the same substrate, and are usually recorded from trees, from stonework (as on buildings, walls and churchyard monuments) and from open ground such as chalk or gravel. The main lichen habitats visited by the Group in the NHC area are described below.

Churchyards and cemeteries

These are classic sites for the lichenologist as they provide a variety of stone (limestone, sandstone, granite, marble) along with gravel and trees. One of the richest in our area is the City Cemetery on Newmarket Road. On a short winter day in February 2018, the Group recorded 106 taxa; there is no doubt that more could be added on further visits. Other sites which have been visited since 2010 include the parish churches at Cherry Hinton (56 taxa), Chesterton (60, with 14 additions on a second visit), Fen Ditton (74) and Teversham (86), as well as St Bene't's Church, Cambridge (39), the Leper Chapel by Newmarket Road (41) and the Ascension Parish Burial Ground (51, with 8 added on a second visit). In one of these churchyards, Chesterton, a single memorial examined in detail yielded 21 species.

Figure 7.15 A view across a small part of the City Cemetery showing the huge number and range of memorials. (MP).

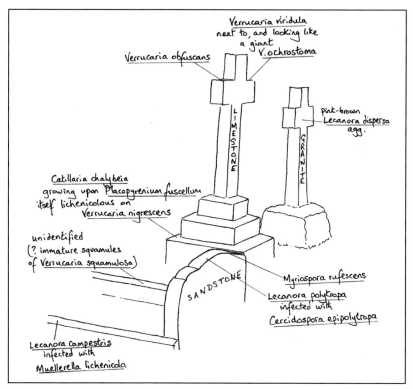

Figure 7.16 A drawing of the memorials in the foreground of Figure 7.15, showing the different habitats and some of their characteristic lichens and lichenicolous fungi. Limestone gravestones support a completely different community of lichens to those on sandstone. (MP).

Many lichens are very specific in their habitat requirements, much more so than bryophytes, and the large City Cemetery provided a wide range of habitats (Figures 7.15, 7.16).

The range of stonework clearly contributes to the richness of cemetery sites, as does the differing ages of the memorials. Lichens on recent stonework are sometimes easier to identify as their colonies are well-grown and discrete (Figure 7.17). With time,

the individual thalli usually converge into a closed mosaic, obscuring important marginal features and confusing the view.

Calcareous groundwater is drawn up by porous stones like sandstone, giving different conditions at the base of the stone to that above (Figures 7.18, 7.19). The tops of gravestones receive much more attention from lichenologists than the bases and so species typical of the basal zone, such

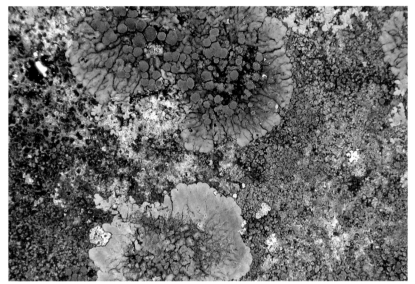

Figure 7.17 Crustose lichens growing as separate individuals on a relatively recent memorial in Teversham churchyard. The large thallus above is *Caloplaca flavescens*; below is *C. aurantia* which differs in having flatter lobes, as if hammered onto the surface, and a more 'eggy' colour. In the background are numerous tiny sprouts of *Caloplaca dichroa*, with *Candelariella medians* at the upper right. (MP).

as *Lecania hutchinsiae*, are seldom recorded on gravestones.

Birds defecating on the top of headstones provide areas of higher nutrient concentrations than those at the top of footstones, where they rarely perch (Figures 7.19, 7.20). The 'nitrophile community' found here comprises a very characteristic suite of species found in many other nitrogen-enhanced situations. Raintracks below metalwork on memorials, such as lead lettering and bronze railings, produce concentrations of heavy metals which inhibit most species but favour a specific few. These differing habitats add to the diversity of the lichens on a site, although the highest concentrations of heavy metals are toxic to all species.

Figure 7.18 Memorials south of St Mary's Church, Fen Ditton, in 2021. On both limestone and sandstone gravestones there are streaks of nutrient-loving lichens which are stimulated by the droppings by perching birds. (CDP).

Figure 7.19 A drawing of the memorials in the foreground of Figure 7.18, made in 2017. *Caloplaca aurantia* forms beautiful orange crusts on the tops of several old limestone gravestones in this part of the churchyard. The lower nine inches or so of sandstone gravestones in this region provide a specialist habitat where the community is different from that of the rest of the stone. (MP).

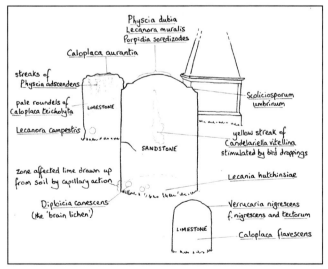

Figure 7.20 Limestone headstone to the south of the church at Fen Ditton. There is almost a complete cover of lichens; even the pale patches are mainly lichen crusts. *Physconia grisea* forms a pale green patch narrowing down from the apex, where it is stimulated by bird droppings. The intensely nutrient-enriched top of the apex is dominated by *Lecania erysibe*. (CDP).

Thick black sooty deposits laid down over the decades of heavy air pollution can still be found on the sheltered stonework of churches such as the Leper Chapel, persisting in places protected from weathering. Even in the open old sandstone can carry a 'toxic legacy'. Pollution-sensitive species such as *Myriospora rufescens* are mainly absent from older sandstone but found on late 20th-century fine-grained sandstone memorials. One feature of the Ascension Parish Burial Ground is a number of wooden crosses. The acidic decaying wood provides a refuge for *Lecanora conizaeoides*.

The City Cemetery is still an actively managed site and this maintains the diversity of its lichens. In many churchyards and cemeteries the largest threat to gravestone communities is ivy, which can quickly engulf a gravestone and kill off lichen communities which have taken many decades to develop. Another potential source of damaging shade is from tree branches, and in the City Cemetery, although some amenity trees have been planted, there are large open areas. Another advantage of a well-kept cemetery is that the grass

sward is kept quite regularly mown which helps to keep the numbers of molluscs in some sort of check. At the much less intensively managed Ascension Burial Ground, molluscs had reduced *Lecanora polytropa* on some gravestones to tightly grazed, rather featureless roundels, and putative *Chaenotheca chrysocephala*, seen on a wooden cross on the first visit, had been reduced six years later to a few barely perceptible blobs and its identification remained uncertain.

As far as we know, none of the molluscs are as dependent on lichens as the **Virgin Bagworm** moth *Luffia lapidella* forma *ferchaultella*. The photograph (Figure 7.21) shows these on stonework in Teversham churchyard, and they can also be seen on tree trunks. Whereas typical *L. lapidella* is represented by both sexes, forma *ferchaultella* is known only as parthenogenetic and wingless females. Like a medieval anchoress, the larva is enclosed in a camouflaged case which incorporates fragments of lichen, and lichens are also thought to comprise a large component of her diet. Occupied cases are usually found in sheltered places but the empty cases remain in exposed sites once the adults have emerged.

Figure 7.21 Larval cases of the Virgin Bagworm moth on an oolitic limestone gravestone in Teversham churchyard. These two incorporate bands of yellow lichen (probably *Caloplaca dichroa*). (MP).

Figure 7.22 Suburban lichenology in Tavistock Road, Cambridge. (MP).

Urban and suburban habitats

The urban and suburban habitats of the ordinary townscape tend not to be visited by lichenologists, who like other naturalists usually prefer to visit 'honeypot' sites such as churchyards and cemeteries. However, the Lichen Group attempted to redress this balance with visits to places such as the Museum of Technology, and the residential streets of north-west Cambridge and Trumpington. Suburban lichenology is always unpredictable; the rewards can be meagre but it takes only a few old wall tops or some rich street trees to

Figure 7.23 Two thalli of *Lecidella carpathica* on either side of *L. stigmatea* on a brick wall in north-west Cambridge. Even on this heavily mollusc-browsed garden wall, the thicker, more warted thallus of *L. carpathica* can be seen. (MP).

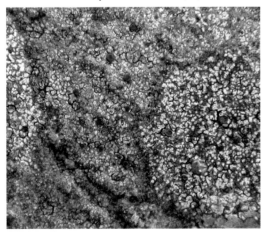

considerably boost the interest. The visit to the streets of the north-west (Figure 7.22) produced 74 taxa, comprising 39 on stonework, 27 on bark, 4 on other lichens, 2 on mosses and 2 on worked or rotting wood. Some species which are more usually associated with churchyards, such as *Caloplaca aurantia*, turned up on weathered old concrete coping stones on wall tops. Old brickwork was also interesting, with one wall supporting a mosaic of *Lecidella carpathica* and *L. stigmatea* (Figure 7.23). The most surprising epiphyte was *Leptorhaphis maggiana*, seen in some quantity on the stems of hazels in an amenity planting on Tavistock Road (Figure 7.22).

Woodland and trees

A few small areas of secondary woodland have been visited in the NHC area during the course of the last decade. The most surprising epiphyte was found at Byron's Pool, where one of the mature Oak trunks supported *Enterographa crassa*. This is usually considered to be a poor coloniser, generally restricted to ancient sites. Its presence, together with *Opegrapha vermicellifera* and *Schismatomma decolorans*, suggests that a relic community of lichens survived here on sheltered tree bases during the many decades of severe SO_2 pollution. There were other interesting species. *Porina byssophila* has until recently been considered to be a nationally scarce lichen of siliceous rocks but is now known to be not uncommon on tree bases, at least in eastern England. *Lecanora barkmaniana* is one of several

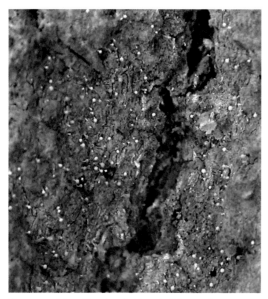

Figure 7.24 The yellow-headed 'pins' of *Chaenotheca brachypoda* on the dry side of an Ash trunk at Paradise LNR, surrounded by *Opegrapha viridipruinosa* on the adjacent bark plates. (MP).

'new' lichen species of which no evidence can be found before the 1980s. It was described new to science in 1999 and seems to be spreading and thriving in the modern eutrophicated landscape. Also seen at this site was an enormous colony of the attractive 'pin-head' lichen *Chaenotheca brachypoda*, which was found on the underside of a gently sloping Willow trunk.

Chaenotheca brachypoda was also found in another patch of riverside woodland at Paradise LNR, this time on the dry, east-facing side of an Ash tree (Figure 7.24), although here the colony appeared to be threatened by the growth of Ivy. Also of interest in this wood was a yellowish, shade form of **Punctelia borreri**, a spectacular species which appears to be spreading out of its former stronghold close to the south coast of England. The wood produced a good haul of *Opegrapha* species, *O. herbarum* as young colonists on Ash stems, *O. vermicellifera* and *O. vulgata* on older bark, *O. varia* and *O. viridipruinosa*.

The riparian common Sheep's Green is only a short walk from Paradise but its impressive Willow trees and large Lombardy Poplars have a completely different assemblage of lichens. Microclimate is a key factor affecting the species present in any situation, and instead of the notable species such as *Chaenotheca brachypoda* and *Opegrapha vermicellifera* in the sheltered and humid conditions in Paradise, the Willows in the open conditions at Sheep's Green are dominated by species such as **Amandinea punctata** and **Diploicia canescens** (Figure 7.25). The various *Opegrapha* species in Paradise are replaced by *O. niveoatra*, a lover of dry trunks.

In the woodland in the long-abandoned chalk pit at Lime Kiln Close, Cherry Hinton, the most interesting species are those on the shaded and sheltered trunks of mature Ash trees. *Opegrapha vermicellifera* is again present (Figure 7.26) along

Figure 7.25 A splendid example of the ubiquitous lichen *Diploica canescens*, growing here on a gravestone at Teversham. (MP).

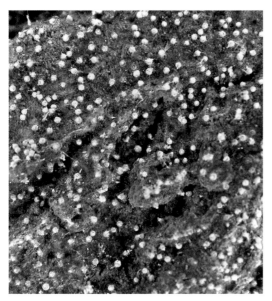

Figure 7.26 *Opegrapha vermicellifera.* (MP).

with two other *Opegrapha* species in a lichen crust community which resembles that on the same host at Chippenham Fen.

On two visits to Adams Road Bird Sanctuary 22 species were recorded on the bark of the trees and shrubs around the lake. In addition one lichen, *Phylloblastia inexpectata*, grew on the evergreen leaves of holly and ivy. Lichens on leaves are generally a feature of humid sites, and they were still rather rare in eastern England when this species was found at Adams Road in 2014.

In its early years the Lichen Group visited the Botanic Garden, but it did not return during the NatHistCam recording period. However, the Garden was surveyed by Jonathan Graham in the winter of 2010/11. He found that where epiphytes were well developed on well-lit trees, the species occurring in the greatest quantity, such as *Evernia prunastri*, *Hypergymnia tubulosa*, *Parmelia sulcata* and *Xanthoria parietina*, all had a degree of resistance to SO_2 pollution. However, a number of species that are more sensitive to air pollution were found in small quantity and often on younger branches. These included *Flavoparmelia caperata*, *Punctelia subrudecta*, *Ramalina fastigiata* and *Pleurosticta acetabulum*. Epiphytes, including *Parmotrema perlatum* (Figure 7.27), have continued to colonise since 2011 but have not been surveyed comprehensively. On the north side of Cambridge, Ash trees at the Observatory also have a good range of the larger (foliose and fruticose) lichens.

Brownfield sites

The old railway sidings at Chesterton are the one brownfield site which has been examined in detail. By the time of the Group's visit, in 2018, these were reduced to a relatively small area mostly colonised by young Birch, Buddleia and other shrubs (Figures 7.28, 7.29). It is unfortunate that no lichenologist visited this site in its heyday, when large areas of open sidings (now redeveloped as Cambridge North station) would presumably have provided excellent habitat for species of

Figure 7.27 The foliose lichen *Parmotrema perlatum* on a well-lit trunk in the Botanical Garden 2021. (CDP).

Figure 7.28 Stacks of old railway sleepers amongst *Buddleia* **scrub on Chesterton sidings.** (CDP).

Figure 7.29 The fruticose lichen *Cladonia rangiformis* **in one of the remaining fragments of young birch scrub on Chesterton sidings, 2021.** (CDP).

Cladonia and *Stereocaulon*. These tolerated the former high levels of SO_2 pollution, but appear to be disadvantaged by the current high levels of nitrogen. Nevertheless, nine *Cladonia* species were recorded on what remains of the sidings including *Cladonia cariosa*, a classic lichen of old industrial sites. The debris lying around in such places

contributes to their diversity. Another *Cladonia*, *C. fimbriata*, appeared to find large, rubberised hoses particularly attractive and *Stereocaulon vesuvianum* var. *symphycheileoides* was found, new to Cambridgeshire, on old, stacked timber. The epiphyte *Scoliciosporum chlorococcum* was seen on birch twigs. This was almost ubiquitous on twigs until the early 2000s, but is now rather rare, having retreated to more acidic substrates.

The scope for future lichenology

Future lichenologists will have much to interest them in the NHC area. It seems highly unlikely that the dramatic changes to the lichen communities seen in recent decades have culminated in a stable climax situation. Instead, it is reasonable to anticipate that many new species will invade the city in the future. The taxonomy of some of the most common lichen species found in the area remains poorly understood. The most common member of the genus *Lecanora* to grow on tree bark, widespread across Cambridge, has been recorded as *L. chlarotera* until recent months. We now realise that most if not all Cambridgeshire. material will be referable to *L. hybocarpa* though these specimens have not yet been formally reappraised. *Lecanora albescens*, almost ubiquitous on walls of all sorts, appears to comprise at least two distinct taxa but all specimens are currently recorded under the one name. An amateur lichenologist armed only with a hand lens and an academic taxonomist with access to a laboratory would both find much left to discover about the lichens of Cambridge.

Butterflies

Introduction

Nationally our butterfly populations have declined significantly since the 1970s both in terms of abundance and diversity (Fox *et al.* 2015). Much of this decline is related to changes in land use and intensification of agriculture. Within the NHC area these changes have not had a negative impact on diversity. Although abundance has probably declined, we do not have sufficient historical data to confirm this.

Twenty-nine species have been recorded within the NHC area over the period 2016–2020, of which 24 are resident. This would appear to be a net increase of two since the 1970s. The once common **Wall** *Lasiommata megera* is no longer found in the city or much of the surrounding county, but its disappearance has coincided with the recent establishment of three other species.

Migratory species and rare visitors

The **Painted Lady** *Vanessa cardui* is our most travelled butterfly. Each year the first generation emerges in the desert fringes of North Africa, the Middle East and central Asia, recolonising mainland Europe and reaching Britain. In most years, small numbers can be seen between May and October, mainly in dry open areas, but some years see a spectacular influx when they can be seen almost anywhere, as was the case in 2019.

The long-term trend for this species in Cambridgeshire is for increasing numbers (Field *et al.* 2008) which is probably linked to climate change

extending the range to more northerly latitudes. Our other common migratory species is the closely related **Red Admiral** *Vanessa atalanta*. Red Admirals can overwinter at more northerly latitudes than Painted Ladies, so have shorter migration and turn up in significant numbers each year, when they are a common sight anywhere in the city. It would seem that our changing climate is also allowing some individuals to survive British winters and sightings of them on warm winter days are not that unusual.

The rarest of our migrant species is the **Clouded Yellow** *Colias croceus*. The numbers arriving in Britain are usually small but occasionally they turn up in significant numbers. 2020 was such a year and several were recorded from Trumpington Meadows.

A single **Purple Emperor** *Apatura iris* was recorded over the period of the survey. This sighting was most probably a vagrant, as the species has not been recorded as breeding in the city historically. There were also two sightings of **Swallowtails** *Papilio machaon*, one at British Antarctic Survey in 2019, the other in Cherry Hinton in 2020. These individuals were either on migration or had been released from captive breeding.

Common city-wide resident species

Large White *Pieris brassicae* and **Small White** *Pieris rapae* butterflies are well adapted to our suburban environment as they are just as happy using cultivated brassicas for their caterpillar food plant as they are wild varieties. The yellow and black caterpillars of the Large White are easily spotted but are unpalatable to birds, as they

Figure 8.1 (left) Red Admiral, (centre) Painted Lady, (right) Clouded Yellow. (PAR).

Figure 8.2 (left) Brimstone, (centre) Holly Blue, (right) Orange Tip. (PAR).

accumulate mustard oils from their food plants, whereas the Small White caterpillars are green and not easily seen on the leaves on which they feed, but are palatable.

Brimstone *Gonepteryx rhamni*, **Peacock** *Aglais io* and **Small Tortoiseshell** *Aglais urticae* butterflies all overwinter as adults and are therefore some of the earliest species to be seen on the wing. All three are regular visitors to our gardens and hibernating adults can often be found in sheds and other outbuildings.

Holly Blues *Celastrina argiolus* are the first of the 'blues' to emerge and the only one to regularly visit gardens, where their food plants of **Holly** *Ilex aquifolium* and **Ivy** *Hedera helix* occur in abundance. They can be seen on the wing throughout April with a second brood in July and a third in October.

Orange Tip *Anthocharis cardamines* and **Green-veined White** *Pieris napi* prefer damp habitats such as meadows, woodland glades, hedgerows and the banks of streams and rivers, but readily visit gardens, so are a common sight throughout Cambridge.

Woodland species

Although **Speckled Woods** *Pararge aegeria* are now a common sight in Cambridge, this has only been the case in recent years. Historically this was a scarce species in the county and has only established itself in the city since the early 1990s. They can be found anywhere in the city where mature trees provide the dappled sunlight they prefer, including larger gardens with mature trees.

Woodland edges and hedgerows are ideal sites to see **Commas** *Polygonia c-album* and **Gatekeepers** *Pyronia tithonus*. Both species are also regular visitors to larger gardens with mature trees and hedges.

The **White-letter Hairstreak** *Satyrium w-album* was only recorded twice between 2016 and 2019. The lack of observations is probably due to the fact they tend to fly at the top of the tree canopy which makes them difficult to see and they are therefore under-recorded. The loss of many elm trees makes this species vulnerable and their long-term status as a breeding species in Cambridge is uncertain. However, there were sightings from Jesus College and Byron's Pool LNR during 2020, so it is possible

Figure 8.3 (left) Gatekeeper (PAR), **(centre) Speckled Wood** (PAR), **(right) White-letter Hairstreak.** (JMO).

Figure 8.4 (left) Ringlet, (centre) Small Copper, (right) Brown Argus. (PAR).

Figure 8.5 (left) Common Blue, (centre) Essex Skipper (right) Small Heath. (PAR).

that colonies are present anywhere small stands of elm still survive.

The **Purple Hairstreak** *Favonius quercus* is even more elusive, spending most of its time high in the tree canopy. It is only driven down to seek fluid and nectar during prolonged drought. This probably explains why this common and widespread species was only recorded twice during 2016–2019, once in the Botanic Garden in 2018 and the other time in Tennis Court Road on the hottest day ever recorded in Britain in July 2019. In 2020 it was recorded on several occasions at Byron's Pool LNR and it can probably be found anywhere in the city where mature oak trees grow.

Grassland and meadow species
Areas of flower-rich grassland including roadside verges are important for many of our common resident species, providing both the appropriate larval food plants and an ample supply of nectar for adults. **Large Skipper** *Ochlodes sylvanus*, **Small Skipper** *Thymelicus sylvestris*, **Essex Skipper** *Thymelicus lineola*, **Brown Argus** *Aricia agestis*, **Common Blue** *Polyommatus icarus*,

Small Heath *Coenonympha pamphilus*, **Ringlet** *Aphantopus hyperantus* and **Meadow Brown** *Maniola jurtina* all depend on such sites. The scarcer **Small Copper** *Lycaena phlaeas* prefers meadows, waste ground and rough grassland with areas of shorter turf.

As well as the larger open green spaces, smaller, more urban sites such as Bramblefields LNR and Mill Road Cemetery provide suitable conditions for these species to thrive.

New colonists
Two of the most exciting events to occur over the period of this project have been the establishment of **Marbled Whites** *Melanargia galathea* as a resident species and the resurgence of **Small Blues** *Cupido minimus* after an absence of over 100 years.

Marbled Whites have been expanding their range northwards and eastwards over the last 20 years. They were first recorded from the West Cambridge Site in 2014 and from Coldham's Common in 2018. Their rapid expansion across the city means that they are likely to be found in

Figure 8.6 (left) Marbled White, (right) Small Blue. (PAR).

any suitable flower-rich grassy habitat. As well as the above sites, they can be seen in large numbers at Trumpington Meadows and along the protected verge by Worts' Causeway from late June through July and August.

The Small Blue was historically recorded in the Cherry Hinton area back in the 19th century (Morris 1870) but was absent from Cambridge in the 20th century. With only small numbers recorded from just four Cambridgeshire sites the species was on the point of extinction in the county (Field *et al.* 2006).

Despite being lost from previous sites close to Cambridge at the beginning of this century, they made a quite stunning appearance in 2018 at the newly-established country park at Trumpington

Meadows. Breeding colonies have been established in both sections of the park, to the north-east and south-west of the M11 motorway, where their food plant, **Kidney Vetch** *Anthyllis vulneraria* is plentiful. They can be seen on the wing there from late May to June followed by a second brood emerging in the second half of August.

Potential new species
It is quite possible that with ongoing changes to our local climate, the Small Blue may not be the last butterfly species to establish itself within the city. One possibility is the **Dark Green Fritillary** *Speyeria aglaja*. This butterfly was considered to be extinct as a breeding species in Cambridgeshire just a few years ago (Field *et al.* 2006), but since then,

Figure 8.7 Dark Green Fritillary. (PAR).

there have been regular records from Fleam Dyke, and a June 2020 sighting from the Fulbourn side of the Gog Magog hills, just 200 metres outside the NHC area.

Moths
Introduction
Although most moth species are nocturnal and therefore go unnoticed by the casual observer, we are fortunate to have a number of individuals and groups of recorders who regularly run moth traps throughout the year. This has resulted in the number of species recorded out-stripping all other animal groups by far.

For this report I have used the records from moth traps run year-round in two private gardens, the Botanic Garden, summer recording from Logan's Meadow and ad hoc records from one-night events. In addition I have casual records of day-flying species and Sam Buckton's records of over 50 species of leaf-miners from the Botanic Garden. In total this amounts to 601 species, of which only a small sample of common and notable species can be covered in the following pages.

Figure 8.8 Paul Rule setting up a Skinner moth trap in his garden. (PAR).

Day-flying moths
Although the vast majority of our moth species are nocturnal, some of our most colourful are on the wing during daylight hours. The largest and most spectacular of these is the **Emperor Moth** *Saturnia pavonia*. Despite its large size and its status as a common species, we have few NHC records. On sunny April and May days, males can be attracted to lures containing artificial female pheromones and this offers one of the best chances to observe them.

Another one of our larger day-flyers, the **Hummingbird Hawk-moth** *Macroglossum stellatarum* can often be observed feeding at nectar-rich flowers in our parks and gardens.

Flower-rich meadows and roadside verges are good places to observe some of our common species such the **Six-spot Burnet** *Zygaena filipendulae*, probably our most common day-flying moth, whose distinctive yellow cocoons can be seen attached to tall flower stems. Adults can be seen in very large numbers, particularly at Trumpington Meadows where in late June and early July nearly every **Common Knapweed** *Centaurea nigra* and **Field Scabious** *Knautia arvensis* flower head will have at least one moth on it.

The **Burnet Companion** *Euclidia glyphica* is a less numerous species but is often found in the company of Burnet moths which is how it earned its common name.

Two other common meadow species that are found alongside Burnet moths are the **Cinnabar Moth** *Tyria jacobaeae*, with its very familiar 'football jersey' caterpillars and the **Mother Shipton** *Euclidia mi*. Several micro-moths are also day fliers and one common species often seen in our gardens is the **Mint Moth** *Pyrausta aurata*. As its name suggests, its caterpillars feed on **Mint** (*Mentha* spp.) and the adults can often be seen sipping nectar from the flowers of mint and other aromatic herbs.

Crescent Plume Moths *Marasmarcha lunaedactyla* are not so common. They are normally on the wing from dusk, but they are seldom caught in light traps and the best chance to see them is to check a suitable patch of their food plant, **Rest Harrow** *Ononis repens* in June and early July where they gather to mate and lay eggs. They prefer dry habitats, such as chalk grassland, and the protected verge along the upper stretches of Worts' Causeway is a hotspot for this species.

Figure 8.9 (left) Emperor Moth (AS), **(right) Hummingbird Hawk-moth.** (PAR).

Figure 8.10 (left) Six-spot Burnet Moth adults on Field Scabious, (centre) Cocoon, (right) Burnet Companion. (PAR).

Figure 8.11 (left) Cinnabar Moth adult, (centre) caterpillar, (right) Mother Shipton. (PAR).

Figure 8.12 (left) Mint Moth, (centre) Crescent Plume, (right) Cocksfoot Moth. (PAR).

Figure 8.13 (left) Yellow-barred Long-horn, (centre) Brassy Long-horn, (right) Feathered Bright. (PAR).

Figure 8.14 (left) Common Plume, (right) Beautiful Plume. (PAR).

The **Cocksfoot Moth** *Glyphipterix simpliciella* is a very common species, but they are so small (3–4 mm long) that most people might not even realise they are moths. They are found in large numbers between May and July visiting flowers, especially those of buttercup *Ranunculus* where there can be 20 or more to one flower head.

The antennae of male long-horn moths are extremely long – up to three times the length of their bodies. The **Yellow-barred Long-horn** *Nemophora degeerella* is a species that prefers deciduous, often damp woodland. In May and June the males can often be seen in groups, 'dancing' in the sunshine at sites such as Logan's Meadow and Byron's Pool. The closely related **Brassy Long-horn** *Nemophora metallica* prefers meadows

and roadside verges where its food plant, **Field Scabious** *Knautia arvensis* grows. Adults can often be seen sunning themselves on the flower heads of this plant.

Male **Feathered Bright** moths *Incurvaria masculella* have large comb-like (pectinate) antennae and can be seen in quite large numbers 'dancing' along **Hawthorn** *Crataegus monogyna* hedgerows.

Spring and summer are the best seasons to observe our day-flying moths, but a few may be spotted all year round. **Common Plume** *Emmelina monodactyla* and **Beautiful Plume** *Amblyptilia acanthadactyla* can be found throughout the year. In winter they can occasionally be seen resting on walls and fence posts.

Nocturnal moths

The number of nocturnal species we recorded over the last four years exceeds 500, far too many to cover in detail so I have provided a snapshot of some seasonal highlights of common and notable species, plus an account of some of our rarer visitors.

Spring moths (March–May)

Moths overwinter in a number of ways, some as eggs that hatch in the spring, some which hibernate as adults and a few which hibernate as caterpillars. Most moths on the wing in spring, however, will be fresh adults that have overwintered as pupae and it is these ones we will concentrate on here.

The well-named **March Moth** *Alsophila aescularia* and the **Early Grey** *Xylocampa areola* are two of the earliest spring species to emerge. In the case of the former only males visit light traps as the females are flightless. The **Oak Beauty** *Biston strataria* is probably our most handsome early moth, especially the males with their feathered antennae.

March and April see the emergence of four of our six 'Quaker' moths. Their common name is derived from the sombre clothing worn by the original practitioners of that religious sect in the 17th century. Common names are based on superficial appearance, which in this case is confusing. Three, the **Common Quaker** *Orthosia cerasi*, **Powdered Quaker** *Orthosia gracilis* and **Small Quaker** *Orthosia cruda* all belong to the genus *Orthosia*, as does another common moth on the wing at this time of the year, the **Hebrew Character** *Orthosia gothica*. The **Twin-spotted Quaker** *Anorthoa munda* is unrelated to these, belonging to another genus.

Another spring specialist to emerge in April is the small but beautifully coloured **Streamer** *Anticlea derivata*. Like all the preceding moths this species is single-brooded, and adults can only be found on the wing for a short period of the year. Other common spring species such as the **Double-striped Pug** *Gymnoscelis rufifasciata* are double-brooded, with the first brood on the wing April to May and a second emerging in August.

Figure 8.15 (left) March Moth, (centre) Early Grey, (right) Oak Beauty. (PAR).

Figure 8.16 (left) Common Quaker, (centre) Powdered Quaker, (right) Twin-spotted Quaker, (far right) Hebrew Character. (PAR).

Figure 8.17 (left) Streamer, (centre) Double-striped Pug, (right) Vine's Rustic. (PAR).

Figure 8.18 (left) Male Muslin Moth playing dead, (centre) Canary-shouldered Thorn, (right) Mating Brimstone Moths. (PAR).

Figure 8.19 (left) Puss Moth, (centre) Sallow Kitten, (right) Pale Tussock. (PAR).

Vine's Rustic *Hoplodrina ambigua* is also double-brooded, but the flight period of the two broods is longer and they overlap, so the moth may be found between May and October.

In May the first **Muslin Moths** *Diaphora mendica* arrive. This species provides a good example of sexual dimorphism. Not only do the sexes exhibit very different colouring, the wings of males being grey and females translucent white, but the males are mainly nocturnal and females diurnal so it is the males that are attracted to light traps. Muslin moths are also one of the species that play dead as a defensive mechanism. Any attempt to handle them may provoke them into letting go of whatever they were clinging to and dropping to the ground.

May also provides a welcome splash of primary colour from the **Brimstone Moth** *Opisthograptis luteolata* and **Canary-shouldered Thorn** *Ennomos alniaria*. Late spring sees the arrival of three 'cat' species; **Puss Moth** *Cerura vinula*, **Sallow Kitten** *Furcula furcula* and **Poplar Kitten** *Furcula bifida*, accompanied by another hairy-legged species the **Pale Tussock** *Calliteara pudibunda*.

Summer moths (June–August)

Summer is when things really get busy for moth recorders, as both the number and diversity of species increase dramatically and a recorder may have two or three hundred moths to count and identify from one night's catch.

June sees two lovely green moths in our local traps. The first is the most vivid green of any of our moths, the **Green Silver-lines** *Pseudoips prasinana*. The **Green Carpet** *Colostygia pectinataria* is one of our many 'carpet' moths. (Carpet in this case referring to their highly patterned wings resembling carpet patterns not their preferred food).

June is also the month when hawk-moths regularly turn up. The **Privet Hawk-moth** *Sphinx ligustri* is our largest resident species with a wingspan of 90–120 mm. It is a common suburban species, its caterpillars feeding on Lilac as well as Privet. Another common hawk-moth found in our garden moth traps is the **Poplar Hawk-moth** *Laothoe populi*. At rest they are unmistakable, with their hindwings held forward of the forewings, and the abdomen curved upwards at the rear.

Our two most colourful hawk-moths are the **Elephant Hawk-moth** *Deilephila elpenor* and **Small Elephant Hawk-moth** *Deilephila porcellus*. Both are common garden visitors.

Figure 8.20 (left) Green Silver-lines, (right) Green Carpet. (PAR).

Figure 8.21 (left) Privet Hawk-moth, (right) Poplar Hawk-moth. (PAR).

Figure 8.22 (left) Elephant Hawk-moth, (right) Small Elephant Hawk-moth. (PAR).

Figure 8.23 (left) Lime Hawk-moth, green form (AM). **(right) Eyed Hawk-moth.** (PAR).

Figure 8.24 (left) Chinese Character, (centre) Scarce Footman, (right) Inlaid Grass-veneer. (PAR).

The three remaining hawk-moths to be found at this time of the year are **Pine Hawk-moth** *Sphinx pinastri*, **Lime Hawk-moth** *Mimas tiliae* and **Eyed Hawk-moth** *Smerinthus ocellatus*. The false eyes of the latter species are a defensive mechanism and are normally hidden, but if the moth feels threatened by a potential predator it will raise its forewings to reveal them in an attempt to scare the predator away.

Counting and identifying all the catch from a heavily populated light trap can be quite a task. This is especially the case for the smaller moths which can easily escape or be overlooked.

The **Chinese Character** *Cilix glaucata* is an unusual-looking moth; from above, its wing-pattern and unusual resting posture give it the appearance of a bird-dropping, thus avoiding the attention of hungry birds looking for a tasty snack.

Footman moths get their name from the uniforms of 18th-century servants. We have several species and despite its name, the **Scarce Footman** *Eilema complana* is commonly recorded.

The **Inlaid Grass-veneer** *Crambus pascuella* is one of several 'grass moths' that spend the day at rest on grass stems where their posture and colouring keeps them well hidden from the eyes of predators. However they can often be observed during daylight hours when disturbed by people walking through tall grass.

The **Golden Argent** *Argyresthia goedartella* is one of our smallest moths at only 5 mm long and 1 mm across at rest. It belongs to the Argyresthiidae family of moths, or the shiny head-standing moths, which all adapt this very distinctive resting posture. Many of our micro-moths have unusual resting postures; for example members of the Gracillariinae family such as the **Small Red Slender** *Caloptilia rufipennella* rest on their long front legs with heads held high.

Figure 8.25 (left) Golden Argent, (right) Small Red Slender. (PAR).

In July the **Water Veneer** *Acentria ephemerella* is often found in very large numbers. As suggested by its scientific name, it is a very short-lived species and many caught in light traps do not survive until morning. The larvae and pupae of this moth are entirely aquatic.

Some species of moth are impossible to identify as adults without dissecting them and examining their genitalia under a microscope. This is the case with the appropriately named **Uncertain** *Hoplodrina alsines* and the near identical **Rustic** *Hoplodrina blanda* and also the **Dark Dagger** *Acronicta tridens* and **Grey Dagger** *Acronicta psi*.

Luckily we do not have to do this to establish the presence of these last two species. We only need to wait until autumn and search out their distinctive caterpillars.

Buff-tip *Phalera bucephala* moths are common throughout June and July and when at rest they create the illusion of being a dead, peeling piece of birch twig, fooling their predators into thinking they are not worth eating. My final selection for summer notables is the exotic looking **Swallow-tailed Moth** *Ourapteryx sambucaria*. With a wingspan of up to 50 mm this is one of our largest Geometrids, and cannot be mistaken for anything else.

Figure 8.26 (left) Water Veneer, (centre) Uncertain/Rustic, (right) Grey/Dark Dagger. (PAR).

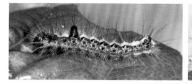 

Figure 8.27 Caterpillars of (left) Dark Dagger and (right) Grey Dagger. (PAR).

Figure 8.28 (left) Buff-tip, (right) Swallow-tailed Moth. (PAR).

Autumn moths (September–November)
Early autumn catches tend to be dominated by the Underwings: **Large Yellow Underwing** *Noctua pronuba*, **Lesser Yellow Underwing** *Noctua comes*, **Broad-bordered Yellow Underwing** *Noctua fimbriata*, **Lesser Broad-bordered Yellow Underwing** *Noctua janthe* and **Lunar Underwing** *Omphaloscelis lunosa*.

Two other moths that are caught in significant numbers at this time of the year are **Square-spot Rustic** *Xestia xanthographa* and **Setaceous Hebrew Character** *Xestia c-nigrum*. The **Old Lady** *Mormo maura* is a very large unmistakable moth. It frequents riverbanks, marshes, gardens, woodland, scrub and hedgerows. By day it hides in old buildings and sheds.

Figure 8.29 (left) Large Yellow Underwing, (centre) Broad-bordered Yellow Underwing, (right) Lunar Underwing. (PAR).

Figure 8.30 (left) Square-spot Rustic, (centre) Old Lady, (right) Setaceous Hebrew Character. (PAR).

Figure 8.31 (left) Red-line Quaker, (centre) Merveille du Jour, (right) Black Rustic. (PAR).

Figure 8.32 (left) Beaded Chestnut, **(centre)** Feathered Thorn, **(right)** Yellow-line Quaker. (PAR).

October sees peak numbers of **Red-line Quakers** *Agrochola lota* and two of our most striking autumn moths; the **Merveille du Jour** *Griposia aprilina* and the **Black Rustic** *Aporophyla nigra*.

Autumn also brings us a number of moths that have adapted to blend in with the predominant colours of the season, including **Beaded Chestnut** *Agrochola lychnidis*, **Feathered Thorn** *Colotois pennaria* and **Yellow-line Quaker** *Agrochola macilenta*.

Winter moths (December–February)

It may surprise you that adult moths are active during wintertime, but we have several species that are. Some of these are actually continuous breeders that can be found year-round in all their life stages.

To do this requires a year-round source of food such as stored grain or 'dead stuff' such as animal skins and wool.

One of the best places to find such food is in our houses, where the **Brown House-moth** *Hofmannophila pseudospretella* and **White-shouldered House-moth** *Endrosis sarcitrella* are very happy to take advantage of poorly stored grain, bran, flour and other cereals. They will also feed on wool and other animal-based fabrics. The **Common Clothes Moth** *Tineola bisselliella* and **Case-bearing Clothes Moth** *Tinea pellionella* are two species you do not want in your home, as they can do significant damage to clothing and wool carpets.

Other moths are true winter specialists. The **Mottled Umber** *Erannis defoliaria* and **Winter Moth** *Operophtera brumata* are on the wing

Figure 8.33. (left) Brown House-moth, **(centre)** White-shouldered House-moth, **(right)** Case-bearing Clothes Moth. (PAR).

Figure 8.34 (left) Mottled Umber, **(right)** Winter Moth. (PAR).

Figure 8.35 (left) Pale Brindled Beauty (PAR), **(right) Dotted Border.** (AM).

Figure 8.36 (left) Satellite, (centre) Dark Chestnut, (right) Herald. (PAR).

from late autumn to January. **December Moths** *Poecilocampa populi* can be found on the wing from November through to late December, although this moth seems to be a bit of a rarity for the NHC area as we only have two records: one from the Botanic Garden and another from Girton College.

With the turn of the year we have three additional winter species visiting our light traps: **Pale Brindled Beauty** *Phigalia pilosaria*, **Spring Usher** *Agriopis leucophaearia* and **Dotted Border** *Agriopis marginaria*. All these moths are males, as the females of all three are flightless.

A few species overwinter as adults. **Dark Chestnut** *Conistra ligula* moths become active on milder winter days so may turn up in light traps in all winter months. The **Satellite** *Eupsilia transversa* tends to stay dormant throughout December and January and starts to reappear from February onward.

The **Herald** *Scoliopteryx libatrix* stays in hibernation throughout the winter months.

Looking rather like a shrivelled leaf, it can often be found hibernating in outbuildings, porches and cellars.

Rare visitors

The first British record of **Clancy's Rustic** *Caradrina kadenii* was from Kent in 2002 and it has been recorded regularly from the most southern counties of England in subsequent years. The first and, so far, only record from the NHC area was from a private garden in 2020.

Cambridge is a long way from any salt marshes, so you would not expect a **Saltmarsh Plume** *Agdistis bennetii* to turn up in your garden, but in July 2018 one was caught in my garden trap and another 20 found in the Trumpington area.

The **True Lover's Knot** *Lycophotia porphyrea* is a common species of moorland and heathland, so again is an unexpected find in a city lacking such habitats, but a single individual was captured in my garden, in the same month as the Saltmarsh Plume.

The **Gypsy Moth** *Lymantria dispar* was once a common species in East Anglia, but around 1900 they became extinct as a breeding species. Since 1995 small colonies have established themselves in parts of London and with a good southerly breeze the odd male turns up in the NHC area. Females are poor flyers so are unable to fly this far north.

The **Jersey Tiger** *Euplagia quadripunctaria* is a species that has until recently been confined to the Channel Islands and the southernmost fringes of England, but is now expanding its range northwards and is established in some parts of London. Cambridge records are increasing and there is a strong possibility that it will become a resident species.

The **White-spotted Pinion** *Cosmia diffinis* has undergone a rapid decline as a result of Dutch elm disease and is now a nationally scarce species, with only a single record within the NHC area between 2016 and 2019.

Defoliators

The adult stages of these moths go mainly unnoticed but the huge numbers of caterpillars they produce in some years cannot be missed, due to the damage they inflict on their host plants.

The **Brown-tailed Moth** *Euproctis chrysorrhoea* is a native species that was historically confined to southern and eastern coasts of England but in recent years has become established further inland. The sight of trees and hedgerows covered in their silken tents has now become rather a common one in Cambridge. These caterpillars feed on a wide range of plants and once they have stripped their original food source of all its leaves, they will disperse to find alternative food supplies.

Figure 8.37 (left) Clancy's Rustic (AM)**, (centre) Saltmarsh Plume** (PAR)**, (right) True Lover's Knot.** (PAR).

Figure 8.38 (left) Gypsy Moth (PAR)**, (centre) Jersey Tiger** (PAR) **, (right) White-spotted Pinion.** (AM).

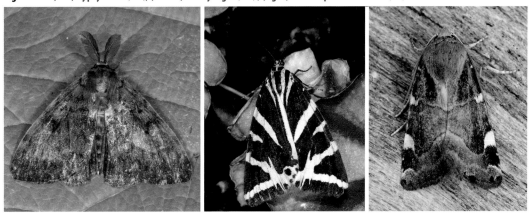

Brown-tailed moths overwinter as small caterpillars which can then go on to defoliate host plants in the spring. Tents created in early summer or later will belong to the small ermine *Yponomeuta* group of moths. There are several species but the two most likely to create expansive webs are the **Spindle Ermine** *Yponomeuta cagnagella* and the **Orchard Ermine** *Yponomeuta padella*. The former feeds solely on **Spindle** *Euonymus europaeus*, the latter on **Blackthorn** *Prunus spinosa*, **Hawthorn** *Crataegus monogyna*, plum & cherry. As well as covering the food plant, their webs can sometimes extend to surrounding objects such as post boxes and the pavement.

Although the damage caused by these species looks terrible it does not normally cause long-term damage to healthy trees and shrubs. This is not the case with the recent accidental introduction to these shores of the **Box-tree Moth** *Cydalima perspectalis*, which can cause die-back in infested **Common Box** *Buxus sempervirens* trees and hedges.

This Asian species reached Cambridge about 2017 but the number of observations then increased dramatically, with a maximum of 50 individuals caught in one night in Trumpington. This is possibly linked to large scale Box planting in nearby new housing estates. The caterpillars overwinter in a dormant state and start feeding again in late March. They pupate in a cocoon made of silk and leaves, with the first adults emerging in May. Two to three further generations occur over the summer.

Leaf-miners

Many micro-moth species (especially in the families Gracillariidae and Nepticulidae) are leaf-miners: the caterpillars eat leaves from the inside and often pupate within the leaf. They excavate characteristic galleries and blotches on the leaves that appear relatively translucent when held up to the light. Many of the leaf-mining micro-moths do not come to light, so are missed by moth-trapping and are best sought by searching for the mines themselves. If you are sharp eyed, adult moths such as this **Garden Apple Slender** *Callisto denticulella* can be spotted during daylight hours.

The Botanic Garden has been a focal point for recording leaf-miners during the NatHistCam

Figure 8.39 (left) Brown-tailed Moth caterpillars, **(centre)** Orchard Ermine webs covering a Hawthorn hedge, **(right)** Orchard Ermine caterpillars. (PAR)

Figure 8.40 Box-tree Moth, adult and caterpillar. (PAR).

Figure 8.41 (left) Garden Apple Slender (PAR), (right) Leaf mine created by a larva of the Scarce Maple Pigmy. (SJB).

Figure 8.42 Adult Horse Chestnut Leaf-miner and larval mines. (PAR).

project, especially during bioblitzes (Buckton 2021). Over 50 species of leaf-mining micro-moth have been found there; the huge diversity of host plants in the Garden must surely boost the leaf-miner diversity. The Garden's checklist includes a considerable number of Local, Nationally Scarce and even Nationally Rare species. One example of a leaf miner is the **Scarce Maple Pigmy** *Stigmella aceris* which mines the leaves of **Field Maple** *Acer campestre* and **Norway Maple** *Acer platanoides*.

Few leaf-miners occur in such numbers as the invasive **Horse Chestnut Leaf-miner** *Cameraria ohridella*. First recorded in Britain in 2002, it originates from southern Europe and is now well established throughout England. By late summer its presence is evident from the premature browning and shedding of Horse Chestnut leaves.

Caddisflies
Introduction
If you put a moth trap out at night, moths are rarely the only type of invertebrate attracted to its alluring light. A common stowaway is a drab brownish winged insect, not altogether dissimilar to a moth. It is indeed closely related, but with hairs rather than scales on its wings (which it holds angled in a steep tent shape at rest), generally a slim and elongate body and long thin antennae. This is a caddisfly, or the 'sedge' of fly-fishers, belonging to the order Trichoptera (meaning 'hairy wing').

There are around 200 caddisfly species known in Britain (Barnard & Ross 2012). Caddisflies are rarely found far from water, as their larvae (bar one species) are aquatic: they can be found in all sorts of water bodies and wetlands, although most species require relatively clean, well-oxygenated water (this can make caddisflies useful indicators of water quality). Caddisflies play an integral role in these aquatic ecosystems, providing an important food source for fish, birds and bats. Most of a caddisfly's life is spent in the larval stage; adults are typically ephemeral and live just long enough for dispersal, mating and egg-laying, although some caddisfly species can live for several months as adults

Figure 8.43 Caddisfly larva. (PAR).

(Barnard & Ross, 2012). Many caddisfly larvae are remarkable architects, constructing beautiful protective cases for themselves out of debris such as sand, gravel and plant fragments, held together with silk.

When you look more closely at adult caddisflies, you realise that many have elegantly understated patterning within their brown palette, with all sorts of attractive speckling, marbling, stripes and blotches. Some of our commonest caddisfly species are identifiable just by looking at the wing patterns, although the majority require microscopic examination for reliable identification to species level: this contributes to caddisflies being a relatively under-recorded group. Although interest in 'moth trap intruders' seems to be growing nationally (there is now a dedicated Facebook group), moth-trappers in the Cambridge area could add much to our knowledge of caddisfly distributions by branching out into the non-moths that also find their way into traps. Many of these non-moth records are likely to be

relatively significant because the species have been overlooked.

The Cambridge species

Thirty-four caddisfly species were recorded from 2010 to 2019 in Cambridge, with one further species recorded in 2020 (Table 8.1). Most records come from nocturnal moth-trapping, although some caddisflies may have been spotted during the day. Adult caddisflies can often be seen in flight over or near waterbodies. Unsurprisingly, most of the records come from locations near water, such as Logan's Meadow LNR, Adams Road Bird Sanctuary and the Botanic Garden. Many records are also of larvae (especially from Environment Agency water quality monitoring) in waterways such as Bin Brook, Cherry Hinton Brook, Hobson's Conduit and those in Coe Fen.

Notable species

Notable species are those which are particularly rare or have a special conservation designation. A rather nice find was *Ecnomus tenellus*, a fairly small mottled caddis that has only been recorded from scattered locations across England and Wales. I recorded it whilst moth trapping at Logan's Meadow in 2018. Its larvae are known to eat freshwater sponges (Wundsch 1943). Two other species with a wide but scattered British distribution, are the striking *Mystacides nigra* – caught in moth traps in Paul Rule's garden and nearby Radegund Road – and *Lype reducta*, whose larvae were recorded in Coe Fen and Hobson's Brook by Environment Agency ecologists.

Other species

The regular moth-trapping at the Botanic Garden continues to reveal an encouraging diversity of

Table 8.1 Checklist of caddisfly species recorded in the NHC area (2010–2020).

Adicella reducta	Hydroptila sp.	Mystacides longicornis
Agapetus fuscipes	Limnephilus affinis	Mystacides nigra
Agraylea sp.	Limnephilur auricula	Oecetis lacustris
Agrypnia varia	Limnephilus flavicornis	Oecetis ochracea
Anabolia nervosa	Limnephilus incisus	Phryganea bipunctata
Athripsodes aterrimus	Limnephilus lunatus	Phryganea grandis
Cyrnus trimaculatus	Limnephilus marmoratus	Polycentropus flavomaculatus
Ecnomus tenellus	Limnephilus sparsus	Sericostoma personatum
Glyphotaelius pellucidus	Lype reducta	Tinodes waeneri
Goera pilosa	Micropterna sequax	Triaenodes bicolor
Halesus radiatus	Molanna angustata	Trichostegia minor
Hydropsyche siltalai	Mystacides azurea	

Figure 8.44 The shady character of *Mystacides nigra*, with its distinctly banded antennae. (PAR).

Figure 8.45 *Limnephilus lunatus*, one of our commonest and most easily recognised caddisflies. (PAR).

Figure 8.46 *Phryganea grandis*, Britain's largest caddisfly. (PAR).

caddisflies, especially those in the highly speciose genus *Limnephilus* (this contains the 'Cinnamon Sedges' of fly-fishers). Many *Limnephilus* species are easily identifiable by their wing pattern. One of our most familiar caddisflies is *L. lunatus*, which has a 'crescent moon' shape at the tip of its wings.

Perhaps the most visually impressive of the Cambridge caddisflies is the well-named *Phryganea grandis*, the female of which is the largest British caddisfly, with a wing length up to 28 mm. Paul Rule recorded this species at the East Pit LNR whilst moth-trapping there in 2020.

Older records

Cambridge has a long history of wildlife recording, extending far back before 2010. The NBN Atlas reveals a large number of pre-2010 caddisfly records from the NHC area, including 25 species which have since been unrecorded (Table 8.2). One species *Limnephilus bipunctatus* was last recorded as long ago as 1837 by the great English entomologist James Francis Stephens (1792–1852), who was often sent records of rare insects by the young Charles Darwin. One caveat with these older records is that their location is often vague, so they may not necessarily be within the precise project area (although all are at least ascribed to 'Cambridge').

All of the species listed in Table 8.1 bar nine *Ecnomus tenellus, Limnephilus affinis, L. auricula, L. sparsus, Micropterna sequax, Oecetis lacustris, O. ochracea, Triaenodes bicolor* and *Trichostegia minor* were also known pre-NHC. This means that the NHC period has seen a net 'loss' of 16 caddisfly species.

It is intriguing to ponder why these species have not been recorded in Cambridge for many decades. Some may still be present, but difficult to find or identify. Indeed, a relatively high proportion of the lost species (compared to the NHC species) are uncommon in Britain, so may simply be harder to detect due to their inherent

Table 8.2 Caddisfly species recorded in the NHC area before 2010, with year of last sighting in parentheses.

Agraylea multipunctata (1996)	*Hydroptila sparsa* (1919)	*Limnephilus vittatus* (1907)
Athripsodes bilineatus (2006)	*Hydroptila tineoides* (1991)	*Lype phaeopa* (1938)
Athripsodes cinereus (1991)	*Limnephilus bipunctatus* (1837)	*Neureclipsis bimaculata* (1913)
Beraeodes minutus (1900)	*Limnephilus extricatus* (1991)	*Notidobia ciliaris* (1911)
Ceraclea senilis (2000)	*Limnephilus fuscicornis* (1918)	*Orthotrichia angustella* (1919)
Chaetopteryx villosa (1991)	*Limnephilus griseus* (1859)	*Polycentropus kingi* (2000)
Cyrnus flavidus (2000)	*Limnephilus politus* (1936)	*Rhyacophila dorsalis* (1920)
Holocentropus picicornis (1950)	*Limnephilus rhombicus* (2002)	
Hydropsyche angustipennis (2006)	*Limnephilus stigma* (1932)	

rarity. *Limnephilus stigma* is local throughout Britain in marshes and ponds, with especially few records from the south. *L. politus* and *Neureclipsis bimaculata* are also local nationally. *Beraeodes minutus*, *L. bipunctatus, L. fuscicornis* and *Notidobia ciliaris* are all uncommon nationally, whilst *Athripsodes bilineatus* is not common in the south-east.

Orthotrichia angustella is the rarest of all, with precious few records in Britain. It was found by Cyril Benoni Holman-Hunt, son of the well-known Pre-Raphaelite painter William Holman Hunt, in the 'Livingstone Temperance Hotel' on Petty Cury, right in the heart of town. Cyril's adult specimen remains in the Cambridge University Entomological Collection.

It is likely that some caddisflies have disappeared from the Cambridge area as a result of human activity. Disproportionately represented amongst the lost species are those associated with gravelly or stony substrates, those with preference for acidic water, and those with a northern or western affinity in Britain. These traits often appear together in a single species (e.g. *Chaetopteryx villosa* and *Rhyacophila dorsalis* show all three), complicating the job of disentangling the factors that produced distributional changes in these lost species, although climate change could well have played a role. All of the new species added by the NHC project are relatively generalist and have a southern or no strong regional affinity.

9. Beetles and bugs

Beetles (Coleoptera)

Introduction

With more than 4000 UK species in about 1300 genera and nearly 100 families, beetles can be very difficult for the casual observer to comprehend and this is reflected in the relatively small number of species recorded during this project.

Many species are nocturnal and, unlike moths, few are attracted to ultraviolet light so are harder to record. Many are also very small and have few visible distinguishing features, making identification very difficult. It is therefore no surprise that the more colourful diurnal species top our table of most-recorded species, especially ladybirds (Table 9.1).

There are records of 251 species, but with the possible exception of the more familiar conspicuous ladybirds, Cambridge's beetles are very under-recorded, with many species and even whole families overlooked entirely.

In the following pages I present an overview of some of the more common and notable beetles found in the NHC area. Peter Brown gives a more detailed account of the ladybirds, and Rhona Watson describes the chafers and their impact on Cambridge college gardens.

Aquatic beetles
Whirligig beetles Gyrinidae

These small beetles will be familiar to most people as they are often seen 'dancing' on the surface of ponds, lakes and slow flowing streams and rivers. There are 12 UK species and although a common sight, all those we found were in the genus *Gyrinus*.

Figure 9.1 Whirligig beetles. (PAR).

Table 9.1 Most frequently recorded beetles during the NHC project (from iRecord and CPERC).

Species	Common Name	Records	Proportion %
Coccinella septempunctata	7-spot Ladybird	174	24.1
Harmonia axyridis	Harlequin Ladybird	129	17.8
Propylea quattuordecimpunctata	14-spot Ladybird	22	3.0
Oedemera nobilis	Swollen-thighed Beetle	21	2.9
Exochomus quadripustulatus	Pine Ladybird	17	2.4
Dorcus parallelipipedus	Lesser Stag Beetle	16	2.2
Lampyris noctiluca	Glow-worm	14	1.9
Adalia decempunctata	10-spot Ladybird	12	1.7
Subcoccinella vigintiquattuorpunctata	24-spot Ladybird	11	1.5
Melolontha melolontha	Common Cockchafer	11	1.5
Chrysolina americana	Rosemary Beetle	11	1.5
Hoplia philanthus	Welsh Chafer	7	1.0

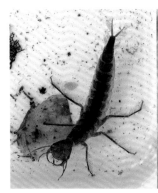

Figure 9.2 (left) Great Diving Beetle larva, (centre) *Acilius sulcatus*, **(right)** *Hydroporus tessulatus*. (PAR).

Figure 9.3 (left) *Hydrobius fuscipes*, **(right)** *Heterocerus fenestratus*. (PAR).

Diving beetles (Dytiscidae)

Diving beetles are highly adapted to aquatic living: both the larvae and adults hunt their prey beneath the surface of ponds and lakes. Eight species of diving beetle have been recorded in the NHC area over the period of the project. Most, including the **Great Diving Beetle** *Dytiscus marginalis* and *Acilius sulcatus* are the larger and more obvious species. The smaller species are very difficult to identify and are very much under-recorded with just one, *Hydroporus tessulatus*, being noted.

Water scavenger beetles (Hydrophilidae)

Although there are 70 British species in this family, they are seldom seen. There is just a single species recorded in the NHC area. The larvae of *Hydrobius fuscipes* feed on small insects and the adults on submerged detritus.

Mud beetles (Heteroceridae)

These small beetles (3–5 mm) have front legs adapted for digging and live in burrows in the mud at the edges of our water systems. Living most of their lives in mud, they are very rarely seen and the

one project record of *Heterocerus fenestratus* was a lucky find from my moth trap.

Small dung beetles (Aphodiini)

These beetles all feed on mammal dung and breed at sites where cattle are grazed such as Coe Fen, Sheep's Green, Midsummer Common and Coldham's Common. Each cowpat may contain many individuals at all stages of their life cycle. Seven species have been recorded, all belonging

Figure 9.4 *Aphodius rufipes*. (PAR).

Figure 9.5 *Geotrupes spiniger.* (PAR).

to the same genus: *Aphodius contaminatus, A. erraticus, A. fossor, A. granarius, A. rufipes, A. sphacelatus* and *A. prodromus.*

Dor beetles (Geotrupidae)
These large powerful beetles are also associated with dung and can be found at the same locations. There are 8 members of this family in the UK with just one, *Geotrupes spiniger*, being recorded during the project. After mating a female excavates a vertical burrow directly beneath a dung pat. From this central burrow, she then excavates horizontal branches and provisions each with a cylindrical brood mass of dung, laying a single egg in each.

Darkling beetles (Tenebrionidae)
Darkling beetles are a diverse group, with the four subfamilies found in the UK appearing to have little in common. The **Mealworm Beetle** *Tenebrio molitor* feeds on stored grain products so is likely to turn up in houses. This beetle is reared commercially, its larvae being used for fishing bait and for wild bird food.

Lagria hirta is very common and may be found in a wide range of habitats including open woodland, grassland and urban gardens. Like most members of this family it is nocturnal, so is seldom seen unless you are running a light trap when it can turn up in large numbers.

Historically *Diaperis boleti* was a rare British species but in recent years has become more common and is expanding its range. It feeds on bracket fungi and was recorded for the first time in Cambridge in May 2020, when at least twenty individuals were found on **Chicken-of-the-Woods** *Laetiporus sulphureus* in Paradise LNR.

Figure 9.6 (left) Mealworm Beetle, **(centre)** *Lagria hirta*, **(right)** *Diaperis boleti.* (PAR).

Figure 9.7 (left) Black Sexton Beetle (PAR), (right) *Nicrophorus vespillo.* (CKL).

Figure 9.8 (left) *Silpha laevigata,* (right) Black Snail Beetle. (PAR).

Figure 9.9 (left) Strawberry Seed Beetle, (right) *Curtonotus aulicus.* (PAR).

Figure 9.10 *Bradycellus verbasci.* (PAR).

Figure 9.11 (left) Black Clock Beetle, (right) Common Sun Beetle. (CKL).

Carrion beetles (Silphidae)

Beetles of the genus *Nicrophorus* are the undertakers of the animal world; they bury dead animals such as mice and birds and feed and breed on the corpses. Three species have been recorded: **Black Sexton Beetle** *Nicrophorus humator*, ***Nicrophorus interruptus*** and *Nicrophorus vespillo.*

We also have records of three *Silpha* species and although they are carrion beetles, ***Silpha laevigata*** and ***Silpha tristis*** supplement their diet with live prey. The third is the **Black Snail Beetle** *Silpha atrata* which, as its common name suggests, is a specialist snail feeder. These beetles are flightless and are most likely to be seen scurrying across paths at night.

Ground beetles (Carabidae)

A large, diverse family found in a wide range of habitats, ground beetles are one of the largest groups of beetles with 360 UK species. They are often encountered as they scurry along the ground. Having said that, they are not easy to identify, as many look very similar to each other, as you can see from the pictures of two of our larger common species, the **Strawberry Seed Beetle** *Harpalus rufipes* and ***Curtonotus aulicus***.

Most ground beetles are nocturnal and for the most part go unnoticed. *Bradycellus verbasci* is a very common species, seldom seen unless you run a moth trap, where it regularly turns up in large numbers.

The **Black Clock Beetle** *Pterostichus madidus* is common throughout most of Britain and with five records, it is our most recorded ground beetle. It is predatory, feeding on ground-living invertebrates, including caterpillars and slugs. The **Common Sun Beetle** *Amara aenea*, as its name suggests, likes to sun itself and is often seen on bare ground. As one of our few common diurnal ground beetles, it is surprising that we only have a single record for this seed-feeding species.

You may be lucky to come across a **Violet Ground Beetle** *Carabus violaceus* in your garden. This flightless black beetle with a distinctive violet sheen is an active predator, coming out at night to hunt slugs, snails and other invertebrates. Another common, but seldom seen, distinctive ground beetle is *Dromius quadrimaculatus*, although this one is mainly associated with deciduous trees. The specimen photographed was found in my garden by searching the trunk and branches of an apple tree by torchlight.

Two of our most interesting and rarest records came on consecutive nights in my garden during a heat wave in August 2020. The **Bombardier Beetle** *Brachinus crepitans* is a scarce species in our region with only a handful of historical county records. For defence these beetles are capable of shooting a hot noxious chemical spray from two glands through their anus. One gland contains hydrogen peroxide and the other hydroquinone, so when the two mix with enzymes in a 'firing chamber' the resulting chemical mix explodes, putting off even large predators.

Polistichus connexus is even rarer with only one county record before 2020. According to UK Beetle Recording (2020) its status is listed as 'Declining and mainly confined to coastal locations

Figure 9.12 (above) Violet Ground Beetle (LKE), **(left)** *Dromius quadrimaculatus.* (PAR).

F**igure 9.13 (left)** Bombardier Beetle, **(right)** *Polistichus connexus.* (PAR).

in the extreme south and east of England'. During the early August heat wave of 2020 there was an explosion of sightings from inland locations in the south of England, including one in my Cambridge garden. It is possible that the extreme temperatures may have uncovered some hidden populations by driving them from their normal hiding places.

Rove beetles (Staphylinidae)

We have 23 species recorded for this family, which is a very small number considering it is Britain's largest with around 1120 known species. There are a number of reasons for this: they are rarely seen in the open, are mostly nocturnal and most are very difficult to identify.

Most rove beetles can be instantly recognised as such by their elongated bodies and short wing cases (elytra). The one species that most people will be familiar with is the **Devil's Coach-horse** *Ocypus olens*. This predator hunts invertebrates after dark in gardens and on grasslands. It is well-known for curling up its abdomen like the tail of a scorpion when it feels threatened.

Platydracus stercorarius is our most colourful rove beetle and despite its large size, we only have a single sighting. The adults and larvae are predators of insect larvae, particularly those of dung flies. This one was found on concrete in the city and was probably attracted in the previous night by the artificial lights from buildings.

Most gardens will have several species of rove beetles hiding away out of sight, but a good place to search for them is in your compost, where species such as *Philonthus cognatus* may be found.

Figure 9.14 (left) Devil's Coach-horse (PAR), **(right)** *Platydracus stercorarius.* (SJH).

Figure 9.15 *Philonthus cognatus.* (PAR).

Figure 9.16 (left) *Tachyporus hypnorum*, (centre) *Tachinus rufipes*, (right) *Oxytelus laqueatus*. (PAR).

Figure 9.17 (left) Tortoise Beetle (PAR), (right) Thistle Tortoise Beetle larva. (MAM).

Tachyporus hypnorum is one of the smaller rove beetles, often found in gardens where it is a useful predator of aphids. A search through damp logs, leaf litter or matted vegetation is likely to turn up several rove beetles including the relatively common *Tachinus rufipes*.

Oxytelus laqueatus is another common species, but this one feeds in dung so is more likely to be found where cattle and horses graze.

Leaf beetles (Chrysomelidae)
Leaf beetles are a large and very diverse family with around 280 UK species, only 19 of which were found in Cambridge in the period 2016–2020. There are several subfamilies with some very distinctive members. Five of these subfamilies are described below.

Tortoise beetles (Cassidinae)
Tortoise Beetles are very distinctive, with their extended wing cases and pronotum covering the entire beetle. If attacked by a predator they clamp themselves to a leaf leaving only their hard protective shell exposed. The larvae also have an interesting defensive mechanism. They possess twin tail-spikes which are used to carry dead skins and droppings in a kind of parasol. The **Tortoise Beetle** *Cassida vibex* and **Thistle Tortoise Beetle** *Cassida rubiginosa* are common species of meadows and road verges, but are hard to spot.

Reed beetles (Donaciinae)
This subfamily consists of large beetles that are found on plants of water margins. *Donacia semicuprea* feeds on **Reed Sweet-grass** *Glyceria maxima*. It has been seen in significant numbers along the stretch of the Cam flowing through Grantchester Meadows and also in the Botanic Garden. Its close relative *Donacia vulgaris* feeds on **Club-rush** *Schoenoplectus* spp. and **Bur-reed** *Sparganium erectum* and was recorded from just one site: the pond at Barnwell East LNR.

Figure 9.18 (left) *Donacia vulgaris*, (right) *Donacia semicuprea*. (PAR).

Figure 9.19 (left) *Altica lythri /palustris,* (centre) **Mallow Flea Beetle,** (right) *Sphaeroderma testaceum.* (PAR).

Flea beetles (Alticinae)

These small beetles are equipped with powerful back legs that enable them to leap like a flea to escape predation. Most species feed on specific plants which typically results in the host plant's leaves being peppered with small holes. Adults of the metallic blue **Altica lythri** and **Altica palustris** can only be distinguished by dissection. In the image, their tell-tale marks can be seen on **Great Willowherb** *Epilobium hirsutum* leaves.

The **Mallow Flea Beetle** *Podagrica fuscicornis* is very common in our meadows and road verges where its host plants *Malva* spp. grow. *Sphaeroderma testaceum* can be found in similar locations, where it feeds on Thistles.

Criocerinae

These colourful beetles might not be too welcome in your garden, particularly if you grow **Asparagus** *Asparagus officinalis* or fill your flower beds with lilies. The **Asparagus Beetle** *Crioceris asparagi* can be found in any larger garden or allotment where

that crop is grown. Both adults and larvae feed on the leaf-like stems.

The **Scarlet Lily Beetle** *Lilioceris lilii* is an Asian species that first became established in Britain in 1939. Since the 1970s it has expanded across much of the country and is now a common sight in our gardens. There are two species of **Cereal Beetles** *Oulema melanopus* and *O. rufocyanea* that, without microscopic examination, appear identical. Both can be a serious pest of cereal crops, but in the NHC area they are more likely to be found in meadows feeding on wild grasses.

Chrysomelinae

We have records for three species of this sub-family, all of them in the genus *Chrysolina*. Two are relative newcomers to Cambridge, including the **Rosemary Beetle** *C. americana*. A native of southern Europe, it is now common in gardens where **Rosemary** *Rosmarinus officinalis* and **Lavender** (*Lavandula* spp.) are grown.

Chrysolina banksii is a native species previously confined to the coastal regions of England and

Figure 9.20 (left) **Asparagus Beetle,** (centre) **Scarlet Lily Beetle,** (right) **Cereal Beetle.** (PAR).

Figure 9.21 (left) *Chrysolina banksii,* (centre) **Rosemary Beetle,** (right) *Chrysolina oricalcia.* (PAR).

Wales. In recent years it has seen a significant expansion to inland areas and since 2019 it has been recorded from Jesus College, Trumpington Meadows and Logan's Meadow LNR. Its food plant, **Ribwort Plantain** *Plantago lanceolata* is very common, so it is likely that it is now well established.

The third beetle of this trio is *Chrysolina oricalcia* which can be found in hedgerows, roadside verges and woodland rides, favouring umbellifer flowers such as Cow Parsley and Hogweed.

Soldier beetles (Cantharidae)

These are our most conspicuous beetles and from mid-spring through early summer they can be found feeding on pollen and nectar in flower meadows and hedgerows. The **Common Red Soldier Beetle** *Rhagonycha fulva* and *Cantharis rustica* are our two commonest species and on a walk around Trumpington Meadows you are likely to see hundreds of them, including many mating pairs.

Soldier beetles are so named after early British military uniforms and most of the 20 species recorded are indeed redcoats, with various amounts of red and black colouring. A minority such as *Cantharis decipiens* would appear to have signed up for another army.

Flower Beetles
Soft-winged flower beetles (Malachiidae)

These small predatory beetles can be found hunting on vegetation and flowers. The adult **Common Malachite Beetle** *Malachius bipustulatus* is the most abundant of this family and can be seen in large numbers on flower-heads in meadows and hedgerows. *Anthocomus fasciatus* is another spring to early summer species, but it is not as common and at 4 mm long is often overlooked. *Anthocomus rufus* is a late summer – early autumn species that supplements its insect diet with pollen, typically from the flower heads of **Common Reed** *Phragmites australis* and various rushes and sedges, so is mainly found in damper areas.

Figure 9.22 (left) Common Red Soldier Beetle, **(centre)** *Cantharis rustica*, **(right)** *Cantharis decipiens*. (PAR).

Figure 9.23 (left) Common Malachite Beetle, **(centre)** *Anthocomus fasciatus*, **(right)** *Anthocomus rufus*. (PAR).

Figure 9.24 (left) Common Pollen Beetle, (centre) *Glischrochilus hortensis*, **(right) Raspberry Beetles.** (PAR).

Pollen/sap beetles (Nitulidae) and raspberry beetles (Byturidae)

Pollen beetles are small beetles that appear in very large numbers on flowers in spring and summer. They are particularly attracted to yellow flowers and will often land on yellow clothing, mistaking it for a very large flower. The most common of these is the **Common Pollen Beetle** *Meligethes aeneus*.

Most members of this family are just 1–2 mm long, but *Glischrochilus hortensis*, a sap feeder, is one of the larger species. This beetle spends much of its time hiding under bark so although fairly common it is seldom seen.

The larvae of the **Raspberry Beetle** *Byturus tomentosus* are fruit feeders, but the adults and those of its close relative, *Byturus ochraceus*, are pollen feeders. They can often be seen in large numbers on the flowers of the buttercup family *Ranunculaceae*.

False blister beetles (Oedemeridae)

The beautiful metallic green **Swollen-thighed Beetle** *Oedemera nobilis* is one of our most common beetles and can be seen in large numbers in parks, meadows, hedgerows and gardens during the summer months, feeding on pollen.

The males are unmistakable, but the females lack the swollen thighs and are difficult to separate from their less common close relatives *O. lurida* and *O. virescens*.

Longhorn beetles (Cerambycidae)

Longhorns are among our most spectacular beetles and the adults can often be seen feeding on pollen and nectar in meadows, hedgerows and woodland margins on sunny spring and summer days.

Ten species have been recorded, including the **Wasp Beetle** *Clytus arietis*, **Four-banded Longhorn** *Leptura quadrifasciata* and *Anaglyptus mysticus*. The larvae of all these species feed within dead wood.

The larvae of the **Greater Thorn-tipped Longhorn** *Pogonocherus hispidus* feed within small dead branches and twigs. *Stenurella melanura* larvae develop within thin dead twigs, branches and surface roots, and generally feed on decaying, or crumbly and slightly damp wood.

The **Fairy-ring Longhorn** *Pseudovadonia livida* is a meadow specialist: its larvae develop in the soil feeding on the mycelium of **Fairy Ring Mushrooms** *Marasmius oreades*.

At 25 mm long *Stenocorus meridianus* is one of our larger longhorns. Its larvae develop in diseased

Figure 9.25 Male and female Swollen-thighed Beetles. (PAR).

trees. Adult beetles can be found frequenting flowers and shrubs on the margins of wooded areas. We currently only have a single record from East Barnwell LNR for this species. Even larger at 40 mm is our most impressive longhorn, the **Musk Beetle** *Aromia moschata*. This metallic green beetle is associated with live willows in damper areas. It has been recorded from three sites in recent years including Paradise LNR, which is probably the best place to find them within the NHC area. From July to September they may be found among low vegetation, feeding on flowers or on sunlit tree trunks.

Figure 9.26 (left) Wasp Beetle, (centre) Four-banded Longhorn, (right) *Anaglyptus mysticus***.** (PAR).

Figure 9.27 (left) Mating Greater Thorn-tipped Longhorns (PAR), **(centre)** *Stenurella melanura* (PAR), **(right) Fairy-ring Longhorn.** (RKW).

Figure 9.28 (left) *Stenocorus meridianus*, **(right) Musk Beetle.** (PAR).

Figure 9.29 (left) *Tatianaerhynchites aequatus*, **(centre)** Acorn Weevil, **(right)** Figwort Weevil. (PAR).

Figure 9.30 (left) Nettle Weevil, **(centre)** Pea-leaf Weevil, **(right)** Vine Weevil. (PAR).

True weevils & bark beetles (Curculionidae)
True weevils
True weevils are small herbivorous beetles with extended snouts. 26 species were recorded in total across a wide range of habitats. Some of these are extraordinary-looking insects: ***Tatianaerhynchites aequatus***, the **Acorn Weevil** *Curculio glandium* and **Figwort Weevil** *Cionus scrophulariae* are among those with very long, narrow snouts.

The **Nettle Weevil** *Phyllobius pomaceus* is one of the broad-nosed weevils (Entiminae). Its green-blue colouring comes from a covering of scales that rub off as they age, so some older specimens may be mainly black.

Several species will be familiar to gardeners as they are considered pests. The larvae of **Pea-leaf Weevils** *Sitona lineatus* attack the roots of legumes and **Vine Weevils** *Otiorhynchus sulcatus* eat the roots of many types of garden plant, especially plants in containers.

Bark beetles
Although there have been very few records, their presence is noticeable by the damage they inflict on our trees, in particular **Elm** *Ulmus* spp. Dutch elm disease is caused by the fungus **Ophiostoma novo-ulmi**, carried by elm bark beetles, in particular the **Large Elm Bark Beetle** *Scolytus scolytus*.

The image below shows an unknown *Scolytus* species boring into the bark of a sick **Rowan** *Sorbus aucuparia* tree shortly before the tree died.

Figure 9.31 *Scolytus* sp. (PAR).

Cardinal beetles (Pyrochroidae)

The Pyrochroidae are a small family with just three known British species, including the **Red-headed Cardinal** *Pyrochroa serraticornis*. This predatory beetle is relatively common in parts of the city containing mature trees, such as Cherry Hinton Hall and Byron's Pool LNR. It is superficially similar to the Scarlet Lily Beetle but can easily be distinguished by the distinctive notched antennae and red head.

Figure 9.32 Red-headed Cardinal. (PAR).

Click beetles (Elateridae)

These bullet-shaped beetles have a unique mechanism that enables them to leap without the use of their legs. A hinge between the thorax and abdomen contains stored elastic energy and when released the beetle is flipped in the air with an audible click. This is used to escape predators or to right themselves if they are overturned or land on their backs.

The larvae of some click beetles are garden pests (wireworms) feeding on vegetable roots.

Figure 9.33 (left) *Athous haemorrhoidalis*, (right) *Stenagostus rhombeus*. (PAR).

However the six species identified for this project are all predatory species including *Athous haemorrhoidalis* and *Stenagostus rhombeus*.

Stag beetles (Lucanidae)

The UK has four species belonging to this family, but only the **Lesser Stag Beetle** *Dorcus parallelipipedus* has been recorded in the NHC area in significant numbers. The larvae feed on rotting timber and they would appear to be common across the city, having been recorded at 15 different sites. Being a large and easily identified beetle may contribute to the higher-than-average number of sightings.

Three records of **Stag Beetles** *Lucanus cervus* have been made within the area during the annual national Stag Beetle survey organised by the People's Trust for Endangered Species (two in 2016 and another in 2018), but there would appear to be no other sightings.

Figure 9.34 Lesser Stag Beetle. (PAR).

Glow-worms (Lampyridae)

Common Glow-worms *Lampyris noctiluca* are not nearly as common as they once were and recent research suggests a 70% decline in numbers in south-east England between 2000 and 2018 (Gardiner & Didham 2020). East Pit LNR in Cherry Hinton is the only site where they can currently be found in the NHC area. They were previously

Figure 9.35 Female Common Glow-worm. (PAR).

present at Coldham's Common but have not been seen there since 1979. It is also worth noting that there is a colony just outside our NHC area in Teversham Fen.

Glow-worms are predators of snails and the females are flightless, so they are vulnerable to changing climate conditions. Hotter, drier summers could see a dramatic decline in snail numbers at this site, which could in turn lead to the extinction of this species in the city.

Ladybirds (Coccinellidae)
Introduction
The UK has 48 resident ladybird species, often divided into two subgroups – the 'conspicuous' and 'inconspicuous' ladybirds. The 27 conspicuous species are larger, shinier and generally much more colourful than their 21 inconspicuous cousins. The latter are small (generally 1–3 mm in length) beetles, many belonging to the genera *Scymnus* or *Rhyzobius*. They are mostly dull in colour (brown or black), hairy and rather difficult to spot. Whilst they are no doubt under-recorded compared to their more obvious counterparts, in many cases the inconspicuous species seem to be genuinely less common.

Many ladybirds do rather well in urban and suburban habitats. Most are predators feeding on small sap-sucking insects, particularly aphids and scale insects. Urban vegetation can provide rich sources of such food. A minority of species feed on mildews or vegetation. Ladybirds tend to favour warm habitats and many species seem more abundant in drier parts of Britain. As with many insect groups, ladybird species richness is high in the south-east and lower in the north: Scotland lacks many ladybird species found in southern England. All of these factors make it unsurprising that Cambridge has rather a rich ladybird fauna, with 25 of the British species being recorded in Cambridge within the period of the NHC survey. I suspect that a few extra species are present but were not recorded.

Common city-wide resident species
The most common ladybird species in Cambridge is the 7-**spot** *Coccinella septempunctata*, the classic ladybird with bright red wing cases and seven black spots. This generalist species may be found on vegetation almost anywhere (usually on herbaceous plants, but also on trees). Next most common is probably the **Harlequin Ladybird** *Harmonia axyridis*, the notorious non-native species that has spread across the country since its arrival in 2003. This generalist species may be better recorded than the other conspicuous ladybirds, as it favours urban

Figure 9.36 (left) 7-spot Ladybird, (right) Harlequin Ladybird. (PAR).

Figure 9.37 (from left to right) 14-spot Ladybird, 16-spot Ladybird, 22-spot Ladybird, 24-spot Ladybird. (PAR).

Figure 9.38 (left) 2-spot Ladybird, (centre and right) 10–spot Ladybird, typical and melanic forms. (PAR).

locations, particularly on deciduous trees, and usually overwinters in buildings.

Other common species include two yellow ladybirds with black spots, the **14-spot** *Propylea quatuordecimpunctata* and **22-spot** *Psyllobora vigintiduopunctata*. The latter is a mildew feeder, as is the **16-spot** *Tytthaspis sedecimpunctata*, a grassland species that also feeds on pollen and nectar. Cambridge has one herbivorous ladybird, the **24-spot** *Subcoccinella vigintiquatuorpunctata*, another small grassland species that is unusual in being hairy.

Two closely-related species which were negatively affected by the arrival of the Harlequin Ladybird are still moderately common in Cambridge, the **2-spot** *Adalia bipunctata* and **10-spot** *Adalia decempunctata* ladybirds. These tend to be found in trees, the 2-spot being rather more generalist and also commonly recorded on herbs such as **Cow Parsley** *Anthriscus sylvestris*. The 10-spot favours hedgerows as well as deciduous and coniferous trees.

Common species on trees

There are several other common ladybird species found on trees in Cambridge. The **Pine Ladybird** *Exochomus quadripustulatus* lives on coniferous and deciduous trees, whereas its close relative the **Kidney-spot Ladybird** *Chilocorus renipustulatus* is usually found on deciduous trees such as **Ash** *Fraxinus excelsior* and **Sallow** *Salix* spp. (Roy & Brown 2018). Both of these species are black with red spots and are often found feeding on scale insects on the trunks and branches of trees, rather than on the foliage. The aptly named **Orange Ladybird** *Halyzia sedecimguttata* is one of a minority of ladybird species doing well in recent decades and may be seen on a variety of deciduous trees where it feeds on mildews. The **Cream-spot Ladybird** *Calvia quattuordecimguttata* is often found in the same places as the Orange Ladybird, and the two species may be confused: both have white spots and whilst the Cream-spot is usually brown, pale individuals look quite similar to darker Orange Ladybirds.

Figure 9.39 (left) Pine Ladybird, (centre) Orange Ladybird, (right) Cream-spot Ladybird. (PAR).

Figure 9.40 (left) Cream-streaked Ladybird (GSM), **(right) 11-spot Ladybird** (CKL).

Figure 9.41 (left) Eyed Ladybird, (centre) 18-spot Ladybird, (right) Adonis' Ladybird. (PAR).

Less common species

There are sparse records in Cambridge of three conifer specialists, the **Eyed** *Anatis ocellata*, **Cream-streaked** *Harmonia quadripunctata* and **18-spot** *Myrrha octodecimguttata* ladybirds. These species are particularly found on **Scots Pine** *Pinus sylvestris* and are much more abundant in the heathland and forested habitats of the Suffolk and Norfolk Brecks. The **Water Ladybird** *Anisosticta novemdecimpunctata* is a species of reeds and other waterside vegetation, whilst the **Adonis' Ladybird** *Hippodamia variegata* prefers dry habitats. The **11-spot Ladybird** *Coccinella undecimpunctata* favours coastal areas, tends to be scarce inland and seems to be declining. All three of the latter species have sparse recent records in Cambridge.

Inconspicuous species

All of the ladybirds mentioned thus far are conspicuous species. Of the smaller, inconspicuous ladybirds, seven species were recorded during the NHC survey, mostly with just one or two records of each. Four species are discussed here and three below, as new colonists.

Although it was only recorded once, the most common of the smaller ladybirds of Cambridge is probably the **Pointed-keeled Rhyzobius** *Rhyzobius*

litura. This little brown ladybird is easy to miss, but is not difficult to find when sweep-netting along overgrown verges by fields or roads. Its close relative, but found in trees, is the **Round-keeled Rhyzobius** *Rhyzobius chrysomeloides*. These two species are very hard to distinguish. The **Four-spotted Nephus** *Nephus quadrimaculatus* is a tiny but pretty little ladybird, black with four red spots and usually found on **Ivy** *Hedera helix*. It was the best-recorded inconspicuous ladybird in the NHC survey and was found at four different sites in Cambridge. Finally, there was a single record of the **Heath Scymnus** *Scymnus femoralis*, a species of dry habitats that had historically been found in Cambridge, but this seems to be the first record for almost 80 years.

Figure 9.42 (left) Pointed-keeled Rhyzobius, (right) Four-spotted Nephus. (PAR).

Figure 9.43 (left) Red-flanked Scymnus (PAR), **(centre) Mealybug Destroyer larva** (PAR), **(right)** *Rhyzobius forestieri.* (MM).

Figure 9.44 Red-headed Rhyzobius. (KL).

New colonists
The **Red-flanked Scymnus** *Scymnus interruptus* is a recent (2016) arrival to the region and was recorded in Cambridge itself for the first time in the NHC survey. *Rhyzobius forestieri* was first recorded in Britain in 2014 and in Cambridge (near Mill Road Cemetery) in 2017. This species, of Australian origin, has started spreading in England, with recent first records from many southern counties (Brown & Roy 2018). The most recent arrival to Cambridge, in 2020, was the wonderfully named **Mealybug Destroyer** *Cryptolaemus montrouzieri*. This is a non-native species frequently introduced to control pest insects in glasshouses. It used not to survive British winters. There are signs that with climate warming, this is no longer the case, based on the record in Cambridge and similar recent records elsewhere in England.

Potential new species
The **Red-headed Rhyzobius** *Rhyzobius lophanthae* is very likely to be found in Cambridge in the near future, having been recorded locally (first in Fordham in 2015) and now spreading rapidly in England (Brown *et al.* 2015). Another species of Australian origin, this inconspicuous ladybird is about 2 mm long and is quite distinctive, with a dull orange head, thorax and legs and black wing cases. Elsewhere it has been found on trees, especially cypresses.

Chafers, chafer grubs and college lawns
Five species of chafer have been recorded in the NHC area in recent years: **Common Cockchafer** *Melolontha melolontha*, **Summer Chafer** *Amphimallon solstitiale*, **Garden Chafer** *Phyllopertha horticola*, **Welsh Chafer** *Hoplia philanthus* and **Mediterranean Spotted Chafer** (*Oxythyrea funesta* – otherwise known as the White Spotted Rose Beetle).

Only 23 chafer records were submitted to CPERC and iRecord between 2017 and 2019. This is a low number, as I believe that quite a few cockchafers end up in moth traps as a summer by-catch. Another possibility is that the Summer, Welsh and Garden chafers look similar to the untrained eye, so people may not have been able to identify them easily for recording. The records come from all over Cambridge, and I have found Common Cockchafers, Summer Chafers, Garden Chafers and Welsh Chafers at Jesus College.

'The crows are destroying the lawns' was the cry that went round the Cambridge colleges in 2014. Suddenly **Carrion Crows** were seen lifting up divots

Figure 9.45 Carrion Crow searching for chafer grubs. (RKW).

Figure 9.46 (left) Common Cockchafer (RKW), **(right) Welsh Chafer.** (PAR).

Figure 9.47 (left) Chafer grub, (right) Summer Chafer. (RKW).

Figure 9.48 (left) Mediterranean Spotted Chafer, (right) Garden Chafer. (CKL).

of grass and many of the colleges' carefully nurtured lawns were beginning to look very scruffy. A second phrase that began to be heard at college High Tables was 'The crows are looking for chafer grubs' as an explanation of what was happening.

About a month after the crows began digging up the lawns at Jesus College in 2014, I also noticed a flock of **Jackdaws** doing the same. It seemed as if this was corvid behaviour, not just crow behaviour. The Botanic Garden have reported that crows, **Rooks** and also **Badgers** have all been digging up

their lawns. A 'large gull' was also seen behaving in this way in Downing College.

When the crows dig up an area, they sometimes turn their heads at right angles to the grass, as if listening, then begin to dig with their beaks. They strip the turf off the lawns in large clumps, then brush away soil, using a side-to-side motion with their beaks. Quite often you can see them having to pull hard. When they get a divot of turf, they fling it away, high in the air, closing their nictitating membrane when they do so. They then stab down to collect a small white grub from the bare ground and eat it before looking around and moving on. They often dig beside an area already dug, creating large patches of bare ground several metres in diameter. Jackdaws have a slightly different technique. They peck and then pull up small bits of turf and are often the first birds to start digging. Crows come along later and clear larger areas where the jackdaws started. The badgers have a more methodical approach: they almost seem to lift the turf and roll it back from areas where there are plentiful grubs.

What are they catching? In the summer of 2019, Jesus College employed BASF Pest Control to sample a small 2.5 m² area in the middle of a lawn in North Court. The result was: 200 chafers per m²; with just over 500 being found altogether. These were mainly 3rd stage Welsh Chafers, but about 50 1st stage larvae were found in this area. They also found about 20 mature Common Cockchafer larvae from a grid pattern search of the same lawn. First Court in Jesus College had an explosion of adult Garden Chafers which emerged on 19th June 2015 and swarms of flying Summer Chafers have been seen in Cherry Hinton Chalk Pits and on Jesus Green.

Chafers emerge as adults in the summer (colloquial names for these beetles are May bugs or June bugs). They mate and lay eggs before dying. The larvae hatch 2–4 weeks later and spend most of their lives eating through grass roots about 2 cm below the turf surface. They can live in the soil or in rotting vegetation and wood for up to five years. They pupate in spring and the beetle then emerges.

This problem has been building up for about 20 years, becoming more serious since 2014. Lawns on soils with more clay are less affected by the grubs than lawns on a sandy loam. The harder-wearing ryegrass on sports fields is less badly affected, as the larvae cannot easily cut through the tougher grass. There was a suggestion that the banning of neonicotinoids in 2013 might have exacerbated the problem, but also that recent mild, damp autumns may have played a part.

Control methods include spraying the affected lawns with parasitic nematodes (for example, Jesus started a trial of **Nemasys G** *Heterorhabditis bacteriophora* in 2019 but with limited success). Other lawns have been stripped and replaced with different, stronger turf or grass seed. Scarifying the lawn down to a depth of 2.5 cm has had some success and there is a new trial of a Tree-oil based product. Downing College managed to keep the crows away by the use of a model hawk, but unfortunately it soon went missing and the birds returned.

Perhaps the new trend for creating lawns full of wildflowers instead of grass will ease the aesthetic problems for some Colleges; or people will simply get used to seeing churned-up lawns. Both grubs and adults provide food for birds and other wildlife, so the sheer biomass of the beetles might be a good thing for wildlife in Cambridge.

There is a single record of the Mediterranean Spotted Chafer, found in the Botanic Garden early one morning in June 2019. A new colonist in Britain, it is thought to be expanding its range but is also moved about with potted plants.

True Bugs (Hemiptera)
Introduction
Many people use the term 'bug' to describe many types of insects, but true bugs *(Hemiptera)* are an order of insects that share a common arrangement of sucking mouthparts. Some species are sap suckers, others are predatory and a few are blood suckers.

This order of insects includes aphids, leafhoppers, shieldbugs and bedbugs. The number of species recorded for this project is 138, and some of the common and notable species are covered in the following section.

Home and garden species
There are three species of blood sucking bugs in Britain, all of which can be found in, or in very close proximity to our homes. They are the **Bedbug** *Cimex lectularius* which feeds on human blood, ***Cimex pipistrelli*** which is found in bat roosts and ***Oeciacus hirundinis*** in **House Martin** nests. None of these species have been reported in Cambridge on any wildlife recording sites, but a trawl through TripAdvisor reviews tells a different story, at least in the case of the Bedbugs.

Reduvius personatus is one of our cohabiting bugs that has been found in Cambridge. This predatory species preys on other invertebrates such as bedbugs, silverfish, booklice and flies, so is a more welcome intruder.

Cambridge gardens, especially larger mature ones, make perfect homes for many true bugs. In my own garden I have recorded 47 species and I have selected a small number of those to illustrate the sort of diversity that can be found across the city.

Figure 9.49 *Reduvius personatus.* (GM).

Aphids are not welcomed by gardeners perhaps, but are an important part of the food chain and attract many other insects to the garden including ladybirds, lacewings and predatory bugs. Some species like the **Black Bean Aphid** *Aphis fabae* are happy to suck the sap of many different plants, so can be found in flower beds and hedges as well as your vegetable patch. Others like *Macrosiphum rosae* (one of several rose aphids) and the **Common Periphyllus Aphid** *Periphyllus testudinaceus* have a less varied diet, the latter being found on *Acer* species such as Field Maple and cultivated on Japanese maples.

Common Green Shieldbugs *Palomena prasina* and **Hairy Shieldbugs** *Dolycoris baccarum* feed on a wide variety of plants and are common garden visitors. The **Juniper Shieldbug** *Cyphostethus tristriatus* was previously confined to southern juniper scrub, but is now common across southern and central England. This expansion has coincided with **Lawson's Cypress** *Cupressus lawsoniana* being included in its diet (Stewart *et al.* 2015). If you have Lawson's Cypress in your garden, look out for this distinctive shieldbug.

Dock Bugs *Coreus marginatus* are our most common squash bug and although the nymphs feed on dock and related plants, in late summer and early autumn adults can be found in quite large numbers feeding on raspberry, gooseberry and sometimes blackcurrant plants. Adult **Common Froghoppers** *Philaenus spumarius* are less noticeable than their nymphs, who protect themselves from predation by producing the very familiar 'Cuckoo-spit' on a wide range of garden plants. Gardens are planted with many non-native plants and over the years a number of non-native bugs that feed on these have become established here. One of them is the **Bay Tree Sucker** *Lauritrioza alacris*. The waxy nymphs of this psyllid bug cause bay leaves to curl and form a gall.

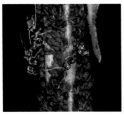

Figure 9.50 (left) Black Bean Aphids, (centre) *Macrosiphum rosae*, (right) Common Periphyllus Aphid. (PAR).

Figure 9.51 (left) Common Green Shieldbug, (centre) Hairy Shieldbug, (right) Juniper Shieldbug. (PAR).

Figure 9.52 (left) Dock Bugs on raspberry leaf, (centre) Common Froghopper, (right) Bay Tree Suckers. (PAR).

Figure 9.53 (left) *Heterotoma planicornis*, **(centre)** *Megacoelum infusum*, **(right)** *Campyloneura virgula*. (PAR).

All these plant-eating species attract many predatory bugs including the exotic-looking *Heterotoma planicornis*, *Megacoelum infusum* and *Campyloneura virgula*.

Aquatic and wetland species

The surface of our lakes and ponds provides a happy hunting ground for several predatory species.

Common Pond Skater *Gerris lacustris*, **Water Measurer** *Hydrometra stagnorum* and **Water Cricket** *Velia caprai* are all hunters, exploiting surface tension to attack passing tadpoles and any insect that happens to get in trouble on the water surface.

The **Common Backswimmer** *Notonecta glauca* does its hunting below the surface using its oar-like rear legs.

Figure 9.54 (left) Common Pond Skater, (right) Water Measurer. (PAR).

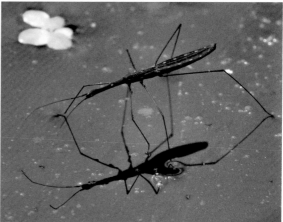

Figure 9.55 Common Backswimmer: (left) upper view (right) lower view. (PAR).

Figure 9.56 (left) *Callicorixa praeusta*, (centre) *Corixa punctata*, (right) Water Scorpion. (PAR).

Figure 9.57 (left) Common Shore Bug, (right) *Conosanus obsoletus*. (LKE).

Also possessing a pair of oar-like legs are the water boatmen, *Callicorixa praeusta* and *Corixa punctata*. Unlike backswimmers, these bugs swim the 'right way up' and are herbivorous. **Water Scorpions** *Nepa cinerea* are ambush predators hiding among dead vegetation, waiting to grab passing tadpoles or small fish.

The **Common Shore Bug** *Saldula saltatoria* can be found at the margins of ponds and lakes; we have just one record, from Adams Road Bird Sanctuary.

The leafhopper *Conosanus obsoletus* is found among rushes. So far it has only been recorded at East Barnwell LNR.

Woodland and tree species
All trees have a number of bugs that are exclusively or mainly dependent upon them. For instance, *Oncopsis flavicollis*, Birch Shieldbug *Elasmostethus*

interstinctus and **Birch Catkin Bug** *Kleidocerys resedae* are all common bugs associated with birch trees.

Most native trees also have their exclusive aphids: some, like the **Sycamore Aphid** *Drepanosiphum platanoidis* feed on leaves but a few like the **Variegated Oak Aphid** *Lachnus roboris* and the **Large Willow Aphid** *Tuberolachnus salignus* are bark feeders and are to be found on twigs and branches.

Other bugs can be found over a wider range of trees. *Ledra aurita* is a large very odd-looking leafhopper which is found on a wide range of lichen covered trees. Although common, it is hard to find as it is well camouflaged against the lichens. Despite its common name, the **Alder Spittlebug** *Aphrophora alni* can be found on a wide range of trees and shrubs.

Predatory species such as *Deraeocoris lutescens* and *D. ruber* also use a wide range of trees on which they hunt aphids and other small invertebrates.

Meadow and hedgerow species
Cinnamon Bugs *Corizus hyoscyami* are found in drier habitats and feed on a range of different plants: their striking colouring and patterns make them an easy bug to identify. The similarly coloured **Red-and-black Froghopper** *Cercopis vulnerata* is both our largest and most colourful froghopper and certainly the easiest to identify.

Figure 9.58 (left) *Oncopsis flavicollis*, (centre) Birch Shieldbug, (right) Birch Catkin Bug. (PAR).

Figure 9.59 (left) Sycamore Aphid, (right) Large Willow Aphid. (PAR).

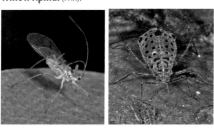

Figure 9.60 (left) *Ledra aurita*, (right) Alder Spittlebug, nymph. (PAR).

Figure 9.61 (left) *Deraeocoris lutescens nymph*, (right) *Deraeocoris ruber*. (PAR).

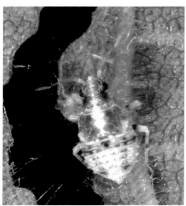

Figure 9.62 (left) Cinnamon Bug, (right) Red-and-black Froghopper. (PAR).

Figure 9.63 (left) Brassica Shieldbug, (centre) Blue Shieldbug, (right) Bishop's Mitre Shieldbug. (PAR).

Figure 9.64 (left) Tortoise Shieldbug, (centre) *Javesella pellucida* long winged form, (right) *Notostira elongata*. (PAR).

Despite its common name you are unlikely to find the **Brassica Shieldbug** *Eurydema oleracea* in your vegetable patch, as they feed on wild Brassicaceae such as **Garlic Mustard** *Alliaria petiolata* which grows in profusion along hedgerows and tree margins.

The **Blue Shieldbug** *Zicrona caerulea* is a predatory bug feeding on the larvae of leaf beetles. It is not a common species, with single records from three sites, including East Barnwell LNR and Trumpington Meadows.

Grass specialists can be found using a sweep-net anywhere patches of long grass grow, such as Trumpington Meadows, Coldham's Common and Logan's Meadow. The **Bishop's Mitre Shieldbug** *Aelia acuminata* and the elongated grassbugs *Notostira elongata* and *Stenodema laevigata* can be caught this way in large numbers.

The **Tortoise Shieldbug** *Eurygaster testudinaria* is much scarcer, only having been recorded at Byron's Pool, but nationally its range is expanding northward so is likely to become more common in Cambridge in years to come.

Javesella pellucida is a common species of leafhopper frequenting grassy areas. It is quite a variable species and has short and long winged forms.

New arrivals and rarities

The **Box Bug** *Gonocerus acuteangulatus* was until the turn of the century a very rare British species, being confined to Box Hill, Surrey. Since then it has expanded its range to much of southern England and is now a common species in Cambridge. This successful expansion seems to be linked to its adaptation to feed on a wider range of plants than **Common Box** *Buxus sempervirens*. In late summer I have found both adults and nymphs feeding on rose hips.

Another species that was once confined to a small area of Britain is *Eremocoris fenestratus*. This

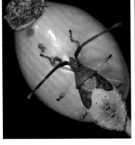  

Figure 9.65 (left) Box Bug nymph, (centre) *Eremocoris fenestratus*, (right) *Asiraca clavicornis*. (PAR).

ground bug was historically known only from the Chilterns, where it was thought to have become extinct, before reappearing in the London area in 2010. There have been just four sightings from NHC Area since 2018, but three of these were from my garden in 2020, so it has possibly become established here.

Asiraca clavicornis is an unmistakable and very strange-looking planthopper. Modern records of this species are mainly restricted to the London area and Thames estuary, where it prefers rough grasslands and wastelands. The first Cambridge record was from a private garden in 2018. Since then it has been found at several other sites including Barnwell East LNR and Coldham's Common LNR.

Climate change would seem to be driving a northward expansion of the range of a considerable number of bugs, with the result that Britain has a significantly higher number of species today than it had 20 years ago. *Acericerus heydenii, Eupteryx decemnotata, Orientus ishidae* and *Synophropsis lauri* are four new city arrivals, none being recorded before 2016.

Three very recent new arrivals are accidental introductions from other continents. The **Western Conifer Seed Bug** *Leptoglossus occidentalis* is a North American species that arrived in Europe around 2010 and is now well established in southern England. It has been recorded from several Cambridge locations since 2018.

The **Southern Green Shieldbug** *Nezara viridula* is an African species that has frequently been imported to Britain in food produce; it is now widespread in southern Europe and has been recorded annually from sites in southern England since 2003, including records from Jesus College and the Botanic Garden in 2019.

As its name suggests the **Japanese Maple Leafhopper** *Japananus hyalinus* is an Asian species, but it is now well established in Europe after hitching a ride on imported cultivated maples. The first British record of this species was from Gwydir Street, Cambridge in 2014 where it has been regularly recorded up to the present day, so it is almost certainly present elsewhere in the city.

Figure 9.66 (left) *Acericerus heydenii*, **(right)** *Synophropsis lauri*. (PAR).

Figure 9.67 (left) Western Conifer Seed Bug (JMO), **(centre) Southern Green Shieldbug nymph** (RKW), **(right) Japanese Maple Leafhopper.** (LKE).

10. Dragonflies, bees, wasps, ants, sawflies and flies

Damselflies and dragonflies (Odonata)

Introduction

Cambridge has a long history of dragonfly research and the Zoology Museum has a good collection of these remarkable insects. Visits to the Cambridge museum and that of Oxford University revealed only about 30 specimens from the city. The Cambridgeshire and Peterborough Environmental Record Centre (CPERC) has a greater number of city records. Up to 1989 it had only 60 Odonata records. This total was significantly enhanced by the three-year Cambridgeshire county dragonfly survey in the early 1990s. Between 1990 and 2016 this figure increased to 522 records.

Since that time, good new field guides combined with websites for posting data have made it easier to record Odonata. In Cambridgeshire, the British Dragonfly Society's identification courses at Wicken Fen have stimulated interest and increased the skills of local naturalists. Then the NHC project focussed on wildlife in and near the city. From 2016 to 2020 the number of records increased dramatically and we now have more than 3000 records for the area.

Climate change is affecting the populations of Odonata throughout the British Isles. Warmer periods in recent summers have coincided with the arrival of previously unrecorded species, some of which have gone on to establish breeding populations. The **Small Red-eyed Damselfly** *Erythromma viridulum* and the **Willow Emerald** *Chalcolestes viridis* are certainly breeding successfully. Their remarkable spread, reported on the British Dragonfly Society's website, shows how quickly new colonists can establish breeding populations and then spread further. It seems likely that **Southern Migrant Hawker** *Aeshna affinis* and **Lesser Emperor** *Anax parthenope* are also breeding locally.

In order to record the species present I have been photographing adult dragonflies and damselflies over the three-year period 2018–2020. This allows accuracy to be checked and any unusual findings can be confirmed. The larvae have not been studied and this is a subject that deserves greater attention but requires many hours of searching with a hand net. This is a shortcoming, because the existence of larvae, and larval cases (exuviae) left behind when the adult emerges, are the best proof of successful breeding. The existence of the Lesser Emperor in the West Cambridge Lake and in Barnwell Lake, where it was recorded ovipositing, is a case in point. It was observed in the Cambridge Science Park in 2009 and it may have been breeding in the city unnoticed until 2019.

The total of 24 species of Odonata recorded in the NHC area is a high figure (as a benchmark Wicken Fen has records for 22 species) and points to the fact that cities have habitats for a wide range of species, some of which may be declining in the wider countryside. Property development within the city can bring with it wildlife benefits. The developments at Clay Farm, Trumpington Meadows and Eddington have excellent aquatic habitats with growing populations of Odonata. Small local nature reserves also make a good contribution to the city environment. Although individually they may be small and have fewer species, when combined together they contribute significantly to the range of species present. Finally the river and smaller water courses are important features which provide a variety of habitats. Where the floodplain on either

Figure 10.1 Hawker Dragonfly exuvia left behind after the adult emerges. (DJM).

Figure 10.2 Banded Demoiselle eating a mayfly, whilst a spider *Enoplognatha* sp. attempts to tie them both down.

side of the river has been retained as undeveloped land, Odonata will make good use of any features such as ditches and pools. Grantchester Meadows, Ditton Meadows and Logan's Meadow are key environments which have good populations of many insect species including the Odonata.

Damselfly species
Banded Demoiselle *Calopteryx splendens*.
Flight season: May–August.
This distinctive and easily recognised species is found all along the River Cam and on the chalk streams Cherry Hinton Brook and Hobson's Conduit. It is widespread and can occur in ponds, though the greatest numbers are to be found on the upper reaches of the Cam. In 2019 the earliest specimen was seen in late April just downstream of the sewage works outfall on the Cam. This is at least two weeks earlier than normal. At the height of summer its numbers along the River Cam can be considerable. It has been seen mating widely in the area and is undoubtedly breeding here.

Large Red Damselfly *Pyrrhosoma nymphula*.
Flight season: April–July.
This is the earliest emerging of all species and is often flying at Easter, but with the main emergence in May and June. Large Red Damselflies are very distinctive and are to be found throughout Cambridge, often colonising garden ponds. Their numbers start to decline by early July. This species has been observed mating and is breeding here. Newly emerged adults have been observed at many locations.

Emerald Damselfly *Lestes sponsa*.
Flight season: July–September.
This species appears later in the summer, reaching peak numbers in August. The ditches of Ditton Meadows are a good place to find it. One male Emerald Damselfly was photographed attempting to mate with a female Willow Emerald. Emeralds in tandem are often observed here as well.

Willow Emerald Damselfly *Chalcolestes viridis*.
Flight season: July–September.
This is a new arrival to Britain. In 2009 Willow Emeralds were regarded as scarce vagrants but by 2018 they had become the most common damselfly recorded in Cambridge in September. Many Willow Emeralds were seen mating. They lay their eggs by injecting them under the bark of waterside trees and shrubs where they will remain protected until they hatch as larvae the following spring. Often willows are used, but they were also seen ovipositing on privet. Their favoured breeding habitat is in slow-flowing and stagnant ditches such as at Ditton Meadows, Barnwell East LNR and the

Figure 10.3 (left) Emerald Damselflies in tandem, **(right)** Willow Emerald Damselflies in tandem while the female deposits her eggs under the bark of a willow tree. (PAR, DJM).

Trumpington Road section of Hobson's Conduit. The classic photo of King's College from the Backs is taken by the boundary ditch and if tourists lowered their cameras, they could photograph this damselfly, which is particularly abundant there in late summer.

White-legged Damselfly *Platycnemis pennipes*.
Flight season: May–August.
White-legged Damselflies have been observed only twice in Cambridge. One was found over 10 years ago in the upper reaches of Hobson's Conduit. Then in July 2019 I managed to photograph a single individual in Grantchester Meadows. Whether this species exists in low numbers along this section of the Cam or whether this was a dispersing individual from another location is impossible to tell.

Azure Damselfly *Coenagrion puella*.
Flight season: June–July.
This very common species is most abundant in June when mass emergence and ovipositing can occur. The numerous paired damselflies dancing above the water as the female deposits her eggs into the floating algal mat is a truly spectacular event, and Hobson's Conduit in front of the Botanic Garden is a good place to stand and watch. This species can occur almost anywhere in Cambridge and breeds throughout the area.

Variable Damselfly *Coenagrion pulchellum*.
Flight season: May–August.
This damselfly is restricted in its range and seems to be declining in England. In Cambridge the best place to find it is beside the ditches in Ditton Meadows, where a sizeable population is to be found. June and July are good months to find the

adults amongst the emergent vegetation of the ditches. This species has been observed mating and egg-laying in Ditton Meadows.

Common Blue Damselfly *Enallagma cyathigerum*.
Flight season: June–August.
A common species reaching peak numbers in late July and early August. Numbers of Common Blue Damselflies increase in June and care is needed to distinguish them from Azure and Variable Damselflies. They are particularly common in Hobson's Conduit, Hobson's Park ponds, Cherry Hinton Lakes and Barnwell Lake. They have been recorded breeding throughout the area.

Blue-tailed Damselfly *Ischnura elegans*.
Flight season: May–August.
This species is found throughout the NHC area. Female Blue-tailed Damselflies can come in five different colour forms (*typica, rufescens, obsoleta, violacea* and *infuscans*) and the tail is not always blue in these forms. All forms have been recorded in Cambridge. They are often to be found in the vegetation surrounding a stream, lake, pond or ditch and do not spend as much time on lily pads as the two Red-eyed Damselflies. Hobson's Conduit, Cherry Hinton Brook, Barnwell Lake and the Botanic Garden Lake are good habitats. They breed throughout the area.

Red-eyed Damselfly *Erythromma najas*.
Flight season: June–July.
Only males of this very common species have red eyes. Red-eyed Damselflies can be found on the river north of Fen Ditton and in any of the lakes within the city. They have been observed paired and egg-laying throughout the area.

Figure 10.4 (left) Male Azure Damselfly, (centre) male Variable Damselfly, (right) male Common Blue Damselfly. (PAR, DJM, PAR).

Small Red-eyed Damselfly *Erythromma viridulum*.
Flight season: July–September.
This species is a newcomer to Britain. It has rapidly spread from Essex where it was first found in 1999, and is now as common in Cambridge as the Red-eyed Damselfly. It flies a little later than the Red-eyed Damselfly. Small Red-eyed Damselflies are particularly fond of floating lily pads and are often to be found resting there. Good places to find them are the River Cam and many of the lakes. They can be observed egg-laying in large groups at Trumpington Meadows when conditions are right.

Dragonfly species
Hairy Dragonfly *Brachytron pratense*.
Flight season: May–July.
The earliest of the dragonflies to emerge in spring, this species has been seen mating on Ditton Meadows in April and ovipositing in the Science Park in early May. It is not as common as some of the other dragonflies and was found in only five locations within the NHC area. However, it may be missed at some sites because of its relative scarcity. Ditton Meadows and Barnwell East LNR are good places to find Hairy Dragonflies. They have been observed in tandem at Ditton Meadows.

Migrant Hawker *Aeshna mixta*.
Flight season: August–October.
This species is found almost everywhere in late summer and has become very common in Cambridge. The earliest sightings are in August and it is present throughout the city until well

into October. It prefers ditches, lakes and standing water. In the 1940s it was considered a rare vagrant but is now resident north to Scotland. The ditches of Ditton Meadows have a particularly large population. They have been observed mating and egg-laying throughout the area.

Southern Migrant Hawker *Aeshna affinis*.
Flight season: July–September.
This species was first seen in Cambridge at Ditton Meadows in August 2019. This coincided with a sudden influx across southern Britain. It looks similar to the much commoner Migrant Hawker, needing care to confirm identification. A single

Figure 10.6 Male Southern Migrant Hawker at Ditton Meadows. (DJM).

Figure 10.7 The brown form of female Lesser Emperor at Barnwell Lake. (DJM).

male was photographed in 2019 but in 2020 there were several more occurrences in Cambridge. They were found once again in Ditton Meadows and also at Paradise LNR. There is a strong suspicion that they are breeding at both locations.

Southern Hawker *Aeshna cyanea*.
Flight season: July–September.
This species is also widespread in Cambridge from July onwards. Its numbers never reach those of the Migrant Hawkers and Emperors, but it is present in a wide variety of habitats and is regularly seen ovipositing. It is often found away from water and hunts in meadows, where it often rests on blackberry bushes. Barnwell East LNR is a particularly good place for Southern Hawkers, both on the pond and hunting in the meadows. They have been observed mating and egg-laying at Barnwell East.

Brown Hawker *Aeshna grandis*.
Flight season: June–September.
A widespread species found in 19 out of the 25 study sites, in streams, rivers, ditches and lakes. It appears in late June and can be found well into September. It has been seen mating and ovipositing at several sites including the River Cam, the Botanic Garden and Hobson's Conduit. It is also common around many of the lakes in the city.

Emperor *Anax imperator*.
Flight season: June–August.
Capable of breeding in ditches, lakes, streams and ponds, the Emperor is the most widespread and common of the large dragonflies. It is one of the earlier species to emerge in June and can still be found flying in August. The females can commonly be seen ovipositing on the edges of lily pads on Barnwell Lake and the Cherry Hinton fishing lakes, and on floating mats of algae and water plants on Hobson's Conduit. They have been quick to colonise the new balancing ponds at Hobson's Park and also the new lake in Trumpington Meadows.

Lesser Emperor *Anax parthenope*.
Flight season: June–September.
This once rare species is now widespread in southern Britain. Lesser Emperor was found in the Cambridge Science Park lakes in 2009 and in the West Cambridge Lake in 2017. It also occurred on the Trumpington Meadows lake in 2020. Whether these intermittent reports are of a localised breeding population or of dispersing individuals from more distant breeding populations is unclear. One female was found ovipositing in Barnwell Lake in July 2019. This individual did not look anything like the illustrations in the field guides, being almost entirely a dull grey brown colour but with distinctive green eyes. There was no sign of the characteristic blue band on the first two segments of the abdomen.

Four-spotted Chaser *Libellula quadrimaculata*.
Flight season: June–July.
This midsummer species has been particularly abundant at the Hobson's Park ponds and also Trumpington Meadows lake. It is often to be found perching on the top of bulrush leaves or other vantage points. It is not as widespread as some species, only occurring at 7 of the 25 study sites. They have been observed ovipositing in Hobson's Park.

Broad-bodied Chaser *Libellula depressa*.
Flight season: June–July.
This species is not as common in Cambridge as elsewhere, and was found in only 7 of the 25 study sites. It is found on some of the more secluded ponds and has been observed mating and ovipositing at Bramblefields and Hobson's Conduit.

Scarce Chaser *Libellula fulva*.
Flight season: June–July.
This species was found on the Cam north of Fen Ditton and in Barnwell Lake. On the Cam close to

Figure 10.8 Freshly emerged female Scarce Chaser on the bank of the River Cam north of Fen Ditton. (DJM).

the A14 bridge large numbers can be seen along the edge of the river on bankside vegetation at times of mass emergence in June. Mating occurs as several individuals emerge from the river and remain coupled for a considerable time. The population extends north down the River Cam and is widespread in the Fens.

Black-tailed Skimmer *Orthetrum cancellatum*.
Flight season: June–July.
Black-tailed Skimmers are found in lakeside habitats. They are very territorial and dart out from the bank after prey. They can often be seen occupying fishing platforms around the lakes. Found in 10 of the 25 study sites, they have been observed mating and ovipositing in Hobson's Park and at Barnwell Lake.

Ruddy Darter *Sympetrum sanguineum*.
Flight season: July–September.
A ubiquitous species, it is found in ditches, streams, ponds, lakes and the river. It starts to emerge in the latter half of July, a little earlier than the Common Darter. It has been observed mating and ovipositing throughout the area.

Common Darter *Sympetrum striolatum*.
Flight season: July–September.
Equally common as the Ruddy Darter, this species was found in 21 of the 25 study sites. It emerges shortly after the Ruddy Darter and tends to remain longer in the autumn. It is found in all aquatic habitats. The sight of paired individuals flying in tandem ovipositing on the surface of many of the ditches and ponds is a fascinating sight throughout the area. This is an especially common sight in August and early September.

Habitats

Dragonflies and damselflies can occur as adults in almost any habitat and are often to be found hunting for insect prey along the edges of woodland and in meadowland. However, they are most commonly found in the vicinity of water and the greatest concentrations are normally close to the water's edge. Since the larvae are aquatic, the eggs are laid either in water or in vegetation around the margins. So, for this study the main focus was around the aquatic habitats, though insects found elsewhere were recorded as and when they were found. Codes for the 24 species of Odonata are given in Table 10.1. The 25 study sites are mapped in Figure 10.9. Species present in each study site are listed along with a description of the site.

Streams

Cherry Hinton Brook (Grid Ref. TL479570)
The brook runs from Giant's Grave in Cherry Hinton to the River Cam on Stourbridge Common. The section running beside Cherry Hinton Lakes is a particularly productive area for a wide variety of species and may benefit from a daily movement of insects from the Lakes when the shallow emergent

Table 10.1 Codes for Cambridge's damselflies and dragonflies.

Damselflies	Code
Azure Damselfly	Az
Banded Demoiselle	Bd
Blue-tailed Damselfly	Bt
Common Blue Damselfly	Cb
Emerald Damselfly	Em
Large Red Damselfly	Lr
Red-eyed Damselfly	Re
Small Red-eyed Damselfly	Sre
Variable Damselfly	Va
White Legged Damselfly	Wl
Willow Emerald Damselfly	We

Dragonflies	Code
Black-tailed Skimmer	Bts
Broad-bodied Chaser	Bbc
Brown Hawker	Bh
Common Darter	Cd
Emperor	Em
Four-spotted Chaser	4s
Hairy Dragonfly	Hd
Lesser Emperor	Le
Migrant Hawker	Mh
Ruddy Darter	Rd
Scarce Chaser	Sc
Southern Migrant Hawker	Smh

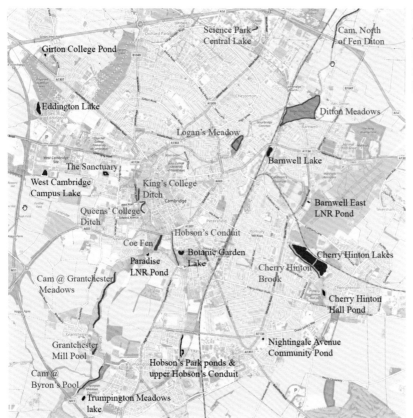

Figure 10.9 Map of dragonfly study sites. The sites are colour-coded: blue = streams and the river, purple = lakes and ponds, green = ditches.

vegetation passes into shadow in the afternoon. Eight species: Bd, Lr, Az, Bt; Mh, Sh, Bh, Cd.

Hobson's Conduit from Empty Common to Lensfield Road (Grid Ref. TL452571)
This section of the conduit has very slow flow, and is more akin to a long linear pond than a chalk stream. Very good viewing of dragonflies can be had where the conduit passes by the Botanic Garden. Nine species: Bd, We, Lr, Az, Bt; Bh, Em, Cd, Rd.

River Cam
Byron's Pool (Grid Ref. TL473548)
This section of the River Cam is adjacent to Trumpington Meadows. The banks are steep and there is only limited emergent vegetation. Early in the summer large numbers of Banded Demoiselles are to be found here. A patch of **Reed Sweet-grass** *Glyceria maxima* below the weir can produce good numbers of Migrant Hawkers during the summer. Ten species: Bd, We, Lr, Az, Bt; Hd, Mh, Bh, Em, Cd.

Grantchester Mill Pool (Grid Ref. TL435551)
Upstream from Grantchester Meadows the bridge

provides a vantage point to observe the pool. There is a patch of Reed Sweet-grass below the bridge which is the hunting ground for Emperors and Migrant Hawkers. 11 species: Bd, Cb, Az, Bt, Re, Sre; Mh, Bh, Em, Bts, Rd.

Grantchester Meadows (Grid Ref. TL436554)
This section of the River Cam runs from Newnham to the cricket pitch at Grantchester. The banks of the river have plentiful emergent vegetation, but this is often damaged during the summer by the very large number of punts on the river. Overhanging willows on the far bank also contribute to a very productive dragonfly habitat. A single White-legged Damselfly has been found. 17 species: Bd, Em, We, Lr, Wl, Cb, Az, Bt, Re, Sre; Hd, Mh, Sh, Bh, Em, Bts, Cd, Rd.

Cam north of Fen Ditton (Grid Ref. TL483613)
It is possible to access the edge of the River Cam north of Fen Ditton via the footpath. The first field is private, but the riverbank can be accessed near the noisy A14 road bridge. The riverbank to the north of this bridge is the best place to find Scarce Chasers

when they emerge in late June or July. Red-eyed and Small Red-eyed Damselflies are both present and Banded Demoiselles can be very abundant. 15 species: Bd, We, Lr, Cb, Az, Bt, Re, Sre; Hd, Mh, Bh, Ep, Sc, Cd, Rd.

Lakes

Barnwell Lake (Grid Ref. TL471593)

This lake is private and access is controlled by a fishing club. It is one of the best habitats for dragonflies and always has a very good population of many species around the margins and hunting over the water. The water depth varies from around 0.8 m in places to deeper zones in the middle of the lake. It has good emergent vegetation as well as extensive lily pads which are good places for Red-eyed and Small Red-eyed Damselflies. 19 species: Bd, We, Lr, Cb, Az, Bt, Re, Sre; Hd, Mh, Bh, Em, Le, Bts Cd, Rd, 4s, Bbc, Sc, Bts, Rd, Cd.

Botanic Garden lake (Grid Ref. TL453571)

This lake in the grounds of the Botanic Garden has a depth varying between 30 and 100 cm. The lake has reed beds at one end which support all the common damselfly species. Emperors and Brown Hawkers together with Four-spotted and Broad-bodied Chasers are the dominant species in June and July. It is very close to Hobson's Conduit and many of the individuals fly between the two stretches of water. 16 species: Bd, We, Lr, Cb, Az, Bt, Re, Sre; Mh, Sh, Bh, Em, 4s, Bbc, Cd, Rd.

Cherry Hinton Lakes (Grid Ref. TL476574)

These fishing lakes are partly owned by Cambridge City Council. Access is by arrangement with the fishing club that maintains and fishes the lakes. For the most part these lakes are over 10 m deep, but there is a marginal area on the southwest shore of the largest lake that is shallow (less than 1.2 m) and has some reed beds and areas of water lilies. Black-tailed Skimmers are abundant and Emperors are often seen egg-laying. Red-eyed Damselflies and Small Red-eyed Damselflies frequent the lily pads. 17 species: Bd, We, Lr, Cb, Az, Bt, Re, Sre; Hd, Mh, Sh, Bh, Em, Bbc, Bts Cd, Rd.

Brook Leys lake, Eddington (Grid Ref. TL422599)

This new lake has been created as part of the development of Eddington. It is well designed and has both shallow and deeper zones with emergent vegetation at the northern end and reed beds around the margins. 13 species: Bd, We, Cb, Az, Bt, Re, Sre; Mh, Sh, Em, 4s, Bts, Cd.

Sanctuary lake

The Sanctuary is a private nature reserve centred round a small lake with an island in the middle. There are extensive reed beds and some small pools on one side. 12 species: We, Az, Bt; Mh, Sh, Bh, Em, 4s, Bbc, Bts Cd, Rd.

Science Park central lake (Grid Ref. TL467617)

In a well sheltered position this lake has a good population of dragonflies and during the height of summer there are constantly Hawkers flying over the lake. Emperors, Brown Hawkers and Hairy Dragonflies breed here. It is a stronghold of the Small Red-eyed Damselfly. It is 0.6–1.5 m deep and has a large carp population, but larvae of Odonata seem to do quite well despite the large number of fish that may eat them. 11 species: Lr, Az, Bt, Re, Sre; Hd, Sh, Bh, Em, Cd, Rd.

Trumpington Meadows lake (Grid Ref. TL434542)

The lake is never more than 1.5 m deep with much of the area considerably shallower. Good reed beds

Figure 10.10 Trumpington Meadows, lake and viewing platform. (DJM).

around the margins provide an excellent dragonfly habitat. Many dragonflies use the viewing platform and reed beds as a launch pad to surf the wind. Good views of many species can be obtained as they fly into the wind to catch insects that are being blown along. It is a very good place to photograph dragonflies. 18 species: Bd, Em, Lr, Cb, Az, Bt, Re, Sre; Hd, Mh, Sh, Bh, Em, Le, 4sp, Bts, Cd, Rd.

West Cambridge Campus lake
(Grid Ref. TL424587)
This lake has great potential as a dragonfly habitat and deserves further study. It is a small lake surrounded by willows with a margin of emergent vegetation. Notable species include Lesser Emperor, Four-spotted Chaser and Willow Emerald. 16 species: We, Lr, Cb, Az, Bt, Re, Sre; Hd, Mh, Sh, Bh, Em, Le, 4sp, Bts Cd.

Ponds
Barnwell East LNR (Grid Ref TL479583)
This small reserve has a pond with a dipping platform and is fed from the airport; the water seems to be pumped. Surrounding trees protect the pond from wind and it can be a sun trap in summer, with temperatures higher than elsewhere. Surrounding scrub and small meadows are used for hunting by Emperors, Southern and Brown Hawkers. The water level in the pond can vary enormously and the pond occasionally dries out in summer. It supports a population of Hairy Dragonflies early in the season and Brown Hawkers and Southern Hawkers are present at the height of summer. Many of the common damselflies also breed here in large numbers, especially Azure. 19 species: Bd, We, We, Lr, Cb, Az, Bt, Re, Sre; Hd, Mh, Sh, Bh, Emp 4s, Bbc, Bts Cd, Rd.

Cherry Hinton Hall (Grid Ref. TL483565)
The water for this large pond comes from Cherry Hinton Brook. The pond is very shallow (30–45 cm deep) and has extensive emergent vegetation and the magnificent display of **Kingcups** *Caltha palustris* in spring occurs when the first Large Red Damselflies are emerging. Other notable species include Willow Emerald and Broad-bodied Chaser. 11 species: Em, We, Lr, Cb, Az, Bt; Mh, Bh, Bbc, Cd, Rd.

Girton College Pond (Grid Ref TL423610)
Due to access difficulties this pond was only visited late in the season. It is a large pond with water lilies

and reed beds, so should be a very suitable habitat. However only 6 species have been recorded here: We, Lr, Bt; Mh, Bh, Cd.

Hobson's Park balancing ponds and upper Hobson's Conduit (Grid Ref. TL454552)
The new ponds created to take surface water from the developments at Clay Farm are located next to the upper section of Hobson's Conduit. They are surrounded by meadows that have been created from farmland. It is not possible to get to the water's edge of the main lake as it is a bird reserve, but the ditches which surround the lake are productive areas for species such as Black-tailed Skimmer, Broad-bodied Chaser and Four-spotted Chaser. 17 species: Bd, We, Lr, Cb, Az, Bt, Re, Sre; Hd, Mh, Bh, Em, 4s, Bbc, Bts Cd, Rd.

Nightingale Avenue community pond
(Grid Ref TL471555)
This community pond is contained within the community wildlife garden at the northern end of the recreation ground. Much effort has been made by the community to build a wildlife garden with many examples of man-made wildlife habitats. The pond is filled with the **Fringed Water Lily** *Nymphoides peltata* and has good populations of Broad-bodied Chasers, Southern Hawkers and Emperors. Nine species: Lr, Cb, Az, Bt, Re; Sh, Em, Bbc, Cd.

Paradise LNR (Grid Ref. TL446572)
This small nature reserve close to the River Cam has a hidden pond which looks ideal for Odonata. Species recorded so far include Broad-bodied Chaser and Southern Migrant Hawker and further study should uncover more. Ten species: Bd, Lr, Az; Mh, Smh, Bh, 4s, Bbc, Cd, Rd.

Ditches
Coe Fen (Grid Ref. TL448574)
The ditch running along the middle of Coe Fen is a productive habitat. It is particularly good for Emperor and Migrant Hawker, both of which hunt over the ditch and the surrounding meadow. The water is slow-flowing and can become stagnant in summer. The ditch is also a good place to find Darters late in the season. Ten species: We, Lr, Az, Bt; Mh, Bh, Em, Bbc, Cd, Rd.

Queens' College ditch (Grid Ref. TL444581)
This is between Queens' College and Queen's Road

and is part of the same ditch system as King's College ditch. The bank is well vegetated for much of its length and has some emergent vegetation. Only Common Darter and Willow Emerald have been recorded here. Two species: We; Cd.

King's College ditch (Grid Ref. TL444583)
A series of ditches run from the River Cam and form boundaries to the various colleges. The ditch around King's College has a steeply sloping bank on the college side and a more gently sloping side facing Queen's Road. In the summer emergent vegetation along the ditch supports Black-tailed Skimmer, Brown Hawker, Banded Demoiselle and Willow Emerald. Ten species: Bd, We, Az, Bt; Mh, Bh, Emp, Bts Cd, Rd.

Logan's Meadow LNR (Grid Ref. TL464593)
This meadow is located beside the river next to the new Chesterton footbridge over the Cam. There is a ditch surrounded by reed beds and bramble patches which joins a small pond to the River Cam. The pond and ditch are less than 0.5 m deep and both support populations of Migrant and Southern Hawkers and Hairy Dragonflies. 11 species: Bd, We, Lr, Az, Bt; Hd, Mh, Sh, Bh, Cd, Rd.

Ditton Meadows (Grid Ref. TL478601)
These old flood meadows with ditches of slow-flowing water have a wide range of species and remain constantly interesting throughout the spring and summer. The ditches are shallow with a deep silt layer and are well vegetated with abundant Reed Sweet-grass and sedges. The water depth varies from 15 cm to 60 cm. The specialities here are the large populations of Variable Damselfly, Emerald Damselfly, Hairy Dragonfly and Southern Migrant Hawker. The site has very productive ditches and a wide section of the River Cam, giving two very distinctive habitats. 21 species: Bd, Em, We, Lr, Va, Cb, Az, Bt, Re, Sre; Hd, Mh, Smh, Sh, Bh, Em, 4s, Bbc, Bts, Cd, Rd.

Figure 10.11 Ditton Meadows is the richest site for Odonata in our area. (DJM).

Wasps, ants and sawflies

Introduction

The Hymenoptera are a vast group, and, with around 8000 British species, the most speciose insect order in the British Isles. They are traditionally split into three major groups: Symphyta (sawflies), Parasitica (parasitic wasps) and Aculeata (ants, solitary and social wasps and bees).

The Symphyta (sawflies) are a fascinating but under-recorded group, named for the saw-like ovipositor sheath the females use to cut into plants to lay eggs. All are plant-feeding and have larvae that resemble caterpillars, though they are distantly related and have evolved the design independently. They are the oldest branch of the hymenopteran family tree and all other hymenopteran families are descended from a sawfly ancestor which lived around 250 million years ago. Twenty-two species of sawfly were recorded from the NHC area over the course of the project. This is certainly only a small fraction of those present within the area as many species are difficult to identify and very few people record the group. The recorded species show a significant (and understandable) bias towards large and easily identifiable species.

The Parasitica are a very species-rich group and include the vast majority of hymenopteran species both in the British Isles and worldwide. They include numerous families of parasites and gall formers. They are very poorly understood and rarely recorded due to the difficulties associated with accurately identifying them. Recent publications, both online and in print, have made the group somewhat more accessible and this situation will hopefully continue to improve. Only thirty species were recorded from the NHC area over the course of the project.

The Aculeata are the most familiar and well-recorded of the major hymenopteran groups. This group includes digger wasps (Crabronidae), social wasps (Vespidae), spider-hunting wasps (Pompilidae), jewel wasps (Chrysididae), several smaller families of solitary wasps, ants (Formicidae) and bees. The bees of Cambridge are better recorded and understood, and are considered in a separate section. The remaining aculeates are discussed here.

To most people, the most familiar wasps are the social wasps so renowned for spoiling late summer picnics. These form large colonies of related individuals and are predators of other insects as well as scavengers. Most non-parasitic wasps, however, have a solitary lifestyle and are often overlooked by the general public. These solitary wasps include several small families and the quite species-rich digger wasps. Jewel or cuckoo wasps are probably Britain's most stunning wasps. These are shining metallic wasps, often with strikingly contrasting red, pink, green and blue coloration created by the structure of the exoskeleton. They are all kleptoparasites (cuckoos) of other hymenopteran species and utilise a fascinating range of adaptations, including mimicking host smell, to gain access to their nests. Spider-hunting wasps paralyse spiders before carrying them to their nest to use as live food for their larvae. In Britain they are generally small to medium-sized black or red and black wasps that are often very difficult to identify.

Ants are effectively a highly specialised family of social wasps that have evolved a complex caste system. Most form large (sometimes truly massive) colonies of a greater complexity than almost any other insect group; others enslave the workers of other species and have no workers of their own.

Thirty-five species of non-bee aculeates, from six families (Crabronidae, Vespidae, Tiphiidae, Pompilidae and Chrysididae and Formicidae), were recorded from the NHC area during the project.

Common garden species

Gardens encompass a diverse range of habitats. Almost any of the hymenopteran species recorded during the NHC project could be found in gardens, and all of the species associated with gardens occur widely in other habitats. Several species of sawfly can be so abundant in gardens that they are

10.12 (left) Large Rose Sawfly *Arge pagana*, (right) Turnip Sawfly. (PAR).

sometimes considered pests. Sawflies in the genus *Arge* are likely to be recognisable to anyone who grows roses. Two species of orange and shining black Argeid sawflies, **Arge ochropus** and **Arge pagana**, are both known as the **Large Rose Sawfly**. Their larvae are infamous for defoliating both wild and cultivated roses. The **Rose-leaf Rolling Sawfly** *Blennocampa phyllocolpa* also attacks roses but their larvae form galls within the leaves of the plant that cause the leaf to roll into a tube. The adults are small, black and nondescript.

The slug-like larvae of the **Turnip Sawfly** *Athalia rosae* feed voraciously on plants in the cabbage family. The adult Turnip Sawfly is easily identified amongst the many attractive orange and black sawflies in the genus *Athalia* by the checkerboard pattern on the top of its thorax. The **Blotch-winged Honeysuckle Sawfly** *Abia fasciata* is a strikingly attractive species with a black and cream body and large dark blotches on its wings. The larvae feed on honeysuckle and snowberry and often occur in gardens and ornamental or amenity plantings in urban areas.

The **Common Wasp** *Vespula vulgaris* and **German Wasp** *Vespula germanica* are the two commonest species of social wasp in Britain and are often abundant in urban and suburban habitats. Both species form large colonies and build elaborate paper nests, usually underground but sometimes in tree cavities and buildings. Anyone who has ever had a garden barbeque will be more than familiar with these species. Despite being an occasional summer nuisance due to their love of sugary food and drink, social wasps are voracious predators of many garden pests and efficient pollinators.

Mason Wasps in the genus *Ancistrocerus* are frequent inhabitants of gardens. They nest in hollow plant stems or holes in walls. They provision their nest with caterpillars to feed their larvae, sealing each larva into an individual cell using clay. All members of the genus are medium-sized yellow and black animals. Three species were recorded from the NHC area, all of which are frequent species in parks and gardens.

The mid-sized yellow and black **Field Digger Wasp** *Mellinus arvensis* is a common species of solitary wasp in gardens and can be found throughout Britain wherever the soil is suitable for building nest burrows, preferably light and sandy. They provision their nest burrows with various species of fly that they capture from leaves and even the surface of animal droppings. They can often be observed hunting on the leaves of garden plants

Auplopus carbonarius is a black spider-hunting wasp that has traditionally been considered a scarce southern species associated with damp clay in woodland habitats. In recent years, however, it has been found to occur regularly in suburban

Figure 10.13 (left) Queen Common Wasp, (right) worker German Wasp. (PAR, NWO).

Figure 10.14 (left) Field Digger Wasp, (right) *Auplopus carbonarius*. (CKL).

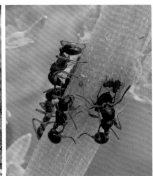

Figure 10.15 (left) Garden Black Ants attacking Nettle Weevil, (right) Common Red Ants farming aphids. (CKL, PAR).

parks and gardens, to the degree that this may be a significant habitat of the species. It is unclear whether this is because the species has recently colonised such sites to a greater extent or is simply being better recorded now. It is significantly under-recorded, due to its secretive nature. It constructs its nest from wet clay in situations ranging from abandoned earthworm burrows to cracks under the bark of trees and even man-made objects. Prey species are generally spiders that can be found amongst low vegetation.

The **Garden Black Ant** *Lasius niger* and the **Common Red Ant** *Myrmica rubra* are both almost ubiquitous in gardens and are likely to be familiar to any gardener. There are, however, several other species of red ant in the genus *Myrmica* that can only be told apart by microscopic examination. It is certain that there are further *Myrmica* species to be recorded in the NHC area.

Common species of open habitats

In the context of the NHC area, open habitats can be considered to include meadows and grassland areas (excluding small lawns) and brownfield sites or disturbed habitats. Such habitats are particularly important to aculeate Hymenoptera, as many species need warm, open habitats with plentiful flowers for nectaring and bare ground for nesting. For these reasons, brownfield sites support richer assemblages of aculeate Hymenoptera than any other British habitat.

Stem Borer sawflies in the family Cephidae are distinctive slender-bodied species that develop in grasses or the stems of rosaceous herbs or shrubs. The **Wheat Stem Borer** *Cephus pygmeus* is the commonest member of the family and can readily be seen crowding flower heads, particularly hogweed, in almost any grassland in summer. There are several other cephid sawflies that may occur in the same habitats.

Many species of digger wasp can be found in open habitats, especially if they have sandy soils. Even small patches of sand, such as those associated with construction, can support colonies of many aculeate species. Several species depend almost entirely on the presence of loose sand for nesting. The **Common Spiny Digger Wasp** *Oxybelus uniglumis* preys on flies and is distinctive in that only members of the genus *Oxybelus* impale their prey on their sting to transport it to the nest.

The **Sand Tailed Digger Wasp** *Cerceris arenaria* and **Ornate Tailed Digger Wasp** *Cerceris rybyensis*

Figure 10.16 (left) Common Spiny Digger Wasp, (centre) Sand Tailed Digger Wasp with weevil, (right) Ornate Tailed Digger Wasp. (NWO, CKL).

Figure 10.17 (left) *Astata boops* with shieldbug prey, (right) *Hedychridium roseum.* (NWO).

Figure 10.18 (left) Common Green Tenthredo, (right) Large Yellow-girdled Tenthredo. (CKL).

prey specifically on small weevils. ***Astata boops*** is a moderate sized orange and black species that preys on shieldbug nymphs. The males of this species are distinguished by their enlarged eyes that occupy almost the entire head. *Hedychridium roseum*, a small jewel wasp with a dull orange abdomen and shining blue-green front half, parasitises *Astata boops*.

The **Common Spider Wasp** *Anoplius nigerrimus* is a black spider-hunting wasp that can be found in dry grasslands and scrub, often in urban areas and brownfield sites. It is quite unfussy in its nesting requirements, having been recorded nesting under stones, in hollow plant stems, deserted aculeate burrows and even inside snail shells. If the soil is suitable, they will also construct their own nest burrows. Their prey includes a wide range of ground dwelling spider species.

The **Yellow Meadow Ant** *Lasius flavus* is common in grasslands. In old unimproved meadows and grassland these ants form impressive anthills and act as significant small-scale ecosystem engineers. In urban areas they usually occur in far less impressive colonies in open grassy habitats including lightly managed lawns.

Common species of woodland, hedgerows and damp places

Woodland, hedgerows and damp habitats are important for many hymenopteran species. They are perhaps the best places to look for a diversity of sawflies and gall wasps, and many aculeates nest in hollow trees, dead wood or hollow plant stems in hedgerows. Many species that nest in open habitats, also regularly feed in flower-rich hedgerows and wood edges.

Many species of sawfly occur in woodland and hedgerows, especially in damp habitats, where some are frequent and obvious. The **Bramble Sawfly** *Arge cyanocrocea* is an attractive species with an orange abdomen, shining blue-black head and thorax and dark wing bands whose larvae feed on bramble. It is abundant in hedgerows, wood edges and any other bramble-rich habitat.

Sawflies in the genus *Tenthredo* are amongst the most obvious of sawflies. They are large, colourful, and often sit on flower heads. Three species were recorded during the project. The stunning green and black **Common Green Tenthredo** *Tenthredo mesomela* can be spotted nectaring on umbellifers at wood edges or paths. The **Large Yellow-girdled Tenthredo** *T. maculata* occurs in the same habitats but is mostly black with a broad yellow band on the abdomen and yellow bands on the legs. The **Figwort Sawfly** *T. scrophulariae* is a striking wasp mimic that is associated with damp habitats where figworts (its larval food plants) grow.

Figure 10.19 European Hornet. (PAR).

The **European Hornet** *Vespa crabro* is the largest social wasp in Europe with the largest queens reaching 2.4 cm in length. Whilst intimidating in size they are less aggressive than Common Wasps and rarely sting. Like smaller social wasps they build large nests out of paper, usually in hollow trees, although nests in buildings and underground do occur. Hornets are traditionally associated with ancient deciduous woodland but can be found in many lowland habitats, especially urban areas with old trees.

Digger wasps in the genus *Ectemnius* nest in holes in deadwood and often occur in hedgerows or at the edges of woodland. Two species, the **Golden-moustached Fly Fox** *Ectemnius cavifrons* and the **Big-headed Digger Wasp** *Ectemnius continuus*, have been recorded. They are mid-sized yellow and black species, quite similar in appearance to many other related species.

Gall wasps are small, often dumpy, unobtrusive wasps that are most easily found and identified by the distinctive galls they cause in their host plants. Sixteen species have been recorded from the NHC area over the course of the project. Most are associated with Oak trees and they include many with interestingly named galls. **Marble Gall** *Andricus kollari*, **Knopper Gall** *Andricus quercuscalicis*, **Oak Apple** *Biorhiza pallida*, **Sputnik Gall** *Diplolepis nervosa*, **Oyster Gall** *Neuroterus anthracinus*, **Blister-gall** *Neuroterus numismalis* and **Common Spangle Gall** *Neuroterus quercusbaccarum* are well worth looking for on any local oaks. Some species also attack shrubs. The **Bramble Stem Gall Wasp** *Diastrophus rubi* causes unevenly swollen galls on bramble stems. One of the most obvious galls formed by gall wasps is the distinctive **Robin's Pin-cushion Gall** on rose stems caused by *Diplolepis rosae*.

The **Slender Ant** *Leptothorax acervorum* is the smallest ant species recorded during the project and nests in dead wood, including relatively small sticks. It can often be found in neglected hedges or shelterbelts. This species is very easy to overlook because of its small size and secretive nature but is quite common.

New arrivals
Several species recorded during the project are relatively recent arrivals to the Cambridge area. A combination of changing climate, human introductions and shifts in land use have allowed many species to expand their ranges over the last few decades.

Figure 10.20 (left) Golden-moustached Fly Fox, (right) Big-headed Digger Wasp. (NWO).

Figure 10.21 Wasp galls: (left) Common Spangle Gall. (centre) Sputnik Gall, (right) Oak Apple Gall. (PAR).

Figure 10.22 (left) Female Bee Wolf, (right) Queen Median Wasp. (CKL, PAR).

Figure 10.23 (left) Birch Sawfly, (right) Female *Hedychrum nobile*. (PAR, CKL).

One recent addition to the fauna of Cambridge is the **Elm Zig-zag Sawfly** *Aproceros leucopoda*. This species arrived in Europe from Asia in 2003 and reached Britain in 2017. It is now fairly widespread in south-east England and East Anglia and is considered a significant threat to our embattled native elm trees. The adult sawfly is a relatively nondescript black species. The most obvious sign of its presence is the distinctive zig-zag feeding pattern of the larvae on elm leaves.

Perhaps the most striking new colonist is the **Bee Wolf** *Philanthus triangulum*, amongst the most impressive of Britain's solitary wasps. This large yellow and black striped species was extremely rare until the 1980s, restricted to a handful of sand dune and heathland sites in southern England. Since then, it has rapidly expanded as far north as Yorkshire and is now locally common in sandy places across southern England, including even small sandy areas in urban and post-industrial habitats. The Bee Wolf feeds its larvae predominantly with **Honey Bees** *Apis mellifera* and can provision its complex burrow with up to a hundred bees.

The **Median Wasp** *Dolichovespula media* is a social wasp that is noticeably larger than the Common Wasp, although smaller than the European Hornet. It is a recent colonist of the British Isles, with the first individual being found in Sussex in 1980. By the mid 1990s it had spread across much of England and continues to become more common. The majority of nests have been discovered in urban gardens, perhaps indicating a preference for such sites. It nests almost exclusively in trees.

The **Brown Tree Ant** *Lasius brunneus* nests under the bark and in the wood of living and dead trees and is a relatively recent arrival in the city. It was first identified in Britain in 1923 and for a long time was rare and confined to high-quality deadwood habitats in the Home Counties. In recent decades it has expanded rapidly through the south and east of England. It is now relatively common in many areas and can be found nesting in trees in gardens and urban green spaces and even on street trees.

Rare species

Several scarce or rarely encountered species were recorded during the NHC project. The **Birch Sawfly** *Cimbex femoratus* is Britain's largest sawfly, growing to 25 mm long. It is a striking animal with a white or red band across a shining black body but is a scarce species, rarely seen in spite of its size. The large caterpillar-like larvae feed on Silver Birch and adults are usually found close to birch trees. Planted birches in parks and gardens are the best places to look for this species in Cambridge.

The **Lesser Horntail Wasp** *Sirex noctilio* is a species of horntail. Unusually for sawflies, members of this family oviposit into the trunks of trees. The host plants of the Lesser Horntail Wasp include a wide range of pine species. Outside its native Eurasian range, it is a serious pest of commercial pine forests. In Britain it is quite scarce.

The most surprising hymenopteran record is that of **Heath Potter Wasp** *Eumenes coarctatus,* a species usually restricted to high-quality lowland heathland in southern England. The species has an elaborate life cycle in which the females construct complex pot-shaped nests from balls of clay which

are provisioned with small moth caterpillars to feed its own larvae. Five nests of this species were discovered on Lavender in the Botanic Garden in 2017. These nests were presumably imported with the plants, and the species seems not to have become established.

Hedychrum nobile is a larger red and green metallic jewel wasp. It is a local species that nests in loose sandy ground and parasitises members of the genus *Cerceris*. *H. nobile* was only relatively recently recognised as a British species, having long been confused with the almost identical *H. niemelai*. It is unclear whether this is a new arrival in the area or just a long-overlooked resident.

The **Five-banded Weevil-wasp** *Cerceris quinquefasciata* is a rare species that collects small weevils to provision the nest it digs in sandy soils. It is very similar to the common Sand Tailed Digger Wasp and its current status is rather uncertain. Until recently, most available records were old and it was thought to have seriously declined. However, it is now frequently recorded from brownfield sites in East Anglia and the East Midlands, where it may be increasing.

The **Two-banded Hopper Wolf** *Lestiphorus bicinctus* is a distinctive yellow and black wasp with a narrow-waisted abdomen and dark smudged forewings. The species is scarce and restricted to southern England. It feeds on leafhoppers and can be found in a wide range of habitats with bramble and sandy soils for nesting.

The **Six-spotted Wasp Cuckoo** *Nysson trimaculatus* is a kleptoparasite of *Lestiphorus bicinctus* and is itself a scarce species, although surprisingly it is more frequently recorded than its host.

Bees

Bees of the Botanic Garden

Amongst the human visitors to the Botanic Garden thousands of wild bees are quietly getting on with their lives, collecting pollen and nectar from the rich variety of plants or hiding away in their nest cells. As well as the familiar **Western Honey Bee** *Apis mellifera*, many kinds of solitary bee and bumblebee are present. Around 155 species of wild bees have so far been recorded in the county of Cambridgeshire and many can be seen in the city itself.

Within the NHC area there are post-1990 records for 95 species of bees, comprising 84 solitary bee species, 10 bumblebees and the

Figure 10.24 Female Five-banded Weevil-wasp. (CKL).

Honey Bee. This represents about one third of the British bee fauna and reflects the importance of Cambridge's open spaces, mature gardens and remaining brownfield sites. The Botanic Garden makes a significant contribution owing to its diversity of flowering plants, habitat features, long establishment and sensitive management. Over seventy bee species have been recorded there. Two Botanic Garden bees, the **Grooved Sharp-tail Bee** *Coelioxys quadridentata* and **Big-headed Mining Bee** *Andrena bucephala*, have not so far been recorded elsewhere in the county.

There is relatively little information about wild bee populations in Cambridgeshire compared with some other counties. In the past, naturalists have tended to focus their attention on nature reserves, such as Wicken Fen. Many of the records from the wider countryside and the city of Cambridge come from the late Peter Yeo, who worked at the Botanic Garden from 1953 to 1993. His excellent bee collection is conserved in the Museum of Zoology. A further major contributor is Peter Kirby, who carried out invertebrate surveys of the Botanic Garden in 2010 and 2011, and surveyed railway tracks and sidings along the route of the now completed Cambridge Guided Busway. Vince Lea, Trevor Grange, Mark and Luke Welch and Steven Boulton have also made important recent contributions. Other records this century, especially in the Botanic Garden, come from Rosie Bleet, Ted Benton and myself.

Wild bees are often overlooked, but play a vital role in pollination. Some bees are declining while others are spreading northwards, apparently in response to climate warming. They all have fascinating lifestyles but many have received little attention. The notes below portray a selection of the Botanic Garden bee species, based on my observations over the past five years. The examples chosen illustrate the diversity of bees that live within the city of Cambridge.

Bee portraits
Hairy-footed Flower Bee *Anthophora plumipes*. This solitary bee is large and round and can be mistaken for a bumblebee. It is a common early spring species which darts quickly from flower to flower. The tongue is long and flowers such as Primrose and Lungwort are particularly favoured. As in many bee species, males usually appear a week or two in advance of the females. Nests are made within the mortar of old walls or in the ground, often in large aggregations.

Four-banded Flower Bee *Anthophora quadrimaculata*. This is a smaller relative of the Hairy-footed Flower Bee and is unusual in being most frequently seen in cities rather than in the countryside. It is most abundant in parts of south-east England including London, but it has an outpost in Cambridge. It can be spotted visiting Catmint in the borders around the café in June and July. The green-eyed males are territorial and often bask on the ground nearby. The Four-banded Flower Bee has a specific cuckoo bee, the **Grooved Sharp-tail Bee** *Coelioxys quadridentata*, which has not been seen in Cambridgeshire since Peter

Figure 10.25 (left) Male Hairy-footed Flower Bee feeding on Early-flowering Borage *Trachystemon orientalis*, **(right) male Four-banded Flower Bee visiting Viper's Bugloss** *Echium vulgare*. (NWO).

Figure 10.26 (left) Willughby's Leafcutter Bee, (right) rose leaf cut by leafcutter bees. (NWO).

Yeo found it in the Garden in 1997. It may still be present but unnoticed.

Willughby's Leafcutter Bee *Megachile willughbiella*. Leafcutters collect pollen under their abdomen and make their nests from cut pieces of leaf, placed in hollow stems like a string of hollow cigars. They sometimes nest in the 'bee hotels' which many people now have in their gardens. Rose leaves and petals are often the nest material of choice. Willughby's Leafcutter is a common species in the Botanic Garden. The bee was named by William Kirby in 1802 in honour of Francis Willughby, who was a younger colleague of John Ray in Cambridge in the 17th century and worked with Ray on various projects and publications before Willughby's early death.

The presence of leafcutter bees is apparent from the distinctive shapes of the sections they cut from leaves. The oval pieces are used for the walls of a nest cell and the round pieces for each end. Bees tend to return to the same leaves to collect more pieces.

Shiny-vented Sharp-tail Bee *Coelioxys inermis*. Some bees behave as cuckoos of other bee species, in a similar way to birds. The cuckoo bee enters a host bee's nest to lay an egg on or near the pollen and nectar collected in one of the host bee's brood cells. On hatching the larva destroys the host's egg or larva and takes over the food. Each cuckoo bee species attacks one or a small number of related bee hosts. The Shiny-vented Sharp-tail bee is a cuckoo of some leafcutter bees. It uses the sharp point of its tail to insert eggs through the leaves covering a nest cell.

Small Scissor Bee *Chelostoma campanularum*. This very tiny black bee, just 4–5 mm in length, specialises on Campanulaceae and Geraniaceae pollen. Nests are made in old beetle burrows in wood. At first sight they might not be recognised as bees. They can easily be found by peering into the bells of suitable flowers, where males sometimes swarm in large numbers in June and July.

Green Furrow Bee *Lasioglossum morio*. This is one of many Furrow Bee species. They are mostly

Figure 10.27 (left) Female Shiny-vented Sharp-tail Bee, (right) female Small Scissor Bee. (NWO).

very small, with the Green Furrow Bee among the smallest at 4 mm in length. Nests are made in the ground, often in clusters on sun-warmed slopes. This is a social species with a queen and sterile female workers, though the queen is usually no larger than the workers.

Blood Bee *Sphecodes* species. Blood Bees, so-called because of their red colour, are cuckoo bees which mostly target Furrow Bees. Each Blood Bee species specialises on one or a small number of different host species. Blood Bees, like other cuckoos, have very little hair since they do not collect pollen. Their black and red colour pattern is shared with many wasp species. They are difficult to identify to species level from photographs.

Yellow Loosestrife Bee *Macropis europaea.* Many solitary bees specialise on flowers from one plant family and some take pollen from just one plant genus. The Yellow Loosestrife Bee usually collects all its pollen and also floral oils from **Yellow Loosestrife** *Lysimachia vulgaris.* The floral oils are used to waterproof the nest. In the Botanic Garden

there is a colony of this bee at the Fen Display, which was established in 1965. The bee was discovered during surveys by Peter Kirby in 2010 and 2011, but may have been present for some time. Pollen is collected on hairs on the hind legs, sometimes in clumps so large that it forages with the legs sticking out backwards from the flowers. Males patrol the site and attempt to pounce on females while they are collecting pollen. At this stage the females usually repel them. Nests are made in the ground, but these have yet to be discovered in the Garden. The bees are active from late June until early September.

Large-headed Resin Bee *Heriades truncorum* This small bee, around 5 mm long, is spreading northwards and reached Cambridge in about 2016. It collects resin from timber to construct its nest, which is usually made in a beetle hole in old wood. It specialises on Asteraceae pollen and can be found in the Systematic Beds. The female's abdomen bobs up and down rapidly as it flicks pollen onto the pollen brush beneath its abdomen, using its hind legs.

Figure 10.29 (left) Female Large-headed Resin Bee, (right) female Yellow Loosestrife Bee. (NWO).

Figure 10.30 (left) Female Gwynne's Mining Bee collecting Primrose pollen, (right) female Fabricius's Nomad Bee. (NWO).

Figure 10.31 (left) Big-headed Mining Bee (female inspected for identification), (right) female Marsham's Nomad Bee. (NWO, PAR).

Gwynne's Mining Bee *Andrena bicolor*. The genus *Andrena* (Mining Bees) is a large one, with about 65 species in Britain. Cambridgeshire has about 36 species and the Botanic Garden 14. Pollen is carried along the full length of the hind legs and under the middle of the body. *Andrena* mining bees often nest in aggregations, but each typically has its own separate nest entrance, leading into a burrow containing a cluster of its own nest cells. Each nest cell is stocked with pollen and nectar, then an egg is laid and the nest cell is sealed. Finally, the whole burrow is sealed. A new generation subsequently emerges, usually in the following year. The bee shown here is collecting pollen from a 'thrum' primrose. In this form of the flower the anthers are exposed at the top of the corolla tube, where this bee can reach them. In the alternative 'pin' form the stigma is exposed but the anthers are about halfway down the corolla tube and the bee is too large to enter. Gwynne's Mining Bee can therefore potentially carry pollen from

thrum to pin flowers but not vice versa. If there were no other pollinators, thrum flowers would set little or no seed.

Fabricius's Nomad Bee *Nomada fabriciana*. This bee is a cuckoo of Gwynne's Mining Bee. There are several different forms of this cuckoo bee of varying size, specialising on different hosts.

Big-headed Mining Bee *Andrena bucephala*. There is an aggregation of the Big-headed Mining Bee in the chalk mound of the British Wild Plants site, where many females can be watched arriving and departing through the same large holes. This bee is one of a small number of *Andrena* species in which many females share a common nest entrance; they nest communally, though each has its own nest burrow leading off an underground atrium. There are four separate entrances, each 5–10 cm wide, to the underground caverns. Pete Michna, who created the feature in about 2002, explained that the chalk lumps were originally stacked loosely with spaces between them.

Figure 10.32 (left) Welted Mason Bee female at nest entrance, (right) Red-tailed Mason Bee. (NWO, CKL).

Sharing the nesting caverns is a second communal *Andrena* species, the **Chocolate Mining Bee** *Andrena scotica*. The latter's cuckoo, **Marsham's Nomad** *Nomada marshamella*, also enters and leaves, but the specific cuckoo of Big-headed Mining Bee the **Long-horned Nomad** *Nomada hirtipes*, which is rare, has not been seen. These nests were discovered by me in 2018, but they may have been present for some time. The chalk mound has recently been extended by the Botanic Garden staff, taking care not to disturb the nests.

Welted Mason Bee *Hoplitis claviventris*. This bee was discovered nesting in the reed fence around the Fen Display in 2016. The only other known sites for this bee in Cambridgeshire are Devil's Dyke and Fleam Dyke. Pollen is collected on the hairs beneath the abdomen from a variety of flowers with a deep corolla, especially members of the Fabaceae.

Another scarce chalk-loving bee present on the chalk mound is the **Red-tailed Mason Bee** *Osmia bicolor*. The bee can be found around Cambridge on chalk grassland and also where limestone ballast has been used for railway tracks. It makes a nest in an empty snail shell then covers the shell with fragments of plant material, which it carries in flight. It is worth watching for its unusual behaviour in the Botanic Garden in April and May.

Wool Carder Bee *Anthidium manicatum*. This is a large and robust bee with a long tongue. Pollen is carried on a 'toothbrush' of hairs under the abdomen. Males are larger than females and defend territories, sometimes making use of the spines on their tail. The nest is packed with soft hairs collected from the leaves of plants such as **Lamb's-ear** *Stachys byzantina*. This was one of the first solitary bees to acquire a common name.

Large Yellow-face Bee *Hylaeus signatus*. This bee collects pollen almost entirely from members of the Resedaceae family, especially **Weld** *Reseda luteola* and **Wild Mignonette** *Reseda lutea*. The bee can be found by searching the flowers of these plants at the British Wild Plants site from late May. Females of the genus *Hylaeus* ingest pollen rather than collecting it on body hairs, then regurgitate it in the nest. There are several *Hylaeus* species in the Botanic Garden, all of them small and black with yellow or white markings.

Ivy Bee *Colletes hederae*. This bee was first recorded in Britain in 2001. It spread north rapidly and within the past five years has become

Figure 10.33 (left) Female Wool Carder Bee, on Marsh Woundwort *Stachys palustris*, (centre) male Large Yellow-face Bee on Weld, (right) Ivy Bee. (NWO, PAR).

common in Cambridge and East Anglia. It nests in dense aggregations on lawns or bare banks and takes pollen almost entirely from Ivy. Nesting aggregations numbering in the thousands are now present around the borders of the Botanic Garden systematic beds, with adults on the wing in September and October. They sometimes cause alarm by their large numbers and audible buzzing, but they are very unlikely to sting. Early in the nesting season most of the bees seen at nesting aggregations are males, which cannot sting.

Bumblebees

Nine species of bumblebee have been recorded in the Garden, two being cuckoo bumblebees. The photographs show some examples. The **White-tailed Bumblebee** *Bombus lucorum* worker has collected pollen from two different sources, with the pollen basket showing both pale and dark pollen, with a distinct line between them. Male bumblebees look similar to workers but, as in all male bees, they have longer antennae and lack pollen-collecting structures. The **Common Carder** *Bombus pascuorum* is one of three very similar brown bumblebees, the others being the **Brown-banded Carder** *Bombus humilis* and **Moss Carder** *Bombus*

muscorum. The latter two species were last seen in the county in the early 1900s at Wicken Fen and are rare nationally.

Cuckoo bumblebees have thin hair with the black cuticle shining through and neither sex has a pollen basket. They tend to be sluggish and fly with a softer buzz. The **Red-tailed Cuckoo Bumblebee** *Bombus rupestris* parasitises nests of the **Red-tailed Bumblebee** *Bombus lapidarius*. Each cuckoo has one or two main hosts, but cuckoo bumblebees are more closely related to each other than they are to their hosts. Even so, cuckoo bumblebees tend to have a similar colour pattern to their host, for reasons which are not fully explained. The Red-tailed Cuckoo disappeared from Cambridgeshire during the last century but it has recolonised from southern counties. The female shown here was observed digging into the ground in west Cambridge in 2011. It can be recognised as a cuckoo by the hind tibia being covered in hairs rather than having a pollen basket. The cuticle is very robust and the wings are darkened, with strong venation.

The **Tree Bumblebee** *Bombus hypnorum* is a relatively recent colonist from mainland Europe and is now common and widespread as far north as the Highlands of Scotland. It is one of the easiest

Figure 10.34 (left) Worker White-tailed Bumblebee, (right) male Common Carder Bee. (NWO).

Figure 10.35 (left) Female Red-tailed Cuckoo Bumblebee, (centre) male Red-tailed Bumblebee, (right) queen Tree Bumblebee. (NWO).

Figure 10.36 (left) Female Red Bartsia Blunthorn Bee, (right) female Violet Carpenter Bee. (SJB, SPT).

Figure 10.37 (left) Female Ashy Mining Bee, (right) Common Mourning Bee. (PAR, NWO).

bumblebees to identify with its ginger thorax, black body and white tail. It often nests in buildings or bird nesting boxes.

Western Honey Bee *Apis mellifera*. Honey Bees have a true pollen basket, as do bumblebees, this being a shiny bare section of the hind legs, surrounded by a fringe of hairs. Pollen with added nectar is collected into a round lump on this part of the hind legs, for transport back to the nest. A worker honeybee's abdomen is usually partly orange, but can be entirely dark. Rather strangely, they have hairy eyes.

Honeybees can overwhelm or outcompete wild bees in some circumstances, with up to 50,000 worker honeybees foraging from each hive by mid-summer. Wild bee species are often more effective pollinators than honeybees, since many have a long tongue, which can reach into deep tubular flowers and, as we have seen, some solitary bees specialise in particular species of wild plants and may be critical to their survival. Bumblebees are able to work at much lower temperatures than honeybees and are vital pollinators of fruit crops and wild flowers, especially during cool spring weather.

Rare and notable bees outside the Botanic Garden

Although most of the bees described by Nick are more widely distributed across the NHC area,

there are two species that have not been found in the Botanic Garden. The first of these is the **Red Bartsia Blunthorn Bee** *Melitta tricincta* which was found in Barnwell East LNR by Stephen Boulton in 2018. This bee collects pollen exclusively from **Red Bartsia** *Odontites vernus*. The bee has not been observed elsewhere in the NHC area, but Red Bartsia is recorded from 46 of the 64 NHC monads so it is worth keeping a look out for the bee elsewhere.

The second is the **Violet Carpenter Bee** *Xylocopa violacea*, a species that most British naturalists will only have come across when holidaying in Southern Europe. Climate change has seen its range expand northwards, with the first record of this species successfully breeding in Britain coming from Leicestershire in 2007. The first record in our area was of a female from Girton in 2019 and remarkably Stephen Tomkins spotted a pristine male in his Girton garden in February 2020, which would indicate successful breeding rather than a migrant from Europe.

With its distinctive black and white colouring the **Ashy Mining Bee** *Andrena cineraria* is one of our easier-to-identify mining bees. It is frequently found in open sunny places, particularly on sites with sandy soil. Females create nests underground by excavating burrows in bare or sparsely vegetated earth. They feed from a wide variety of spring

Figure 10.38 (left) Female Grey-patched Mining Bee, (right) male Gooden's Nomad Bee. (PAR).

Figure 10.39 (left) Female Buffish Mining Bee, (right) Female Chocolate Mining Bee. (CKL, RKW).

flowers and shrubs, including buttercups, hawthorn, blackthorn, gorse and fruit trees.

Another very distinctive black and white bee you may be lucky to find in your garden is the **Common Mourning Bee** *Melecta albifrons*. It is a kleptoparasite, invading the pre-stocked nests of Hairy-footed Flower Bees to lay its own eggs. The larvae hatch before the host's and consume the competition as well as the stored pollen, emerging as adults the following spring. There are few records of this parasite, which unlike its host does not appear to be common in our area.

Gooden's Nomad Bee *Nomada goodeniana* is our largest and probably most common nomad bee. Like the Common Mourning bee this wasp mimic is a kleptoparasite, using several species of mining bee as hosts. Potential hosts in the NHC area are the **Grey-patched Mining Bee** *Andrena nitida*, **Buffish Mining Bee** *Andrena nigroaenea*, and to a lesser extent the **Chocolate Mining Bee** *Andrena scotica*.

True Flies (Diptera)
Introduction
The true flies (Diptera) are the second most species-rich insect order in Great Britain with 7216 species on the British list as of October 2020. The term Diptera (two wings) refers to the unifying distinguishing feature of all true flies, the fact that they only possess a single pair of functional wings. The hindwings found in all other flying insects have adapted into structures called halteres in true flies. These club-like structures act like gyroscopic stabilisers, giving flies an almost unmatched level of manoeuvrability in flight. Most people's first thoughts when they hear the word fly tend to be of species such as house flies, bluebottles, or perhaps the much-maligned mosquito. These are only a small component of the diversity of this huge order, and there are flies that lead almost any conceivable lifestyle. True flies fill many important ecological roles. From a human perspective perhaps the most important of these roles is pollination. Flies are

probably the most important pollinators globally, although bees tend to get more attention, and some groups, such as hoverflies, are obligate flower visitors.

Only 157 species of true fly were recorded from the NHC area between 2015 and 2019. Flies are generally fairly poorly recorded, and this total is a low one. There must undoubtedly have been many other species present.

Common species of the home and garden

There are a number of fly species associated specifically with human habitation, and they are almost universally maligned. The **Housefly** *Musca domestica* was once a common species inside houses, where both the adults and larvae feed on decaying organic matter. They do not carry diseases themselves but can transmit harmful bacteria, viruses and fungi to surfaces and foodstuffs. The Housefly is now increasingly scarce, perhaps as a result of increased cleanliness in homes. Most 'houseflies' encountered now are **Lesser Houseflies** *Fannia* spp. The **Common Bluebottle** *Calliphora vicina* is another species commonly associated with human habitation. It both feeds on and lays its eggs in carrion. It is a particularly useful species in the field of forensic pathology as it lays its eggs on corpses at a consistent time after death, thus providing a useful indication of time of death.

The **Common Greenbottle** *Lucilia caesar* is one of several very similar species of shiny green fly. It is the commonest species of the genus and the most human-associated. Unlike Common Bluebottles and Houseflies it is rarely found indoors, more

usually being encountered on flowers or foliage in gardens and other areas close to human habitation.

Some of the more obvious garden visitors are hoverflies (family Syrphidae). The **Narcissus Bulb Fly** *Merodon equestris* is a common species of hoverfly whose larvae feed on the bulbs of daffodils and other members of the Amaryllis family. The large hairy adults are bumblebee mimics, with several colour forms that mimic different bumblebee species. They can be most frequently seen sunning themselves on leaves or stones near daffodils grown in gardens.

The **Marmalade Hoverfly** *Episyrphus balteatus* is probably the most abundant hoverfly in Britain and can be found in almost any habitat. They can be found in large numbers nectaring on garden flowers. The local British population is reinforced to varying degrees by adults migrating from Europe. The number of migrants varies from year to year, with some years having vast influxes. These small flies can migrate truly extraordinary distances given their size.

The **Common Dronefly** *Eristalis tenax* is the commonest of a genus of hoverflies known as droneflies. They are called this due to the fact that they mimic male honeybees (drones). They can be found in a wide range of habitats and are common in gardens where the males can be seen hovering in the open to aggressively defend their territory from other males. You will often hear the distinctive droning buzz before you see the fly itself.

Common meadow species

Numerous fly species can be found in meadows and grasslands. Many can be observed feeding on

Figure 10.40 (left) Narcissus Bulb Fly, (right) Marmalade Hoverfly. (CKL).

Figure 10.41 (left) Signal Fly, (right) Broad Centurion. (CKL, PAR).

Figure 10.42 (left) Migrant Field Syrph, (right) Spear Thistle Gall Fly. (PAR).

flowerheads. The **Broad Centurion** *Chloromyia formosa*, a striking, medium-sized, metallic green and bronze soldierfly that is common in grassland, woodland, hedgerows and gardens, can often be spotted nectaring on flowering Hogweed. The **Signal Fly** *Platystoma seminationis* is another species readily encountered crawling over flowerheads to take nectar. It is a distinctive and attractive medium-sized fly with a dark mottled body, white-spotted grey wings and large red-brown eyes. It is fairly common in southern England but scarcer further north.

The best-known group of flower-visiting flies are the hoverflies. Amongst the commonest of these is the **Migrant Field Syrph** *Eupeodes corollae*. It is an attractive yellow and black hoverfly that can be exceptionally abundant in Britain. Like the Marmalade Hoverfly its numbers are usually boosted by migrants from the European mainland. It can be found in almost any flowery habitats including meadows, gardens, along hedgerows and at the edges of woodland.

Other species feed on the stems and leaves of plants in their larval stage. Some groups, such as gall flies (families Agromyzidae and Cecidomyiidae) and fruit flies (family Tephritidae)

form galls or mines in plants within which their larvae develop. *Tephritis formosa* is one of the commoner species of gall fly in Britain. It is a small grey fly with black marked wings and is one of several very similar species, all of which are frequent. The fly forms galls on flower heads of Cat's-ear, Hawk's-beard and Sow-thistle within which their larvae feed. It can be found in a wide range of habitats but is most frequently encountered in meadows and grasslands where the larval host plants grow. The **Spear Thistle Gall Fly** *Urophora stylata* is another common gall fly that leads a similar lifestyle, forming galls on thistles.

The **Marsh Brown-edged Tipula** *Tipula oleracea* is a moderately sized grey-brown cranefly (family Tipulidae). Their larvae live in the soil feeding on the roots of grasses, sometimes in such numbers that they are considered a pest by turf growers. It is probably Britain's commonest cranefly and can often be seen flying low over damp grassland. Later in the year large numbers can also be found in and around houses and other buildings. It is one of several very similar species, flying from April to October.

The abundant herbivorous invertebrates in grassland inevitably support many predators. Some species such as the **Kite-tailed Robberfly**

Machimus atricapillus are aggressive predators of other insects. This is a fairly common species in open habitats throughout Britain and can often be spotted perched on fenceposts or leaves watching carefully for prey. Its close relative the **Striped Slender Robberfly** *Leptogaster cylindrica* is a smaller and less active species, often seen hanging lazily on grass stems in the summer. Although less active than most robberflies, it is still a formidable predator of aphids. This species is abundant in grassy habitats and undoubtedly the commonest member of its family in Britain.

Other species have a more complex life cycle. Bristle flies (family Tachinidae) are parasites whose larvae develop inside other invertebrates, consuming them from the inside out. *Eriothrix rufomaculata* is one of the commonest British species and is almost ubiquitous in open flowery habitats in summer. It is a medium-sized black bristlefly with distinctive orange patches on its abdomen whose larvae feed on moth caterpillars.

Common species of woodland and hedgerows

Woodland and hedgerows support many fly species; niches such as deadwood, leaf litter, tree foliage, plants and flowers are important features. One of the most distinctive British fly species is the **Dark-edged Bee-fly** *Bombylius major*. It is a bee-mimicking fly with a densely furred body, large eyes, dark-edged wings and a long proboscis used for feeding on nectar. These features give it a distinctly 'cute' appearance. In spring it can be found abundantly along hedgerows, woodland rides and in gardens. The fly's life cycle is rather more gruesome than its appearance might suggest. The fly flicks its eggs into the nest burrows of solitary bees and wasps where its larvae feed on the original inhabitants of the nest.

Another attractive fly species often found resting on the leaves of trees and bushes is the **Dull Four-spined Legionnaire** *Chorisops tibialis*, a small soldierfly (family Stratiomyidae) with a shining green four-spined thorax and an orange and

Figure 10.43 (left) Kite-tailed Robberfly, (right) Striped Slender Robberfly. (CKL, PAR).

Figure 10.44 (left) Dark-edged Bee-fly, (right) Grey-backed Snout Hoverfly. (PAR, CKL).

Figure 10.45 Pied Plumehorn. (PAR).

black abdomen. It is a common species in many moist and shaded habitats. The larvae can be found in wood debris and rot holes in trees.

Many hoverfly species are strongly associated with woody habitats. The **Common Snout Hoverfly** *Rhingia campestris* is the commoner of a pair of orange-bodied, long-snouted, hoverflies. It can be distinguished from the rarer **Grey-backed Snout Hoverfly** *Rhingia rostrata* by the black edges of its abdominal segments and is very common throughout Britain at the edges of woodland or along hedgerows. The larvae develop in cow dung. The **Gossamer Hoverfly** *Baccha elongata* is a small and very distinctive hoverfly, with a long thin, bulbous-tipped body. It is common along hedgerows, woodland rides and sunny woodland glades, especially where there are nettle beds or other lush ground vegetation.

The **Pied Plumehorn** *Volucella pellucens* is a large and striking hoverfly, pied in black and cream. Males can be seen hovering conspicuously along woodland rides, defending their territory from competitors and keeping an eye out for females. Both sexes can also be found feeding on flowers including bramble, umbellifers such as hogweed and, later in the year, flowering ivy. The larvae live in the nests of social wasps and bees, feeding on waste products and larvae.

Common wetland species

Wetland habitats such as ponds, ditches, marshes and fens are important for Diptera. Numerous species, including many rarities, are found exclusively in wetland habitats. The **Little Snipefly** *Chrysopilus asiliformis* is a small, delicately built snipefly (family Rhagionidae) with striking green eyes. It is a common species that can be found in a range of damp habitats, including woodland, hedgerows and wetlands and is most often observed sitting on foliage.

The **Tiger Hoverfly** *Helophilus pendulus* is a common, large and attractive hoverfly, also known as 'The Footballer'. Both of its common names refer to the neat yellow stripes that run along its black thorax. Its larvae develop in wet, often very unappealing, habitats rich in organic matter such as ponds, marshes, drainage ditches, puddles, and even wet manure. The adults can be found near to such habitats, often sunbathing on vegetation.

The **Semaphore Fly** *Poecilobothrus nobilitatus* is a relatively small metallic green fly that is common at the edges of ponds, marshes and other wetlands. It is easy to overlook this species as it tends to be found on mud or low vegetation, often below the notice of passers-by, but is attractive once noticed. The male is particularly striking, performing a courtship dance to attract females by flicking its white-tipped black wings in a pattern reminiscent of semaphore messaging, giving rise to its common name.

Figure 10.46 (left) Little Snipefly, (right) Tiger Hoverfly. (PAR).

Figure 10.47 Common Phantom Cranefly. (PAR).

The **Common Phantom Cranefly** *Ptychoptera contaminata* is the commonest of seven British species of phantom cranefly. The shining black body is marked with yellow-orange and it has strongly black spotted wings. The aquatic larvae have a long retractile breathing tube that works much like a snorkel and they live amongst decaying vegetation and mud in shallow water. This is a common species at the margins of still and slow-flowing water, but the flies often lurk low amongst tall marginal vegetation and are easily overlooked.

New arrivals

As with most invertebrate groups, Britain's fly fauna has changed over the past few decades in response to habitat change and climate change. Several species of Diptera recorded from our area are relatively recent arrivals in Cambridge.

Probably the most noticeable of these new arrivals is the **Hornet Hoverfly** *Volucella zonaria*, one of the largest and most spectacular flies in Britain, growing to almost 2 cm in length. It is an excellent mimic of the **European Hornet** *Vespa crabro*, with a largely orange-yellow abdomen with dark bands and a dark brown thorax. The larvae of this species live in the nests of social wasps, including Hornets, where they feed on wasp larvae and pupae. Previously known only as a rare vagrant to southern coasts, the Hornet Hoverfly became established in a few places in southern England in the 1940s and 1950s but remained uncommon. It has spread much more widely in recent years and is now frequent in Cambridge gardens and open spaces in late summer, when it can be found nectaring on garden plants and ivy.

Another recent arrival is the bristlefly *Cistogaster globosa* which was, until fairly recently, considered a significant rarity, restricted to a handful of warm sites in southern England. In recent years it has expanded rapidly northwards,

Figure 10.48 Hornet Hoverfly. (CKL).

Figure 10.49 (left) Ivy Waspgrabber, (right) Banded General. (PAR).

perhaps in response to climate change. It is a small (5 mm long) but eye-catching fly. It is a parasitic species whose larvae develop in **Bishop's Mitre Shieldbug** *Aelia acuminata*. It is now a frequent species in dry grassland and brownfield sites around Cambridge. Adults can be found on the flower-heads of umbellifers such as wild carrot and hogweed in summer.

Rare species

Several scarce species of fly have been recorded from the NHC area. The **Ivy Waspgrabber** *Leopoldius signatus* is a narrow-bodied, yellow and black fly with smudge-marked wings which is usually found on ivy blossom in autumn. The larvae are internal parasites of the Common Wasp and probably also the German Wasp. It gets its name from its habit of waiting near ivy flowers to grab adult wasps as they arrive to nectar before laying eggs between the abdominal segments of the unfortunate prey. The genitalia of the female are specially adapted to lever apart the segment to allow this. The fly then releases the wasp and the parasitic larvae will hatch and consume the prey from the inside. It is generally considered scarce but is likely to be under-recorded because of its late flight season.

Verrall's Wasp Hoverfly *Chrysotoxum verralli* is a mid-sized hoverfly whose bright yellow body and bold black markings make it an effective wasp mimic. This scarce species is found in sheltered sunny places such as wood margins or along hedgerows from midsummer to early autumn. The larvae live in the nests of ants. It is usually found in small numbers and only occasionally visits flowers,

so despite its conspicuous appearance it is easily overlooked.

The **Black Colonel** *Odontomyia tigrina* is a medium-sized entirely black soldierfly with aquatic larvae, found in well-vegetated margins of ponds and ditches. It seems to be a quite good, if erratic, colonist, and large populations can sometimes be found in quite isolated and recently-made ponds in urban areas. It is very local, but has proved rather more frequent in recent years. Adults can most easily be found on the flowers of umbellifers close to water in early summer.

The **Banded General** *Stratiomys potamida* is a large and impressive black and yellow soldierfly with carnivorous aquatic larvae which live amongst moss, decaying vegetation and mud in shallow water and are tolerant of summer drying. It was considered scarce in the past and is still an uncommon species but can now be found quite frequently in many wetland habitats, including garden ponds. Adults are usually seen on flowers, where they are often conspicuous, but spend most of their time amongst marginal and emergent vegetation where they can be difficult to see.

The **Drab Wood-soldierfly** *Solva marginata* is a black and yellow fly which is found around poplar trees. Larvae develop beneath the bark of recently dead trunks and branches. It is an efficient colonist and can find small patches of suitable habitat even on quite isolated trees, so can be looked for on any poplar, even in the most urban of situations, provided there is a small amount of dead wood. Adult flies can be found resting on the bark but are quite inconspicuous and very fast-moving when disturbed.

Spiders

Introduction

In the period 2016–2019, 84 spider species were recorded within the NHC area. Of these, 36 were found only in the Botanic Garden; but as none of these are rare, this is no doubt because the Botanic Garden was surveyed more thoroughly than other sites.

Although the majority of the 84 are common species for the region, we only have a small number of records for most of them. Even the very common **Giant House Spider** *Eratigena atrica* has only two records, and with so few recorders, we do not have a clear picture of diversity or distribution across the area or, with the exception of a few newcomers, of changes from the past. In the following pages I present an overview of some of our common, notable and rare species and the sort of environments in which to look for them.

Common species around the home

Giant House Spiders are the most noticeable species we share our homes with, especially in late summer when males emerge from their hiding places and are seen scurrying across our floors in search of females.

Less noticeable is the **Fleecy Jumping Spider** *Pseudeuophrys lanigera* which is one of the smallest spiders (3–4 mm) to share our homes. First recorded in Britain in 1930, this relative newcomer is now widespread in England and is almost exclusively associated with human habitation.

Daddy Long-legs Spiders *Pholcus phalangioides* are responsible for most of the cobwebs in your home, but they are also effective predators of household pests such as flies and mosquitoes. They throw silk at their victims, and will even hunt other spiders including the much larger Giant House Spiders.

Figure 11.1 (left) Giant House Spider, (right) Fleecy Jumping Spider. (PAR).

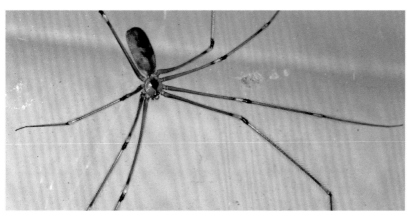

Figure 11.2 Daddy Long-legs Spider. (PAR).

Figure 11.3 (left) Noble False Widow, **(right)** Lace-weaver. (PAR).

We have three species of false widows; they are all common and on occasions may be found in homes. Of the three, it is the appropriately named **Cupboard Spider** *Steatoda grossa* that is most likely to be encountered in the home, with the **Rabbit Hutch Spider** *Steatoda bipunctata* more likely to be found in outbuildings. The third species is the **Noble False Widow** *Steatoda nobilis* which although the only non-native of the three, is probably the most numerous. A night-time torchlight survey of your garden is likely to uncover many individuals that have been hiding away during the day in cracks and crevices in window frames, fence panels and out-buildings.

Another common spider associated with houses is the **Lace-weaver** *Amaurobius similis*. These spiders spin a web of bluish coloured silk around the entrance of holes and crevices in walls and other man-made structures.

Common garden species

The **Garden Spider** *Araneus diadematus* will be familiar to most people and there cannot be a single Cambridge garden that is not home to them. There are also two other orb-web spiders present in many gardens that go largely unnoticed as they are mainly nocturnal. The first of these is the **Missing Sector Orb Spinner** *Zygiella x-notata*; so called because the spiral threads of their unique webs do not extend 360° around the web. The other is the **Toad Spider** or **Walnut Orb-weaver** *Nuctenea umbratica*.

Figure 11.4 (left) Garden Spider, **(right)** Toad Spider. (PAR).

The **Zebra Spider** *Salticus scenicus* is our most common jumping spider. It is sometimes found indoors, but more often seen hunting prey on sunny walls, fences and other vertical surfaces.

Nursery Web Spiders *Pisaura mirabilis* are very common and are often seen on tall vegetation and shrubs. Females can often be seen carrying their egg sac or sitting in the nursery web guarding their young. Males looking for females to mate with can sometimes be seen carrying prey wrapped in blue silk, an offering to reduce the risk of being eaten.

The male approaching the female in our image is not going to have any luck with the female he is approaching; she has already mated and is carrying a large egg sac.

Common meadow species

Two species that are hard to miss are the large and strikingly marked **Four-spot Orb-weaver** *Araneus quadratus* and the equally large **Labyrinth Spider** *Agelena labyrinthica*. The latter's presence is given away by its large conspicuous sheet web with a

Figure 11.5 Male Missing Sector Orb Spinner (left) approaching a female. (PAR).

Figure 11.6 (Left) Zebra Spider, **(right)** Nursery Web Spider. (PAR).

Figure 11.7 (Left) Four-spot Orb-weaver, **(right)** Labyrinth spider. (PAR).

Figure 11.8 (left) *Xysticus* sp., (centre) Common Candy-striped Spider with large meal, (right) *Heliophanus flavipes.* (PAR).

Figure 11.9 (left) Cucumber Spider *Araniella cucurbitina* (PAR), **(right)** *Diaea dorsata* (CKL).

funnel retreat, where the owner spends most of its time hidden from sight. Two species of *Xysticus* crab spiders can be captured in considerable numbers using a sweep net in long grass. *X. cristatus* and *X. ulmi* are difficult to tell apart, although the former prefers wetter habitats and the latter drier ones.

The **Common Candy-striped Spider** *Enoplognatha ovata* is a small orb-web spider that prefers open habitats with low vegetation, but may also be found in larger gardens. *Heliophanus flavipes* can be found on low vegetation and the shrub layer, or on lower branches of trees, but like some other jumping spiders always shows a preference for sunny conditions.

Common species of woodland, hedgerows and damp places

Cucumber Spiders *Araniella* spp. are found along woodland edges, hedgerows and other well wooded areas. There are actually two species of Cucumber Spider, *Araniella cucurbitina* and *A. opisthographa*, which can only be identified precisely through detailed examination.

Diaea dorsata is a very distinctive green crab spider which is found on the leaves of bushes and trees such as oak, box, yew and conifers.

The **Sputnik Spider** *Paidiscura pallens* is a tiny spider (around 1.5 mm), which could be

mistaken for a very young spider rather than an adult. Variable in colour with green and dark forms occurring, they are often overlooked because of their small size, but their strangely shaped, 'sputnik-like' white egg sac is distinctive and unmistakable.

The **Humped Orb-weaver** *Gibbaranea gibbosa* is a distinctive orb-weaver, but due to its very small size is often overlooked, with only one record from the Botanic Garden and a second from a private garden.

Tetragnatha extensa and *T. montana* are long-jawed orb-web spiders that prefer wetland sites. *T. extensa* spins its web in grass or low vegetation

Figure 11.10 (left) Sputnik Spider with distinctive egg sac, (right) Humped Orb-weaver. (PAR).

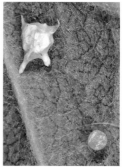

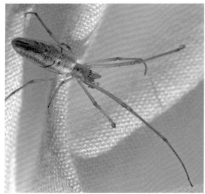

Figure 11.11 (left) *Tetragnatha extensa,* **(right)** *Larinioides cornutus.* (PAR).

close to or over open water, while the very similar *T. montana* can usually be found in bushes and trees slightly further away from open water.

The distinctively patterned ***Larinioides cornutus*** orb-weaving spider can be found on reeds, grasses and other waterside vegetation and in tall herbage and rough damp grassland, although it is nocturnal and stays well hidden during the day.

New arrivals

The **Green Leaf-web Spider** *Nigma walckenaeri* is a small species (5 mm long) that was first recorded in Britain in 1880 and until 1993 was only found in London and the Home Counties. Since that time it has been steadily extending its range northwards and was first recorded in Cambridge in 2014. It is now a common species and one that is likely to be found in many Cambridge gardens and parks. It gets its common name from its habit of spinning a web on the upper side of a leaf, where it will sit waiting for a small invertebrate to fall into its trap. It appears to favour lilac and ivy leaves to construct its webs on.

Segestria florentina spins a tubular web, often in cracks of buildings, with six or more silken lines radiating from it. The spider waits in the entrance, touching the lines with its front legs and emerges to catch any prey that trigger the lines. Notable for its green chelicerae (jaws), it was discovered new to Cambridgeshire in August 2017 at the Devonshire Arms and now appears to be a resident species on the Anglia Ruskin University site.

Ero aphana is a very small spider (3 mm) so easily overlooked. It is a member of the Mimetidae family (pirate spiders) that typically hunt other spiders. A species of lowland heath, it now appears to be expanding its habitat range to include gardens and brownfield sites. Three individuals were found

in a private garden. There are no other records.

First recorded in Britain in 1922, the **Wasp Spider** (*Argiope bruennichi*) was until recently confined to the most southerly counties of England but the last few years has seen a rapid northward expansion of its range. It reached Cambridge in

Figure 11.12 (left) Green Leaf-web Spider, (right) *Ero aphana.* (PAR).

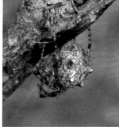

Figure 11.13 Wasp Spider with captured wasp. (PAR).

Figure 11.14 Cricket Bat Spider. (PAR).

2016, and is now becoming well established. It is most likely to be found in fields and meadows where grass and other vegetation is left unmown, although there have been records from gardens as well. It is our largest orb-web spider and spins a large distinctive web low down in tall vegetation. Public sites where this species has been found are

Figure 11.15 Comb-footed Cellar Spider. (PAR).

Logan's Meadow, Trumpington Meadows and East Pit, Cherry Hinton.

At just 4 mm the **Cricket Bat Spider** *Mangora acalypha* is one of our smaller orb web spiders. A species of heathland and open woodland in southern England, the project records from two private Cambridge gardens would appear to be only the second and third records for the county. Since 2019, I have found it in several other sites, including Mill Road Cemetery and in quite significant numbers in my own garden. This would suggest that it is both well established within the NHC area and expanding its range northwards and into more suburban habitats.

Rare Cambridge species

The **Comb-footed Cellar Spider** *Nesticus cellulanus* is a species that is locally common in Britain but is considered rare in Cambridgeshire with only a very small number of county records. These spiders like to hide away in dark damp places such as cellars, sewers and hollow trees so they may not be as rare as currently believed if such sites are concealing a hidden population.

Xysticus erraticus is a crab spider that is rarely recorded in Cambridgeshire, and is only known from Wicken Fen and the Botanic Garden.

The **Spitting Spider** *Scytodes thoracica* is a small (3–6 mm) nocturnal hunter which catches its prey by the unusual technique of squirting a sticky venomous fluid at its victim. Normally to be found in heated buildings, it is an uncommon species with only a handful of county records and recorded at three sites within the NHC area. Two of these were in private homes so it is worth taking a closer look at any small spiders you may come across trying to escape your bath.

Figure 11.16 (left) *Xysticus erraticus*, **(right) Spitting Spider.** (PAR).

Molluscs

Introduction

There are some excellent old records of molluscs in Cambridgeshire, notably by Rev. Leonard Jenyns (1800–93) who lived in Swaffham Bulbeck. He documented 82 species of mollusc in his notebook on the natural history of Cambridgeshire entitled *Fauna Cantabrigiensis*, now a Ray Society Monograph (Preece & Sparks 2012). However, most of Jenyns' records fall outside the NHC area and changes in classification and nomenclature complicate their interpretation. Jenyns' contemporary, Charles Darwin, was sadly more interested in beetles than molluscs! Another source of early records is Brindley's (1904) account of molluscs in Cambridgeshire. Brindley includes many observations from the gardens, ditches and ponds of Cambridge.

In 1929, Hugh Watson, a graduate of Cambridge where the Curatorship of Malacology bears his name, published a list of the 27 species of land molluscs he had found in the Botanic Garden (including the hot houses) and adjoining Benet House. Kerney (1976, 1999) mapped British land and freshwater Mollusca and listed 72 species from the NHC area. Michael Kerney was the National Recorder of non-marine molluscs for the Conchological Society from the 1960s to 1999 and in that capacity, he authenticated many records, but was not necessarily the collector of the Cambridge specimens. In addition, although the date ascribed to most was 1965, this will have covered a wider date range.

In 2011, a bioblitz that included molluscs was carried out in the Cambridge Botanic Garden (Preece & White 2012). Since then, there have been several other studies. Separately, molluscs were recorded in the grounds of Peterhouse between 2017 and 2019.

2011 Cambridge Botanic Garden bioblitz
16   Aquatic snail species
16   Land snail species
11   Slug species
5   Hot-house snail species

The current NBN Atlas produced a list of 382 records of 125 mollusc species from the NHC area. Some of these date back to 1670, others to the early 1900s, but most relate to records made after 1965. These records and those held by CPERC were accessed in order to build up a picture of the modern distribution of species, with changes over time.

Observations and records

Many people are aware of the ubiquitous **Garden Snail** *Cornu aspersum* and perhaps the banded **Brown-lipped Snail** *Cepaea nemoralis* and **White-lipped Snail** *C. hortensis*, but are not very interested in the many smaller species. Most gardeners detest slugs but do not distinguish between them and use some sort of poison to reduce their impact on plants. Systematic surveys of molluscs are rare.

In one small suburban back garden, 1284 adult Garden Snails were captured and removed over a three-month period between June and September 2015, an impressive illustration of how abundant this species can be.

Habitats

Much of the information about land molluscs in Cambridge comes from the Botanic Garden. Other notable habitats are the historic college and university sites, especially riverside areas such as

Figure 11.17 (above) Garden Snail (PAR), **(below)** Chart of numbers of Garden Snails removed from a single garden over 100 days.

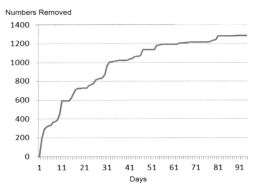

Figure 11.18 (left) White-lipped Snail, (right) Brown-lipped Snail. (PAR).

the Backs. Other habitats include riparian grassland and woodland, farmland, residential areas, and towards the south, the chalk pits of Cherry Hinton and Stapleford. There has been no systematic investigation of these. Hothouse aliens have been recorded from the Botanic Garden on two separate occasions. Aquatic records include species found in the River Cam and also the various lakes, ponds and ditches around the city.

Mollusc species
In total, 126 species have been recorded from the NHC area. Since 2000, 14 new species have been added, the latest in 2020 (Table 11.1). Nine disappeared before 1965 (Table 11.2) and a further 29 have not been seen since 1965 (Table 11.3).

Land species
Of the 73 species of mollusc identified in the Botanic Garden (20 aquatic snails, 8 hothouse alien snails, 31

Table 11.1 New slugs and snails recorded since 2000.

Common Name	Species	Comment
Balkan Threeband Slug	*Ambigolimax nyctelius*	
Greenhouse Slug	*Ambigolimax valentianus*	
Toothless Chrysalis Snail	*Columella edentula*	only record is Peterhouse
Tramp Slug	*Deroceras invadens*	
Wautier's Limpet	*Ferrissia californica*	
Girdled Snail	*Hygromia cinctella*	
Carthusian Snail	*Monacha cartusiana*	found 2020
Glossy Glass Snail	*Oxychilus navarricus*	only record is Peterhouse
Bladder Snail	*Physella acuta*	
Tadpole Physa	*Physella gyrina*	
Globular Pea Mussel	*Pisidium hibernicum*	
Humpbacked Pea Mussel	*Pisidium supinum*	
Fine-lined Pea Mussel	*Pisidium tenuilineatum*	
Rock Snail	*Pyramidula umbilicata*	

land snails and 14 slugs) almost all of the terrestrial species recorded in 1929 were still present, with the exception of the **Smooth Jet Slug** *Milax gagates* (last found 1961), the **False-keeled Slug** *Arion circumscriptus* (last found 1929) and the **Two-toothed Door Snail** *Clausilia bidentata*.

The 2011 bioblitz was carried out over one weekend and may well have missed several common species. The Peterhouse Deer Park, half a mile away, has been undisturbed by building for over 800 years and between 2015 and 2019, produced 3 snail species not found elsewhere since 1965: **Toothless Chrysalis Snail** *Columella edentula*, **Glossy Glass Snail** *Oxychilus navarricus helveticus* and **Smooth Grass Snail** *Vallonia pulchella*. Shells of *Testacella haliotidea* which were thought to be recent (though no live specimens) were found in the Botanic Garden in 2011 (Richard Preece, pers. comm.). *Testacella haliotidea* is a shelled slug first recorded here in 1904, subsequently in 1920 and in Chaucer Road in 1960 (Naggs *et al.* 2008). These carnivorous Mesozoic relicts are rare and for unknown reasons are generally declining in Britain. During the day the animals are hidden in the soil, perhaps some

Figure 11.19 *Testacella haliotidea.* (MF).

Table 11.2 Mollusc species not recorded since 1962. Key to habitat types: A aquatic, W wetland, C calcareous grassland and woodland.

Common name	Species	Years recorded	Hab type	Comment
Iridescent Pea Mussel	*Pisidium pulchellum*	1922	A	Widespread
Shining Ram's-horn (Red data species)	*Segmentina nitida*		A	*Carex-Juncus-Eleocharis-Oenanthe* community.
Thames Door Snail	*Balea biplicata*	1909, 1920, 1949	W	Mainly along the Thames
Smooth Jet Slug	*Milax gagates*		W	
Desmoulin's Whorl Snail	*Vertigo moulinsiana*		W	Calcareous wetlands
Tree Snail	*Balea perversa*	1670, 1909	C	Largely absent from cities, many colonies in lowland England have disappeared
Lapidary Snail	*Helicigona lapicida*		C	Shady rocks and walls
Round-mouthed Snail	*Pomatias elegans*	1962	C	Dry conditions, loose limestone/ chalk
Cylindrical Whorl Snail	*Truncatellina cylindrica*		C	Dry conditions, stone walls; now very rare in Britain

Table 11.3 Mollusc Species last recorded in 1965/6. Key to habitat types: A aquatic, W wetland, C calcareous grassland and woodland, Wid widespread in terrestrial habitats.

Common name	Species	Hab type	Comment
White-lipped Ramshorn	*Anisus leucostoma*	A	Widespread around freshwater
Nautilus Ramshorn	*Gyraulus crista*	A	On water plants in clear still freshwater
Smooth Ramshorn	*Gyraulus laevis*	A	On water plants in clear still freshwater
Lake Orb Mussel	*Musculium lacustre*	A	Freshwater mussel, widespread in England
Common Bladder Snail	*Physa fontinalis*	A	Freshwater
Horny Orb Mussel	*Sphaerium corneum*	A	Freshwater lakes and rivers of moderate hardness
Marsh Pond Snail	*Stagnicola fuscus*	A	Flooded margins of medium to large water-bodies
Freshwater Nerite	*Theodoxus fluviatilis*	A	Widespread south Britain in rivers and lakes on stones
Flat Valve Snail	*Valvata cristata*	A	Widespread south Britain stagnant and slow-moving water
Valve Snail	*Valvata piscinalis*	A	Clear-water habitats, nearshore zones
Lister's River Snail	*Viviparus contectus*	A	Slow flowing rivers and canals, unpolluted with high O_2, hard water, many water weeds
Silky Snail	*Ashfordia granulata*	W	Widespread but uncommon, damp shady places
Marsh Slug	*Deroceras laeve*	W	Common and widespread, also found in greenhouses
Pfeiffer's Amber Snail	*Oxyloma elegans*	W	Widespread, usually near to water
Hairy Snail	*Trochulus sericeus*	W	Common south Britain, woodland and damp places
Marsh Whorl Snail	*Vertigo antivertigo*	W	Widespread but patchy, in wet, unimproved pasture, marshes and tall fen
Shiny Glass Snail	*Zonitoides nitidus*	W	Widespread in any damp conditions
Two-toothed Door Snail	*Clausilia bidentata*	C	Nocturnal, common, widespread, woods and hedges
Plaited Door Snail	*Cochlodina laminata*	C	Relatively common and widespread south Britain. Old, established woodlands, tree trunks after rain
Heath Snail	*Helicella itala*	C	Widespread but increasingly uncommon inland, dry calcareous grassland
Roman Snail	*Helix pomatia*	C	Loose chalk/limestone
Rayed Glass Snail	*Nesovitrea hammonis*	C	Widespread, wide range of habitats, dry to humid conditions, woods especially beech
Dwarf Snail	*Punctum pygmaeum*	C	Not in heavily disturbed habitats, more abundant on calcareous substrate, litter layers of forests
Moss Chrysalis Snail	*Pupilla muscorum*	C	Dry meadows and sand dunes, in open and sunny habitats, old calcareous grasslands
Long-toothed Herald Snail	*Carychium tridentatum*	Wid	Common, widespread, habitat varied
Short-toothed Herald Snail	*Carychium minimum*	Wid	Common, widespread, habitat varied
Least Slippery Snail	*Cochlicopa lubricella*	Wid	Common, widespread, meadows on dry slopes
Sowerby's Keeled Slug	*Tandonia sowerbyi*	Wid	Found in most lowland habitats

10–30 cm below the surface, but come to the surface in the evening. They feed mainly on earthworms.

Aquatic species

The 2011 Botanic Garden survey recorded 16 species of aquatic molluscs, including two that were new to the Garden: the introduced **Wautier's Limpet** *Ferrissia californica* and the native **Lake Limpet** *Acroloxus lacustris*. (The Lake Limpet had been found elsewhere in Cambridge in 1965.) The introduced **Bladder Snail** *Physella acuta*, another aquatic mollusc first recorded here in 1904, was still present. The **Swan Mussel** *Anodonta cygnea* has also been found there. In the Cam, at the boat houses, are **Duck Mussel** *Anodonta anatina* and **Painter's Mussel** *Unio pictorum*.

There remains the threat from invasive alien species such as the **Asian Clam** *Corbicula fluminea*, recorded from the River Ouse, and **Zebra Mussel** *Dreissena polymorpha*. While these have not yet been reported from Cambridge, there is one record of Zebra Mussel from the Cam, downstream and just outside the northern border of our area. Unfortunately, in 2018, as part of a Cambridge City Public Art project celebrating the River Cam, river water was carried from Baits Bite Lock, where Zebra Mussel had been found, up to Byron's Pool above the city and released there – an ecologically irresponsible action.

Hothouse species

As in 1929, five exotic hothouse species of snail were found in the Botanic Garden. However, only two of the 2011 species were the same as those found in 1929, suggesting that, while introductions continue to occur, they do not necessarily persist. In 2011, they included *Gulella io*, a tiny Liberian snail found in hothouse conditions in only nine British locations.

Figure 11.20 *Gulella io.* (FWS).

Appearances since 1965

For a full list see Table 11.1.

Slugs

One of the slugs found in the bioblitz, the **Green Cellar Slug** *Limacus maculatus*, is a recent introduction to the county and seems to be displacing the closely related **Yellow Cellar Slug** *L. flavus*, which has declined or disappeared from

Figure 11.21 (above) Green Cellar Slug, (below) Greenhouse Slug. (PAR).

most of its former sites in the last 20–30 years, while the Green Cellar Slug has colonised them. The Green Cellar Slug seems to do particularly well in plastic compost bins, now a very common feature of gardens. Intriguingly, in the last 10 years the Green Cellar Slug has been found in woodlands some distance from houses, a habitat that the Yellow Cellar Slug never colonised, but which the Green Cellar Slug occupied in Ireland by the 1970s (Brian Eversham, pers. comm.).

Another species which turned up in 2018 Botanic Garden bioblitz was the **Greenhouse Slug** *Ambigolimax valentianus*, classed as a hothouse alien till the 1970s, then noted as occurring in gardens in the 1980s and 1990s, until in the last decade it has started occurring in natural woodland and other habitats. The closely related **Balkan Threeband Slug** *A. nyctelius* has rapidly followed suit and both species are predicted to be found together in woodlands before long (Brian Eversham, pers. comm.)

The number of *Arion* slug species has increased due to recent reclassification of *A. ater, A. hortensis, A. circumscriptus* and other species. It is impossible to determine which of these might be newcomers.

Land snails

A warming climate has produced several snail newcomers. The **Girdled Snail** *Hygromia cinctella*, a Mediterranean species first found in Devon in 1950, has spread widely in southern Britain and is now frequent in Cambridge.

The **Rock Snail** *Pyramidula umbilicata*, previously recorded from Cambridgeshire in 1880, is likely to have been reintroduced to the Botanic Garden rock garden in the 1950s with Carboniferous limestone from Westmorland. The rare **Carthusian Snail** *Monacha cartusiana* was found in 2020, on chalk grassland by Worts' Causeway. Much rarer than the related **Kentish Snail** *M. cantiana*, it is thought to have been introduced by Neolithic farmers from Europe and is largely confined to the south-east of England.

Decline of native species

The aquatic and wetland species **Thames Door Snail** *Balea biplicata*, **Smooth Jet Slug** *Milax gagates*, **Iridescent Pea Mussel** *Pisidium pulchellum*, **Shining Ram's-horn** *Segmentina nitida* and **Desmoulin's Whorl Snail** *Vertigo moulinsiana* were all last recorded before 1965 (Table 11.2) and a further 12 aquatic and 7 land molluscs dependent on damp conditions have not been seen since 1965 (Table 11.3). Some extinctions are part of a massive national decline, such as Shining Ram's-horn (now confined to a small handful of clean-water fen pools and ditches).

Calcareous grassland and woodland species which have not been recorded in Cambridge since 1965 include **Tree Snail** *Balea perversa*, **Plaited Door Snail** *Cochlodina laminata*, **Heath Snail** *Helicella itala*, **Lapidary Snail** *Helicigona lapicida*, **Round-mouthed Snail** *Pomatias elegans*, **Dwarf Snail** *Punctum pygmaeum* and **Moss Chrysalis**

Figure 11.22 Carthusian Snail. (PAR).

Figure 11.23 Roman Snails at Stapleford Pit 2019. (PAR).

Snail *Pupilla muscorum*. However, this may be artefactual, due to under-recording. (See Table 11.3 for full list.)

The **Roman Snail** *Helix pomatia*, although not a native, was introduced to Britain long ago. It needs loose chalky soil and Cambridge is near the northern edge of its main British distribution. In 1826 it was found by Henslow in Cherry Hinton chalk pit, from where it has now vanished. It was later introduced to Stapleford chalk pit, just outside the NHC area. Ernie Pollard (1973) wrote about the introduction: 'Three pits, managed by the Cambridgeshire Trust, seemed particularly suitable, those at Stapleford, Ickleton and Heydon, and the Trust agreed that these could be used. The snails were taken from a road verge site in Hertfordshire and fifteen were put in each pit in June 1972. Although the summer has been very dry and unsuitable for breeding, eggs and young snails have been recorded at all three pits. This is still a long way from the successful establishment of breeding populations but it is a promising start.' It was indeed successful at Stapleford, as in the summer of 2019 more than 100 were recorded.

Conclusion

Climate change seems to be a factor in species gain, warmer winters allowing species to survive which could not do so previously. Loss of habitat, pollution and drainage probably account for the loss of some species, especially those associated with wetland. Under-recording means that some species that are still present have been missed. Although most of the species in Table 11.2 have gone for ever, many of those in Table 11.3 may still be waiting to be discovered.

12. Fish, amphibians and reptiles

Fish

Introduction

Anglers fishing in the Cam are a familiar sight to all Cambridge residents, but few local naturalists know much about fish. However, the Environment Agency Great Ouse and Fenland Fisheries team monitors Cambridge fish stocks closely. As a result, we have more quantitative information about fish numbers than about most other taxa. This account is based largely on detailed reports for the Lower River Cam made by the Environment Agency (2016, 2019). The EA surveyed five sites on the River Cam, of which two, Midsummer Common and Fen Ditton, are in the NHC area. The fish are caught by seine netting,

encircling the fish in a 100-metre-long net with a lead line at the bottom and floats at the top.

There are 23 wild fish species in our area (Table 12.1), of which 13 belong to the Carp family *Cyprinidae* and 2 to the Perch family *Percidae*. These constitute most of the fishes that are caught by anglers. There are three other large fishes, the **Eel**, the **Pike** and the **Brown Trout**. The other five are small, as indeed are the **Gudgeon**, **Bitterling** and **Minnow** which are members of the Carp family. Several other fish species, notably **Goldfish** *Carassius auratus*, are kept in ornamental ponds. The Cherry Hinton lakes are stocked with carp.

Table 12.1 Wild fish in Cambridge. Values for density (fish > 10 cm, individuals per 100 m²) and standing crop (all fish, grams per 100 m²) are means for Midsummer Common and Fen Ditton averaged for years 2016 and 2019. Other columns show presence in the Cam (excluding the part above Byron's Pool), the Rush on Sheep's Green, the Byron's Pool fish pass and Hobson's Conduit.

English name	Scientific name	Dens	St crop	Cam	Rush	Byr	Hob
Carp family *Leuciscinae*							
Silver bream	*Blicca bjoerkna*	+	1		x		
Common bream	*Abramis brama*	1.4	140	x			
Chub	*Squalius cephalus*	0.3	26	x	x	x	
Dace	*Leuciscus leuciscus*	1.2	33	x	x	x	
Roach	*Rutilus rutilus*	29.9	3210	x	x	x	
Rudd	*Scardinius erythrophthalmus*			x			
Bleak	*Alburnus alburnus*	5.6	231	x			
Carp family (other)							
Crucian Carp	*Carassius carassius*						
Common Carp	*Cyprinus carpio*			x			
Tench	*Tinca tinca*			x			
Perch family							
Perch	*Perca fluviatilis*	0.7	190	x	x	x	
Ruffe	*Gymnocephalus cernuus*	+	2	x			
Other large fish							
Pike	*Esox lucius*	0.1	192	x	x		x
Brown trout	*Salmo trutta*			x	x	x	
European eel	*Anguilla anguilla*			x	x		
Small fish							
Gudgeon	*Gobio gobio*	0.9	26	x	x	x	
Bitterling	*Rhodeus amarus*	4.7	6	x			
Minnow	*Phoxinus phoxinus*			x	x	x	x
Spined loach	*Cobitis taenia*			x	x	x	
Stone loach	*Barbatula barbatula*				x	x	x
10-spined stickleback	*Pungitius pungitius*			x	x		x
3-spined stickleback	*Gasterosteus aculeatus*			x	x	x	x
Bullhead	*Cottus gobio*	+	+	x	x	x	x

Figure 12.1 Quality roach from the River Cam at Midsummer Common. (EA).

Figure 12.2 Two large Chub in the ditch around Jesus College. (DJM).

Carp family (subfamily Leuciscinae)

The **Roach** is by far the most abundant fish in the Cam. The numbers shown in Table 12.1 are perhaps inflated by shoaling, but the dominance of Roach is not in doubt. The next most abundant were **Bleak** and **Common Bream**. The high abundance of Bleak may be a chance result of the 2019 survey at Midsummer Common; Bleak were not nearly as plentiful elsewhere in the river. **Chub** are less frequent in the river but were observed in April 2019 at a time when fish are migrating into small streams to spawn. **Rudd** have not been caught in the Cam by seine netting, but are present in Barnwell Pit. Several species in subfamily *Leuciscinae* form hybrids, which are present in our area but not considered further.

Carp family (other than Leuciscinae, excluding small fish)

Tench and **Common Carp** are known from the Cam. **Crucian Carp** is not reported from the Cam but, according to the Cambridge Fish Preservation and Angling Society, Barnwell Pit holds the local record for this species, a 1.3 kg fish caught in 2006.

Perch family

Perch and **Ruffe** have been caught in the Cam by seine netting, with Perch having a comparable standing crop to Bleak, Common Bream and Pike. Perch are regularly caught by Cambridge anglers. **Zander** *Sander lucioperca* are present in the river below Baits Bite Lock, but there are no reports from the NHC survey area.

Other large fish

Pike are small in numbers but large in standing crop (biomass), because they are highly efficient cannibals. Small Pike do not stand much of a chance of surviving, but if they do they become one of the kings of the river. The largest one caught by seine net at Fen Ditton was 69 cm long. **Brown Trout** are present in the main river and have been observed in the Byron's Pool fish pass. Their main Cambridge habitat is the Rush, where they can grow to a good size. Electro-fishing in 2021 revealed trout fry in Vicar's Brook near the Botanic Garden. The **European Eel** is unique among Cambridge fish because it breeds in the sea. It is now uncommon, having suffered a major decline since the 1950s. It is hoped that this decline can be reversed. Eel ladders have been installed at the Baits Bite and Jesus Green locks. The Rush also serves as an eel pass.

Figure 12.3 A large Brown Trout from the Rush, September 2019. (MFPF).

Small fish

Gudgeon, **Bitterling** and a single **Bullhead** were the only small species caught by seine netting. The relatively high standing crop of Gudgeon at Fen Ditton was a surprise to the EA survey team, who expected their seine netting technique to be inefficient at capturing a small bottom dwelling species. However, this was not the case. Gudgeon are also abundant in the Rush where they and Dace were the most plentiful species when the EA electro-fished it in 2017. The Bitterling is a remarkable small member of the Carp family. It is an introduced species, which was first observed in the Great Ouse catchment near Waterbeach in 1984. Since then it has spread widely in the catchment, attaining moderately high densities in Cambridge. Nevertheless, it remains very rare in much of Britain. Its life cycle depends on a good supply of river mussels, into which it lays its eggs. Inside the shell, they are sheltered from predation but do not harm the mussel. After hatching, the larvae swim off.

The third small member of the Carp family is the familiar **Minnow**. This is ubiquitous in the smaller streams in Cambridge, and must sometimes enter the Cam itself as it has been observed in the Byron's Pool fish pass. The familiar **3–spined Stickleback** and much rarer **10-spined Stickleback** occur in the same streams, along with the bottom-dwelling **Stone Loach** and **Spined Loach**. The Spined Loach is Cambridge's rarest native fish, confined to central and eastern England. Finally, there is the **Bullhead**, also frequent in small streams, but once caught in the main river at Fen Ditton.

An angler's perspective

Alan Stebbings is a local angler who often fishes in the lower river at the back of Darwin College. He has caught Roach and Perch up to a pound in

Figure 12.4 Three-spined Stickleback, a common species in Cambridge streams. (PAR).

weight, Chub to 2–3 lbs and Gudgeon, all in good numbers. The Chub can often be seen swimming in the Mill Pond. There are also Bream and Carp present and occasional Eels. In the winter there are good numbers of Pike between 5 and 8 lbs. Before its closure for construction of a cycleway tunnel under Newmarket Road he regularly fished Barnwell Pit. It contains large numbers of small Roach, Bream and Perch plus Tench to about 5 lbs, Pike over 10 lbs (a 20 lb Pike is rumoured) and Carp up to 20 lbs. There is talk of a big Catfish but it definitely falls into the 'one-that-got-away' category.

Change in Cambridge's fish population

Some anglers claim that fish numbers have been reduced by Cormorants and Otters and by illegal fishing by Eastern Europeans. By contrast, the EA reports show a generally stable fish population since 2000. The correct explanation of the anglers' difficulties seems to be that fish are now more difficult to catch because the water is clearer and cleaner than in the past. This has also resulted in an increasing trout population.

In the second half of the 20th century the Cam was intermittently polluted by effluent from an agrochemicals factory at Hauxton. This closed in 2004, and in 2010 the site was remediated for housing development. There have also been occasional fish kills as a result of sewage being pumped into the river. The most recent such event was in 2013, when a failure at the Milton sewage treatment works raised ammonia to toxic levels in the river, killing hundreds of fish. This incident had no long-term effect.

Fish passes

Weirs on the Cam prevent the upstream passage of fish. There are now two fish passes in Cambridge. The first, at Byron's Pool LNR, was completed in 2011. It is a 'nature-like' channel, which mimics a natural side-channel and adds habitat for juvenile fish. It is 110 m long and 2 m wide, with a series of pools providing areas of rest for fish on the way up. The Rush, a former course of the River Cam, flows through Sheep's Green and Coe Fen to the Newnham Mill Pond. It had silted up and did not provide an effective passage for fish. Stimulated by the Cam Valley Forum, Cambridge City Council with additional funding from the EA, installed a fish pass in 2017. The original sluice gate was replaced by a solar-powered automated gate which increased the year-round flow. The upper part of the channel

Figure 12.5 Counting and measuring fish in the Rush, September 2017. (OW).

was raised by the addition of a large amount of gravel to produce artificial pools connected by riffles. In 2016 and 2019, the EA monitored the fish present in the Rush by electro-fishing. The fish are listed in Table 12.1.

In addition to the two fish passes, there are now eel ladders at Baits Bite lock and Jesus Green lock.

Amphibians and reptiles
Introduction
The city of Cambridge, with its mosaic of habitats such as green spaces, urban centres and plentiful waterways, provides a number of opportunities for both reptiles and amphibians (collectively known as *herpetofauna*) alike. With a large network of

garden ponds, amphibians can be found breeding right across the city, even in areas where you would not expect to find them. Of the 13 native amphibian and reptile species found in Britain, six of them are widespread across Cambridge, with a further two having restricted ranges. Additionally, a small number of introduced species can also be found within Cambridge, although like most populations of introduced reptiles and amphibians in Britain, their distribution is severely limited (Allain *et al.* 2017).

Amphibians
Four species are widespread: the Common Frog, the Common Toad, the Great Crested Newt and the Smooth Newt. The Palmate Newt is more restricted while the Midwife Toad is an introduced species.

The **Common Frog** *Rana temporaria* is by far the most easily distinguished species and has the most widespread distribution of any amphibian in Cambridge (Figure 12.6). Between 2010 and 2019, 165 records of Common Frogs or their spawn were made on the internet portals Record Pool and CPERC. Frogs were often found in garden ponds but also in Local Nature Reserves across the city.

The **Common Toad** *Bufo bufo* is the largest species of toad found in Britain and has a limited distribution in Cambridge (Figure 12.6), restricted mainly to larger water bodies that are unsuitable for other amphibian species. There were 78 records between 2010 and 2019, less than half of those of Common Frogs. Both the spawn and tadpoles

Figure 12.6 Distribution of (left) Common Frog, (right) Common Toad in Cambridge.

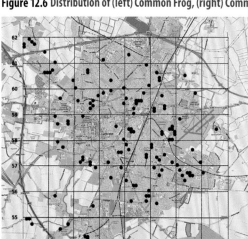

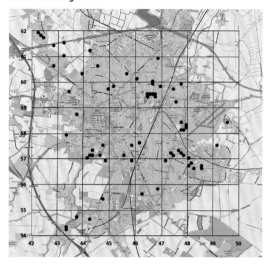

of Common Toads are toxic and so they are able to persist in ponds and lakes that contain fish, whereas Cambridge's other amphibians cannot. There are a couple of toad crossings in Cambridge, the most active being along Stanley Road, where volunteers help move toads out of harm's way and safely escort them to their breeding pond. Other such areas that are deemed important for toads can easily be recognised by the presence of toad warning road signs (Figure 12.7).

The **Great Crested Newt** *Triturus cristatus* is the largest of the three native newt species in Britain and they are present in the city, with most records from north of the River Cam (Figure 12.9). There were only 30 records of Great Crested Newts between 2010 and 2019, but given their patchy distribution there may be other populations that are yet to be recorded. They are fully protected by law (both under the Habitats Directive and the Wildlife & Countryside Act) and this often brings them into conflict with developers, who may have to implement costly mitigation if newts are found when the site's Environmental Impact Assessment is carried out. Like most amphibians, they have suffered huge declines since the 1950s due to a loss of habitat as a result of an expanding human population and agricultural intensification. This is one of the reasons why they are strictly protected.

Figure 12.7 Toad crossing sign (MS).

The **Smooth Newt** *Lissotriton vulgaris* is a small and widespread species that is often mistaken for the larger Great Crested Newt as the male also possesses a crest. Smooth Newts are fairly widespread in Cambridge, with most records coming from the northern half of our area (Figure 12.9). Smooth Newts are often present in residential gardens and may be found when turning over paving slabs, with the newts sheltering underneath. It is a common

The Midwife Toad *Alytes obstetricans*

The **Midwife Toad** *Alytes obstetricans* is a non-native species of toad first introduced to Britain around 1903. Current evidence suggests that the Cambridge population has persisted since at least 2006. The Cambridge population has been the subject of research since 2015, including establishing how large the extent of occurrence is, how large the population is and whether the toads are infected with any infectious diseases (thereby posing a risk to our native species). So far, the evidence suggests that the Cambridge population is free from the pathogenic chytrid fungi that have been linked to dramatic declines in amphibians globally (Allain & Goodman 2017b; Allain & Goodman 2018a). They are also

Figure 12.8 Male Midwife Toad (SJRA).

currently restricted to a small number of private gardens in the Mill Road area with no signs of dispersal.

Midwife Toads are quite small in size, only growing to about 5.5 cm in length. Populations are usually identified by the males' call in late spring, which is often compared to an electronic beeping sound. They get their name from the fact that males carry strings of eggs on their hind legs, until they are ready to hatch (Figure 12.8). Unlike our native amphibians, Midwife Toads live wholly terrestrially and even breed on land. They only spend time in a pond as a tadpole. They also breed at a different time of year to our native amphibians, sometimes having multiple clutches of eggs per year. Due to this, there can be tadpoles of varying ages in the breeding ponds Midwife Toads choose to use. If a tadpole is unable to grow large enough to metamorphose come the autumn, it may overwinter and grow to a large size, giving it an advantage when it eventually metamorphoses in the following spring.

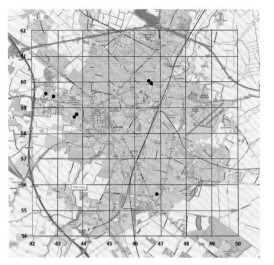 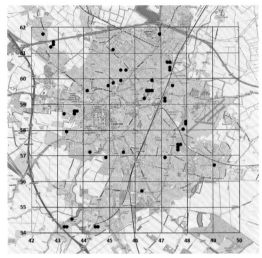

Figure 12.9 Distribution of (left) Great Crested Newt, (right) Smooth Newt in Cambridge.

misconception that amphibians spend all of their life in water. The larvae do but adults only return to water to breed. For the rest of the year they live terrestrially.

The **Palmate Newt** *Lissotriton helveticus* looks superficially like the Smooth Newt but they are rarely found in East Anglia as they prefer more acidic waters. So far in Cambridge, Palmate Newts have only been found living in ponds alongside the introduced Common Midwife Toad (Allain & Goodman, 2018c). It is not certain whether the newts themselves have been introduced like the toads or if they are remnants of a relic population.

Reptiles

The Grass Snake and the Common Lizard are both widespread species, while the Slow Worm is restricted and the Red-eared Slider is an introduced terrapin.

The **Grass Snake** *Natrix helvetica* is the largest native snake species found in Britain, usually growing to 1.2 m in length although individuals may be larger, with females longer than males (Arnold & Ovenden 2002). If a snake is seen swimming in a lake, pond, or other body of water is it almost certainly a Grass Snake. They are often seen swimming in the River Cam or along Hobson's Conduit.

Between 2010 and 2019, there were 30 records of Grass Snakes in Cambridge, mainly from central areas (Figure 12.10). Although in these areas there are also a large number of amphibians, their distribution may be a reflection of egg incubation sites. Despite their widespread distribution across

Britain, there is a lack of data on the population trends in Grass Snakes. As their main prey source, amphibians, have declined in recent times it is likely that Grass Snakes have as well unless they have been able to adapt their diet. The scientific name of the Grass Snakes found in Britain used to be *Natrix natrix helvetica* but this subspecies has been reclassified as a full species *Natrix helvetica*, sometimes called the Barred Grass Snake to distinguish it from the continental *Natrix natrix,* which is not naturally found in Britain.

The **Common Lizard** *Zootoca vivipara* is the most widespread of the three lizard species in Britain. Common Lizards can mainly be found in the north of Cambridge (Figure 12.10), where they occur in isolated populations; which is reflected by the fact there were only nine records between 2010 and 2019. Common Lizards used to be quite common across Britain but in recent times they have declined due to habitat loss and fragmentation. As with the Grass Snake, there is no significant data on population trends over time across the country. We know that populations are declining or becoming extinct, but the rate at which this is happening is not known. Conservation efforts should be targeted towards Common Lizards so that they are not lost from the Cambridge landscape forever.

The **Slow Worm** *Anguis fragilis* is a species of burrowing legless lizard. Slow Worms occur in a number of habitats, usually spending their time in dense vegetation or underground and tending to disappear during periods of hot weather. This makes them very difficult to monitor and survey,

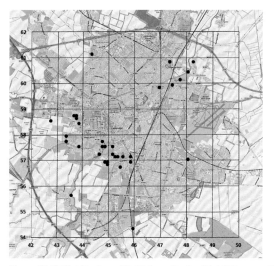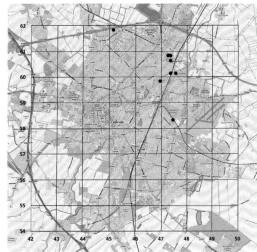

Figure 12.10 Distribution of (left) Grass Snake, (right) Common Lizard in Cambridge.

and so their conservation status nationwide is not fully understood. There is only a single record of Slow Worms in Cambridge between 2010 to 2019 and this comes from Chesterton. It is not certain if the record represents an introduced population but in general Slow Worms are very rare throughout the rest of Cambridgeshire, due to unsuitable habitat acting as a barrier to dispersal from populations in the surrounding counties. The nearest known population of Slow Worms to Cambridge is at Wandlebury Country Park, which was introduced following a mitigation-led translocation from a site in Essex (Allain *et al.* 2019).

There are no native species of terrapins in Britain, making those that are seen basking around the edges of ponds or lakes very conspicuous. The **Red-eared Slider** *Trachemys scripta elegans* is one of the terrapin species that was imported into Europe in the latter half of the 20th century, being a particularly popular pet in the 1990s. Red-eared Sliders are voracious eaters that grow quickly; which may explain why so many have been released or dumped, perhaps because their owners could no longer care for them. They are unable to breed in Britain as it is too cold but they are relatively long-lived, and so may survive in the wild for several decades after release. The only records in Cambridge of Red-eared Sliders are within the ponds at the Science Park.

Sites

Barnwell East LNR is the perfect place to observe amphibians breeding in the spring, being home to Smooth Newts, Common Frogs and Common

Toads. There is a medium-sized pond near the entrance on Barnwell Road.

Bramblefields LNR provides both a haven for people and wildlife. Two ponds have been dug, which are home to Smooth Newts and Common Frogs. Bramblefields has also been managed for a small population of Common Lizards, though patience is needed to observe them due to their skittish nature.

Byron's Pool LNR is situated right next to the River Cam, with four small ponds at the northern end of the reserve that are home to Common Frogs and Smooth Newts. With such a high number of amphibians present, Grass Snakes may also be seen swimming along the Cam whilst on the hunt.

Logan's Meadow LNR on the northern bank of the River Cam in Chesterton was formerly a grazing marsh, but it is now managed for wildlife. Common Frogs and Smooth Newts have been found breeding at the reserve, particular in the pond in the centre. The areas of surrounding scrub provide the perfect habitat for juvenile amphibians to mature before returning to the pond to breed once they reach adulthood.

Paradise LNR is on the west bank of the River Cam, south of Lammas Land with a central lake and marshy area and wet woodland dominated by willows. Here amphibians such as the Common Frog have been found to be breeding, and predatory Grass Snakes can be seen basking or hunting.

Sheep's Green and Coe Fen LNRs are two areas of grassland providing a mosaic of habitats in close proximity to the River Cam. They are seasonally flooded in wet years. This provides potential breeding habitat for amphibians and therefore food for their predators. Grass Snakes may be seen basking in the grassy tussocks that can be found throughout Sheep's Green and Coe Fen.

Stourbridge Common LNR is an extensive riverside floodplain. The grassland at the reserve is seasonally wet and several scrapes have been created to provide winter foraging for birds as well as breeding habitat for amphibians such as Common Frogs, Common Toads and Smooth Newts. Winter rainfall is sometimes not sufficient for these scrapes to allow amphibians to breed, so a new pond has been created on the southern margin of the site which should provide extra breeding habitat. The grassland is managed by grazing cattle in the summer months, with tussocks providing habitat for Common Lizards.

Conservation

Partly due to their ectothermic nature, female amphibians and reptiles tend not to breed every year as the production of eggs or young is a huge and costly metabolic investment. Males however will return to breed every year as sperm is relatively less expensive to produce. This helps us to understand the unequal sex ratios in some of Cambridge's herpetofauna such as Common Toads. This can also explain why at some sites there have been huge fluctuations in the amount of frogspawn present each spring, with females tending to breed in cyclical episodes.

Cambridge's amphibians and reptiles face a number of threats. The single biggest one is habitat loss and modification. Due to the high level of urbanisation, road mortality is a big threat to amphibians, especially when they migrate towards their breeding ponds in the spring. Thankfully a number of vulnerable populations have been identified and mitigation measures are in place, such as the appropriate road signs to warn motorists that amphibians may be on the move, the use of volunteer patrols to help reduce road mortality, and the implementation of ladders in gulley pots so that any wildlife that falls into them can escape. Roads are not the only threat to Cambridge's herpetofauna as there are a large number of cyclists, so cycle paths may also lead to mortalities in amphibians (Allain & Smith 2016). Research conducted in 2016 showed that Common Toads declined in Britain by 68% over the period of three decades, which make these conservation efforts even more vital (Petrovan & Schmidt 2016).

Amphibians are also threatened globally by the presence of diseases such as the amphibian chytrid fungus and *Ranavirus*. With the limited opportunistic and targeted sampling, no diseases of concern have been detected in Cambridge's herpetofauna.

13. Birds

Introduction

Changes in bird life in our NHC area over the last 20–30 years reflect changes nationally and observations during our project reflect these changes. The bird story is mixed; there are winners and losers. The specialist species are in decline but the generalist species are doing well as they can adapt to a human-dominated landscape. The main losers are specialist woodland and farmland species which fits a national pattern.

Hawfinches once bred in the Botanic Garden and along the Backs but are now long gone. The loss of **Spotted Flycatchers** and **Lesser Spotted Woodpeckers** may be due to the loss of elms and mature orchards, predation by Grey Squirrels and Great Spotted Woodpeckers and/or an asynchrony between available food supply and a warming climate (phenology). **Lesser Redpolls**, typically a finch of cool northern pine forests, no longer breed; the last confirmed breeding in the city was in 2002. Nationally, numbers of this finch have receded north and west, probably because warmer summers have disrupted its insect food supply for chicks.

Our **Rook** survey has shown that numbers have dropped in the city by 90% since the 1960s. Rooks are birds of open farmland and pasture and their decline mirrors the decline in many bird species in the farmed countryside. A major shift in farming from spring crops to winter crops, from the late 1970s, ended the availability of over-winter weedy stubbles as a source of food. Our local rookeries are now on the northern and eastern edges of our NHC area adjacent to neighbouring farmland. Rookeries along the 'Backs' and in college gardens have gone.

There are winners! Other species of corvids are doing well, probably due to less persecution and changing land-use. Over 80 **Carrion Crows** can be seen on Parker's Piece clearing dropped food and food take-aways, especially on Sunday and Monday mornings. **Magpies** and **Jays** are now frequent garden visitors. **Ravens** are expanding eastwards. They have been seen over our NHC area and now breed in west Cambridgeshire.

Grey Wagtails have become a common wagtail across the city, not just near waterside habitats. **Woodpigeons** now breed throughout the city (perhaps the countryside is too full of them!). **Blackcaps** are now frequent garden visitors in winter. The increase in non-breeding **Little Egrets** may be influenced by the creation of new wetland habitats outside the city at Ouse Fen at Needingworth, the expansion of Wicken Fen, the Ouse Washes and within the NHC area at Hobson's Park, Trumpington Meadows, Logan's Meadow and Eddington.

Protective legislation, with the ban on toxic seed dressing in agriculture and the ban on egg collecting, which was consolidated into the Wildlife and Countryside Act (1981), has been followed by spectacular increases in breeding birds of prey within our NHC area. **Sparrowhawks** became extinct in Cambridgeshire between 1960 and 1985. They returned and are now a common sight in our city once again. **Peregrines** which were thought of as raptors of mountains, moorlands and sea cliffs, have adapted to city life. There are now more Peregrines breeding in our NHC area than regularly breed on the Shetland Isles: two pairs compared to one! **Red Kites** have bred in the NHC area and flyover Buzzards can be seen regularly in large gardens and soaring over the Market Square.

From the 1960s to the 1980s there was a sequence of records of **Serins** across southern England and they were seen in the Botanic Garden. This small finch, which breeds just across the Channel in France, was expected to colonise but it has not yet despite warmer temperatures. In contrast **Cetti's Warblers**, a non-migratory warbler, have colonised from continental Europe. Their success is linked to survival in milder winters associated with climate change (cold periods can significantly reduce numbers). Breeding species in the near future may include **Firecrests** and **Stonechats**.

Farmland birds breeding on the margins of our NHC area have suffered the greatest losses. Red Listed species that have declined nationally by more than 50% over the last 30 years and show no signs of recovery include **Grey Partridge**, **Skylark**, **Yellow Wagtail**, **Linnet**, **Meadow Pipit** and **Corn Bunting**. **Turtle Doves**, common birds in farmland on the edge of the city 20–30 years ago, have now vanished; this is part of a catastrophic national decline in this migratory species. Farmland birds are being forced to the very margins as the city expands using available land for housing and business development.

The importance of Cambridge as a major highway/flyway for migrating birds is being discovered. The north-east/south-west trajectory of the Ouse/Cam river valley may be an important cross-country route for autumn and spring migrants to and from Iberia, the north Atlantic, the North Sea and breeding grounds in northern Europe. Visual sightings of the autumn Skua passage in the 1980s and 1990s, the remarkable records from the old Cambridge Sewage Farm

and recently the spectacular results of recording and identifying the calls of birds at night over the city, may be keys to a clearer understanding of migration over Britain. **Tree Pipits** are a county rarity but were recorded 29 times over Chesterton from nocturnal calls during our study period (see 'noc-mig' below).

The city's position on a migration route might explain some of these records but the city also has a range of habitats that enables a diverse bird life to flourish (see opposite – Bird Habitats). Habitats are stable within the city's historic centre and the Cam's riverside meadows. However, on the margins of the city, agricultural and Green Belt land is under intense pressure from building development (Chapter 3).

Figure 13.1 (left) Siskins on a Chesterton garden feeder, **(right)** Common Terns at Riverside. (RJJ).

'**Noc-mig**' or nocturnal migration is a bird-detection method that uses sound-recording equipment to capture overhead night-time flight calls. Calls are then identified using computer software. This allows bird calls from a whole night's period to be detected in a relatively short time. Migrating bird calls are significantly easier to pick out during the nocturnal period as diurnal bird activity and other background noise tend to be much reduced.

Migrating birds will often fly over the British Isles on a broad front, which means that, despite being situated well inland, Cambridge picks up its fair share of nocturnal migration. It is suggested that many nocturnal migrants fly straight through overnight, perhaps even from the east to west coast of the British Isles (or vice versa) in one night. Evidence for this includes the frequency of recorded coastal species, such as **Common Scoters**, **Pink-footed Geese** and **Sandwich Terns** which have been recorded on multiple occasions but are very rarely seen in the NHC area. 'Noc-mig' can reveal migrating species which are unexpected and would otherwise not be seen in daytime observations

During the peak migration periods of spring and autumn the diversity of species nocturnally migrating over Cambridge can be surprisingly high. With the right weather conditions conducive for migration, there be good numbers of common passerines such as **Blackbird**, **Song Thrush** and **Redwing** and water birds like **Little Grebe**, **Wigeon** and **Water Rail**, waders (particularly in late summer) such as sandpipers, plovers and **Curlew**. A garden in north Cambridge has recorded 64 species by this method including **Quail**, **Bittern**, **Stone-Curlew**, **Avocet**, **Curlew Sandpiper**, **Grey Plover**, **Bar-tailed Godwit**, **Ring Ouzel**, **Pied Flycatcher**, **Tree Pipit** and **Hawfinch**.

Bird habitats

The historic centre

The colleges and college gardens of the city's historic centre offer a remarkable diversity of stable woodland and parkland habitats, mostly in west Cambridge. A survey during the project period by college head gardeners produced a list of 61 bird species. There have been significant losses including Hawfinch, **Wryneck**, Lesser Spotted Woodpecker, **Spotted Flycatcher** and Rook. **House Sparrows** were common in the 1960s and 1970s but are now rare and only found on the edges of the central city in residential areas. The lack of breeding **Nuthatches** is difficult to understand.

Species which have become more regular include Grey Wagtails, Sparrowhawks, a pair of breeding Peregrine Falcons, flyover Buzzards and Red Kites. The abundance of Mistletoe may be due to the frequency of **Mistle Thrushes** as its main vector; 15 of the 23 singing male Mistle Thrushes recorded in 2017/2018 were in the University part of west Cambridge. The Backs probably have 8–10 breeding pairs of **Tawny Owls**. Rooks, once abundant in central Cambridge, have gone. They are now birds of the northern and eastern edges of the city; persecution is the likely cause as college grounds staff and gardeners wanted pristine lawns and sports fields unimpaired by Rooks digging for chafers and grubs (anon., pers. comm.). **Black Redstarts** are seen or heard most years but confirmed breeding is rare. Similarly, Firecrests have been seen and heard singing but breeding has not yet been proven.

The Botanic Garden

This is a special, unique and diverse habitat within the NHC area. Its bird life mirrors much of west Cambridge and the University gardens and college grounds.

River Cam and riverside meadows

The Cam, and its riverside meadows and parks, is the corridor that unites the University and west Cambridge with the rest of the city. Here are the most accessible, diverse, exciting and stable habitats for wildlife. They are probably the most under-watched but valuable sites in our NHC area from Byron's Pool, Grantchester Meadows, Paradise and Coe Fen to the manicured lawns of the riverside colleges to Jesus Green and Midsummer Common, Logan's Meadow and Riverside to Stourbridge Common and Ditton Meadows. **Cormorants**, grebes, terns, rails, at least

eight species of warblers, **Barn Owls**, **Kestrels** and other flyover raptors, feeding hirundines, **Kingfishers**, and many more species of birds make these habitats the real ornithological treasure of Cambridge. The meadows in Fen Road used to be important local breeding sites for **Redshank** and **Snipe** but are now heavily grazed and mostly drained. In 2016, a **Cattle Egret** and passage **Ring Ouzels** were recorded there.

> From the 1920's until 1966, the **Cambridge Sewage Farm** was one of the most watched inland sites in Britain. Its position on the Cam flyway, neighbouring gravel pits (now Milton Country Park) and the ballast pits (now the site of Cambridge North station), attracted a remarkable sequence of vagrant birds such as **Squacco Heron**, **Great Snipe** and rare waders such as **Temminck's Stint**, **Wood Sandpiper** and phalaropes. This 'evil smelling bird paradise' was converted into sewage works in 1966 and the ballast pits, site of the infamous **Moustached Warbler** record (see below), were filled in 1955.

Recently created 'wild space'

Trumpington Meadows, Logan's Meadow, Hobson's Park and Eddington complement the diversity of greenspace at the river and its meadows. All look suitable habitats for future breeding Stonechats. The city has a number of Local Nature Reserves at: East Barnwell, north Chesterton and Orchard Park. The East Barnwell site used to be part of Coldham's Common where **Red-backed Shrikes** last bred locally in the 1960s.

> Up to autumn 2018 **Trumpington Meadows** had recorded 105 species of birds but no House Sparrows. In the 1970s, when this area was a trials ground for the Plant Breeding Institute hundreds, perhaps a thousand House Sparrows would feed on the ripening cereal crops, especially the winter wheats, compromising the yield trials. Efforts were made to control numbers but with little effect. The demise of the House Sparrow came in the late 1970s onwards with the move to repeat rotations of winter crops – winter wheat, winter barley and winter oilseed rape – ending the practice of leaving overwinter weedy stubbles on which farmland birds could feed.

Gravel pits, farm reservoir and open water

There are few accessible large areas of open water in the NHC area. Bolton's Pit is a private lake, though **Goosander** have been seen flying over, and the small lake at Adam's Road Bird Sanctuary nature reserve is open to members only. A gravel pit on the north edge of the NHC area (Impington Lake) is difficult to access and under-watched; it has breeding grebes and **Great Northern Diver** has been recorded there. A small farm reservoir in the north of the NHC area that was regularly watched had three species of passage terns, **Whooper Swans, Arctic Skua, Goldeneye**, regular passage **Whinchats** in autumn as well as breeding **Coots, Little Grebes** and Meadow Pipits on the embankments. The edge of Dickerson Pit at Milton Country Park just enters our NHC area with wintering wildfowl, flocks of **Greylag** and **Canada Geese** and a complement of scarce migrants such as **White-fronted Goose, Scaup, Osprey** and **Siberian Chiffchaff**.

A new area of permanent open water was 'discovered' during the Covid-19 lockdown – the small Washpit Lake between Eddington and the M11 motorway.

> **Cherry Hinton Lakes** are the largest areas of open water and include the private Territorial Army Pit; Wilson and Jarman (1995) compiled a list of 143 bird species from records in the annual reports of the Cambridgeshire Bird Club. Up to the late 1990's this area, with the exception of the TA pit, was well watched but access has since become restricted and the growth of scrub has further reduced viewing from the public footpaths. This area boasts a significant list of rare passage migrants including **Red-throated Diver** (1986 and 1989), **Red-necked Grebe** (1985, 1990), **Ferruginous Duck** (1984, 1985), Eider (1981, 1991), White-fronted Geese (1989), **Bewick's Swans** (1992, 1993), Arctic Skua and **Little Gull** (1991), Osprey (1992), **Alpine Swift** (1969), **Golden Oriole** (1978), **Grasshopper Warbler** (1994), **Wood Warbler** (1991), **Twite** (1986) and Bittern. **Great Crested Grebes** are regular breeders at this site. A juvenile **Puffin** found injured was rehabilitated and released at Nene mouth (1989).

The Cherry Hinton Lakes may become public amenity and recreation areas in the near future. Barnwell Pit on Coldham's Common has occasional feeding **Common Terns** and **Cetti's Warblers** have been recorded. A planned cycle-way may disrupt this site and hedges that had breeding **Whitethroats** and **Lesser Whitethroats** were removed in 2018 and 2019.

Residential areas parks and gardens
Cambridge is an expanding city, developing mainly to the north and east, leaving the south-west and west of Cambridge dominated by the University. The Victorian terraced houses of Petersfield, Romsey, Riverside and Market have important breeding populations of our common tits, thrushes, finches, Starlings, **Jackdaws, Green** and **Great Spotted Woodpeckers**. Sparrowhawks can be seen displaying over these areas most years. The major residential developments of Arbury and Kings Hedges were originally farmland, the old farm house in Carlton Way was demolished in the 1960s and Manor Farm was developed in the 1970s to become North Arbury/King's Hedges. Arbury, Cherry Hinton and King's Hedges are the council wards with the largest breeding populations of House Sparrows.

The birds of these residential areas and gardens are much the same as the college gardens. In winter Blackcaps are regular visitors and roadside trees can become a life-saving source of berries for winter thrushes and **Waxwings** in invasion years. In spring, singing Blackcaps can be heard across the city in residential gardens, although few breed. Many mature roadside trees and hedges are now under threat in these areas from road projects to alleviate congestion into the city by commuters. Occasionally, unusual spring and autumn migrants pass through residential gardens: **Reed Warblers, Yellow-browed Warblers, Dartford Warbler** and **Black-headed Bunting**.

Many residents across the city feed their garden birds. This is an important contribution to the birds' survival, providing a food supply to wintering

> **Garden Birdwatching:** a garden in the north of the city has recorded 107 species and an additional 18 species as sound recorded nocturnal flyovers. Unusual garden species include Reed Warbler, **Sedge Warbler** and Spotted Flycatcher. Overcast days with light winds from September to November are best conditions to observe visible overhead migration ('vis-mig'). On particularly good days 'vis-mig' can produce hundreds, sometimes thousands, of **Redwings** and **Fieldfares** as well as the chance of locally rare species: **Mediterranean Gull, Short-eared Owl, Merlin, Hen Harrier, Great White Egret,** Osprey, Tree Pipit, Lesser Spotted Woodpecker and Ring-necked Parakeet. In winter Brambling and Waxwing have been recorded in the garden and weather-displaced birds flying over: **Lapwing, Golden Plover** and **Woodcock**. In February 2019, the warmest February on record, four soaring **Cranes** were seen.

Figure 13.2 Cranes (main picture) and Mediterranean Gull (inset) over north Cambridge. (JH).

Blackcaps and less common visitors such as **Siskins**. Gardens with mature ornamental pines and yews often have their own insular breeding populations of **Goldcrests** and **Coal Tits**, which can be uncommon outside the city.

Churchyards

Many churchyards and cemeteries, as well as offering an important quiet space for reflection and remembrance, are also managed well for wildlife; some meticulously, others less so. Many have planted yews and holly bushes, which are important habitats for breeding tits and Goldcrests and one day may reveal breeding Firecrests, as has happened in London.

Farmland

The State of Nature 2016 report (Hayhow *et al.* 2016) found that 56% of UK bird species declined between 1970 and 2013 and this was mostly driven by agricultural changes. The change from spring to winter sown crops reduced over-winter weedy stubbles as a source of feed for finches, buntings and sparrows. As a result the countryside House Sparrow became extinct (see below and Trumpington Meadows above) and it is now an entirely urban nesting species in our NHC area. Many birds are still present in farmland near Cambridge. Skylarks are common, plus Kestrels and

more recently Buzzards and Red Kites hunt these areas. **Hobbies** also nest on the fringes of our NHC area. Darwin Green was originally an agricultural trials ground that was left fallow for 8 years and during this period it attracted **Short-eared Owls** and a **Hen Harrier**.

On the southern edge of the NHC area is an area of chalk land which includes the Nine Wells LNR, the source of Hobson's Brook (see Chapter 15). It is mainly arable farmland with mature hedges and small copses. It is widely used by cyclists and walkers but its northern edge is threatened by the expansion of Addenbrooke's Hospital and the Biomedical Campus. It has a remarkable density of breeding Red Listed farmland birds (see above for definition): Skylarks (57 pairs), Linnets (15 pairs), Grey Partridge (15 pairs), Yellowhammers (15 pairs), Corn Buntings (10 pairs), Yellow Wagtails (2 pairs) and other declining species. It is an important migration stop-off habitat and a hunting area for breeding Kestrels and Tawny Owls (Meed 2021).

Species list
Wildfowl including Swans

Whooper Swans are occasional flyovers, probably from the Ouse Washes; on 1 October 1995 an exhausted pair arrived on a farm reservoir, probably newly arrived from Iceland, and stayed until 22 October. **Mute Swans** commonly breed along the Cam Valley from Grantchester in the south to Ditton Meadows and Milton Country Park (Milton CP).

Greylag and **Canada Geese** are common breeding birds on most water bodies. These two naturalised resident species have vigorous populations and regularly graze the riverside college gardens; in winter a flock of about 150 Greylag moves between Milton CP, Horningsea and Barnwell. **Barnacle Geese** are scarce naturalised residents in the NHC area; four were at Hobson's Park in winter 2020/2021. **Brent Geese** are rare winter flyovers occasionally stopping, as on St Bede's sports field in winter 1991 and 1999 (a flock of nine!) and at Hobson's Park in autumn 2017. **Egyptian Geese** are uncommon naturalised residents; one was recorded at Milton CP in 2013 and flyovers have been recorded by noc-mig. **Pink-footed Geese** are occasional flyovers, with

Outside the breeding season **Common Scoters** are sea ducks but have been known to migrate overland. Only small numbers are seen each year on large inland water bodies. It was not until sound-recording equipment was regularly used during the night ('noc-mig') that the true extent of their overland passage was revealed. Nocturnal recordings by Simon Gillings and Jon Heath have shown that Common Scoters frequently migrate over Cambridge nocturnally during spring (Mar/Apr) and autumn (Aug/Sep) – detected by the Scoter's characteristic short 'peep' call. This matches recordings across much of Britain and suggests overland Scoter passage is much more common and widespread than previously thought.

records mainly during the autumn passage and occasional single birds such as one at Hobson's Park that joined the Greylags in the first winter period in 2021. **Shelducks** are rare and occasional flyovers, often in spring when looking for nesting opportunities.

Mallard commonly breed on any suitable water body in the NHC area. Other breeding wildfowl are fairly scarce; **Gadwall** and **Tufted Duck** breeding is confined to the few larger areas of open water: Hobson's Park, Milton CP and Cherry Hinton Pits.

The number of wildfowl species increases over winter; **Wigeon**, **Teal**, **Shoveler** and **Pochard** can usually be found on the gravel pits, a farm reservoir in the north of the city and Bolton's Pit near Barton Road. **Goldeneye** are rare and occasional, similarly the sawbills – **Smew** and **Goosander**, the latter is probably annual involving just one or two individuals. Goosander bred for the first time in Cambridgeshire in 2018 on the River Cam at Little Shelford just outside our project area. The southern edge of Dickerson's Pit at Milton CP is an important deep-water habitat for diving ducks and can attract scarce winter visitors, such as a female **Scaup** in winter 2018. **Muscovy Duck** are occasional stragglers on the river, probably from the naturalised population in Ely.

Gamebirds

Pheasant and **Red-legged Partridge** are naturalised residents which frequent the edges of the city and are often seen in big gardens; large numbers of both species are released annually on surrounding farmland for shooting. **Grey Partridge** have breeding populations in the north (1–2 coveys of 5–12 birds) and the chalk arable hills south of the

Figure 13.3 (left) Scaup in Milton Country Park, (right) Goosander in Milton Country Park. (JH).

Figure 13.4 (left) Grey Heron near the Mill Pond, (right) Little Egret on Snakey Path, Cherry Hinton. (RJJ).

city (88 were counted at Nine Wells in autumn 2017). Both areas are threatened by building developments; pairs were also seen at Missleton Hill opposite the Beech Woods and Grantchester in February 2019. **Quail** are rare summer visitors but do turn up occasionally at Nine Wells on the chalk hills; nocturnal migrants were also recorded over the city in 2018 and 2019 (see 'noc-mig' box on page 208).

Cormorants
Cormorants of the European race *Phalacrocorax carbo sinensis* are now common on the river and seen flying over the city. There is a regular roost of 6–12 birds at Logan's Meadow, opposite Riverside and at Fen Ditton. **Shags** are rare storm-driven vagrants with the occasional influx; the winter of 1993/4 produced a remarkable 11 birds on the Cam in the Midsummer Common/Jesus Lock area.

Egrets and Herons
Little Egrets were first confirmed breeding in Britain in 1996 (Balmer *et al.* 2013) and in Cambridgeshire on the Ouse Washes in 2004 (Ward 2005). In the last ten years, Little Egrets have become common overwintering birds of streams and riverside meadows throughout the NHC area; there may be 10–12 individuals. These birds have probably dispersed from their breeding colonies on the Ouse Washes and do not breed in the NHC area (though they may in the near future). Two over Harding Way in January 2016 would have been unthinkable in the 20th century!

Grey Herons are common by deeper waters; they can be very confiding along the river margins through the city and are notorious early-morning raiders of garden ponds. There is a small breeding colony of three to four nests in Newnham. **Bitterns** have been recorded at the Territorial Army Pit off Coldham's Lane (see above) and rare night flying birds recorded over Chesterton – see above noc-mig. **Cattle Egrets** are becoming commoner in East Anglia, often with occasional influxes; a single bird was found in a grazing meadow along the Fen Road in April 2015. **Cranes** are possible future regular flyovers from the increasing Cambridgeshire breeding population; four flying north over the city on 24th February 2019 – see Garden Birdwatching above – and two over Hills Road on 17th March 2021 (Martin Walters, pers. comm.).

In December 2020 at least six individual **Glossy Ibises** were present in the county, including one on Chesterton Fen from 24th to 31st December 2020 (Cambridgeshire Bird Club E-Bulletin 90, December 2020).

Divers and Grebes
A **Great Northern Diver**, an uncommon inland species, was found at a gravel pit in the north of the NHC area in January 1993.

Little Grebes are regular on the Cam in winter and are early colonists of all new areas of open water, e.g. Eddington, Hobson's Park and Trumpington Meadows. **Great Crested Grebes** breed on the larger open waters and can occasionally be seen on the Cam in harsh winter weather.

Raptors

The spectacular increase in most raptors has been a UK conservation success. From 1960 until 1985 **Sparrowhawks** were extinct as a breeding bird in Cambridgeshire, largely as a result of toxic bioaccumulation of agricultural pesticides, including DDT and mercuric seed dressings, which severely affected breeding success. Since these pesticides were banned the population has recovered and Sparrowhawks are now common birds in the city with at least 10 breeding pairs. **Kestrels** are common on arable field margins, riverside meadows around the edge of the NHC area and even larger church cemeteries and college grounds. In winter Kestrels can be seen more often over the city and frequently hunt in newly created wild spaces such as Logan's Meadow wherever the turf is short; there are probably 10–12 breeding pairs. **Merlins** are rare winter visitors to the northern edge of the city. In the 1990s, Merlins were regular winter visitors to the NIAB's Trials Ground near Huntingdon Road. **Hobbies** are uncommon summer visitors and can be seen hunting high over the city; there may be two or three nest locations within the NHC area. One nest site just outside the NHC area has been used for about 25 years and young birds can be seen hunting over Orchard Park and Histon Road in early autumn. One seen over the Washpit Lake on 14th March 2021 was the earliest county record.

Buzzards have recolonised from the west; they returned to breed in Cambridgeshire in 1999, which was the first breeding record since 1976. Buzzards are now a common sight over the city, particularly on warm spring days when breeding birds display and interact with other prospecting pairs; 3–4 pairs may breed on the very edge of the NHC area. Eddington is the best place to see them. In June 2017, a dead **Honey Buzzard** was found near the nest site of one of the breeding Peregrines and probably died from a Peregrine strike. **Red Kite** bred successfully on the northern edge of the city in 2016 and raised one chick. They are seen regularly over the northern fringe of the city and, in 2019, there was a sequence of records over Mill Road Cemetery at the very centre of our NHC area (Andrew Dobson, pers. comm.) and Cherry Hinton Hall (Roger Horton, pers. comm.).

Marsh Harriers are scarce passage migrants over the NHC area, breeding in the neighbouring

Two pairs of **Peregrine Falcons** have been breeding in the city since 2014 (see above) and one pair can be seen most days from the Market Square. In winter they can be seen heading north over Huntingdon Road out of the city – the general trajectory seems to be the Ouse Washes between Earith and Sutton Gault and birds have been seen here and on the radio tower at Over village. Black-tailed Godwit feathers have been found underneath the Cambridge roost site, which suggests the Ouse Washes may be a hunting ground. In autumn 2013 a juvenile Peregrine seen on the Catholic Church had been ringed as a chick earlier that year on Chichester Cathedral. The increase in Peregrines in lowland Britain contrasts with the decline in the uplands and National Parks managed for driven-grouse shooting (Cox *et al.* 2018).

Figure 13.5 Peregrines near City Centre nest site (AR).

Figure 13.6 Common Buzzard at Eddington. (RJJ).

fenland. In winter 2016/2017, an area set aside for the Darwin Green housing development, that had been left fallow, attracted a 'ring-tail' **Hen Harrier**. **Ospreys** are rare and irregular flyovers in spring and autumn.

On the 22nd April 2020 James Cadbury reported a **White-tailed Eagle** over Bolton's Pit, Newnham. It was probably one of the released birds from the Isle of Wight reintroduction scheme. They had been seen over Greater London and a bird was tracked up the Suffolk and Norfolk coasts during March 2020.

Rails

Water Rails are secretive and uncommon winter visitors which are regularly seen along waterside margins in Lammas Land and Logan's Meadow. **Moorhens** are very common and can be found along the whole stretch of the Cam and neighbouring

ditches. Up to 25 Moorhens can be seen in the ditch behind Jesus College and occasionally graze on Parker's Piece; in 2018, a pair built a nest in the middle of the weir at Jesus Green Lock! **Coots** are scarce away from larger open waters and are mainly restricted to the flooded gravel and chalk pits in the NHC area.

Waders

Two, perhaps three pairs of **Little Ringed Plovers** bred at the Cherry Hinton Pits (see above) until the late 1990s when the site was redeveloped as a retail park and gymnasium; more recently birds may have bred from 2010 during preliminary excavations at the Eddington site. Up to 450 **Golden Plovers** are regular winter visitors to arable fields on the edge of the city near Trumpington Meadows and near Histon Road. In 2016 four pairs of **Lapwings** nested on farm stubble on the northern edge of the city although nesting failed due to predation and/ or subsequent farm operations. These were possibly the first Lapwing nests in our NHC area for about 50 years! Lapwing chicks hatched at Hobson's Park in 2019. Nest-site prospecting **Oystercatchers** are occasional springtime flyovers; a pair was seen over the main railway station in May 2018.

Woodcocks, usually singles, can turn up anywhere in winter, often in gardens and particularly during prolonged cold weather when the warmer urban environment provides suitable feeding areas. Sites include the gardens along Lensfield, Tavistock, Tenison and Huntingdon Roads, and Jesus College, but in November 2017 one was disturbed from the small garden of a terrace house in Petworth Street and in November 2020 one was disturbed from the same place, suggesting a returning bird (Salim Algailani, pers. comm.) **Redshanks** and **Common Snipe** used to breed in the

Figure 13.7 Water Rail near A14 bridge over the river Cam. (JH).

Dotterels were once common spring migrants on Limekiln Hill and neighbouring arable chalk fields within our NHC area. In the 19th century hundreds of this tame wader were shot there for upmarket London restaurants and hotels. The confiding nature of this bird made them easy targets for hunters and gave them the name 'dotard' from the old English meaning idiot or old fool! They no longer occur regularly in flocks or 'trips' but should still be looked for from mid-April to early May. One was heard over Coldham's Common on 6th August 2012.

wet meadows off the Fen Road (Chesterton Fen) but they no longer do so because of drainage, housing and increased stocking. Both species are now passage or wintering birds; up to 60 Common Snipe were at Hobson's Park in winter 2018/19 and 110 there in winter 2020/21. **Jack Snipe** are uncommon winter visitors with recent records from Ditton Meadows in winter 2017/2018, Hobson's Park (5) and Eddington (1) in winter 2018/2019.

Common Sandpipers are uncommon passage migrants with occasional sightings along the Cam and at the large open water pits. **Green Sandpipers** are also uncommon passage migrants, as well as infrequent winter visitors to watersides and the river meadows. Recent noc-mig findings have shown that **Dunlin** are regular nocturnal passage migrants in late autumn. During the 2018 'Beast from the East' the harsh weather drove a number of Dunlins into the NHC area including three at Milton Country Park, one at Ditton Meadows and another at Stourbridge Common which sadly succumbed to the conditions.

Generally, the NHC area lacks suitable wading bird habitat and most sightings involve flyover birds. **Whimbrels** have been seen over Trumpington Meadows, Clay Farm and Chesterton. A flock of 43 birds over Little Shelford in August 2017 probably passed over our NHC area. Whimbrels are also regular nocturnal migrants and have been recorded annually along with **Ringed Plovers**, **Curlews** and **Black-tailed Godwits** in the last few years since noc-mig detection methods have been used for recording. A single Black-tailed Godwit was disturbed from the Washpit Lake on 6th April 2021.

Other nocturnal waders recorded over the city include **Greenshank** (September 2017) and **Turnstones** (October 2017 and 2019). Nocturnal sound recording will doubtless reveal much more in the future.

Figure 13.8 Dunlin in Milton Country Park. (JH).

Skuas, Gannet

Skuas are very rare passage migrants to our NHC area. Observations at Ouse Mouth at the base of Wash suggest that many skuas pass down the Ouse and Cam valleys and probably high over Cambridge in autumn on southward migrations (Easy 1994; Easy 2007); see box below. There is also an unusual record of a juvenile Arctic Skua on a foggy day in January in 1989 at a farm reservoir in the north of the NHC area.

On 18 April 1985 an adult **Gannet** was swept inland, likely from the Norfolk coast, on a northerly gale and was seen flying over Girton College heading south and one seen over Newmarket Road in October 2020 was heading towards the city centre!

In the 1970s and 1980s Graham Easy saw flocks of skuas (**Arctic** and **Great Skua**) passing south-west overhead in autumn at great height over Milton and Cambridge. He speculated that there were major overland migration highway/flyways for skuas and thousands of **Kittiwakes** following the north-east/south-west trajectories of the Ouse/Cam, Nene and Welland river valleys. The birds would exit in the Bristol Channel to take an overland short cut on their way to wintering grounds off the coast of Senegal.

On 16 October 2019 St John's college staff found the fresh corpse of a juvenile **Long-tailed Skua** outside Merton House at the junction of Queen's Road and Madingley Road (Shaun Mays, David Brown, Jonathan Bustard, pers. comm.). This was the first record for our NHC area and possibly only the 12th record for the County. Injuries to the dead bird suggested a Peregrine strike.

Terns

Little Tern is a very rare spring migrant – one was seen feeding on a farm reservoir in the north of the NHC area in May 1995. **Common Terns** are regular summer visitors along the Cam from Fen Ditton to Jesus Lock. In 2018 and 2019 birds with food were seen heading south over the city, probably to a newly established breeding colony at Hobson's Park. However, Common Terns did not breed at Hobson's Park in 2020, possibly because the vegetation on the island rafts was not cut back. In September 1996 an adult **Sandwich Tern**, harassed by a juvenile, was seen over Vinery Road; nocturnal sound recordings suggest there is a previously undetected annual passage of birds over the NHC area in early autumn. **Black Terns** are rare passage migrants to farm reservoirs and gravel pits in the NHC area.

Figure 13.9 Common Gull with green ring. (RJJ).

Gulls

Black-headed Gulls are the common over-wintering gull (the familiar 'sea-gull') in the NHC area, with large flocks frequenting the commons, sports fields, parks and the riverside meadows; 6–10% of these are first-year birds. They are joined by smaller numbers of **Common Gulls**. In November 2020, 400+ Black-headed Gulls were regularly seen flying NNW in the evenings over Chesterton to roost – probably at Fen Drayton RSPB reserve. About 30 pairs of Black-headed Gulls breed at Hobson's Park.

Little Gulls are rare passage migrants in our NHC area: five were at Hobson's Park on 26th March 2020. Single **Mediterranean Gulls** turn up occasionally and are probably birds dispersing from a breeding site in the west of the county. In March 2020, a single Mediterranean Gull with nest material was seen in the Black-headed Gull colony at Hobson's Park.

Herring Gulls are present in small numbers either as flyovers or as winter visitors with the Black-headed Gulls on parks and the riverside meadows. **Lesser Black-backed Gulls** are common flyovers but their increasing presence over the city centre buildings in spring and summer has suggested breeding attempts. **Great Black-backed Gulls** are uncommon flyovers. **Yellow-legged Gulls** are uncommon but regular spring and autumn visitors, mostly to open water sites in the NHC area such as Hobson's Park.

An aberrant Herring Gull showing some plumage characteristics of Audouin's Gull was seen on Parker's Piece in winter 2018.

Ringing histories reveal that some of the gulls visiting our NHC area migrate considerable distances. A Black-headed Gull seen on Parker's Piece in March 2017 had been ringed 13 years earlier in the Netherlands on 5th January 2004 (distance 415 km). A Common Gull seen at Eddington in November 2019 had been ringed as an adult near Stavanger, Norway, in 2016. Another Common Gull ringed in Norway in 2014 was seen on Parker's Piece for three consecutive winters in 2017–19.

Pigeons and doves

Woodpigeons have experienced a huge expansion in numbers, becoming familiar garden birds that are no longer restricted to open farmland; the population increase coincided with the expansion of oilseed rape crops from the late 1970s. They occur throughout the NHC area, often in flocks of several hundred and increasingly nesting in city gardens. They are one of the few bird species that can survive on green vegetable material alone. **Stock Doves** are easily overlooked but are widely distributed in the NHC area; a pair nests undisturbed, most years, close to one of the Peregrine nests. In February 2017 a flock of 117 was seen on farmland in the north of the NHC area; they are hole nesters and often use nest boxes intended for Kestrels and owls (Histon Road Cemetery, Paradise) and can sometimes visit gardens.

Feral Pigeons are found throughout the city. The Market Square population seems largely ignored by the Peregrines but a flock in Carisbrooke Road is regularly harassed. A

Peregrine with a feral/homing pigeon kill was once watched being mobbed by a Red Kite over the junction of Gilbert Road with Histon Road at roof top height!

Collared Doves were first recorded in Lincolnshire in 1952. They first bred in Britain in Norfolk in 1955 and in Cambridge in 1963. They are now a familiar garden bird and occur throughout our NHC area; flocks of 250+ have been seen on maize stubble close to the Histon Road/ Huntingdon Road footpath. **Turtle Doves** have disappeared from the NHC area. The BTO *Bird Atlas 2007–2011* (Balmer *et al.* 2013) shows that this species has suffered the most dramatic decline of any UK breeding bird by an estimated 98%. This decline is mirrored across Europe; habitat loss and unsustainable hunting are thought to be the main reasons for this population collapse of a once common migratory dove.

Cuckoo

In the 1960s and 1970s **Cuckoos** were regular summer visitors to gardens in the new housing estates in the north of the city, parasitising Dunnocks. They are now rare birds in the NHC area with very few records each year including one in Rustat Road in June 2018 (Jane Denney, pers. comm.).

Owls

Barn Owls have hunted the fields in the north of the city for the last 70 years at least. As the Arbury Estate expanded, then the 'McManus' estate (Tavistock Road/Carisbrooke Road area)

and most recently Darwin Green, they have had to move breeding territories further and further away and may soon be forced out and beyond our NHC northern boundary. There are possibly 8–10 pairs within the NHC area, hunting the riverside meadows and adjacent fields including Trumpington Meadows and the University Rugby Club's training ground in Grange Road. There may be 8–10 breeding pairs of **Tawny Owls** mostly in the west side of the city.

There is a 1990s winter record of a **Long-eared Owl** on Coldham's Common and this secretive nocturnal owl may be regular in the area; there is a well-established breeding site just outside the NHC area. In the winter of 2015/2016 four **Short-eared Owls** hunted over the fallowed fields that are now the Darwin Green housing development; the fields had been left uncultivated for eight years. Only two territories of **Little Owl** were recorded during the study period, both in the West Cambridge research site.

Swifts

Swifts are declining breeding birds in the city as building improvements and modifications seal access to regular nest sites. An important breeding site, St Regis House on Chesterton Road, was demolished in winter 2018/2019. It was rebuilt by Clare College with new nest boxes for swifts installed and a vivid motif of a flock of 'screamers' on the front of the building including two in the college colours of red and gold (see Figure 13.11). The Swift tower in Logan's Meadow, Chesterton, attracts 6–8 nesting pairs annually although it

Figure 13.10 Short-eared Owls at Darwin Green. (JH).

Figure 13.11 (left) St Regis House, Chesterton Road, (right) Kestrel in Hobson's Park. (RJJ).

comprises 221 nest boxes held together in a steel frame of urban art inspired by the African sun. Swifts arrive faithfully in early May each year and their pre-departure 'screaming' over the city is a feature in the last two weeks of July. **Alpine Swift** is a very rare vagrant which has been recorded once in Cherry Hinton in 1969.

Action for Swifts, inspired by Cambridgeshire Bird Club member, Dick Newell, has been proactive in the NHC area installing swift nest boxes in churches, houses, council properties, schools, the East Tower of the David Attenborough Building and the rebuild of St Regis House by Clare College in Chesterton Road (www.actionforswifts.blogspot.com).

Woodpeckers

Bircham (1989) described the **Lesser Spotted Woodpecker** as 'the commonest of its genus in the county' and the Cambridge population as 'substantial'. It could be seen across the city from the Backs to gardens in Romsey Town and orchards near the Huntingdon Road/Histon Road footpath (Jarman, 2012). Since then they have ceased to breed in the city and the population across East Anglia has crashed to just nine breeding territories in 2018: Cambridgeshire one, Norfolk three and Suffolk five (Eaton *et al.* 2020). Failure to compete with Great Spotted Woodpeckers, predation by Grey Squirrels, loss of dead wood offered by dying elms and phenology – asynchrony between breeding season and food available for nestlings, due to climate changes – have all been cited as reasons for this decline.

The long-term national trends for both **Green Woodpeckers** and **Great Spotted Woodpeckers**

are an increase in both species; the loud yaffling call of Green Woodpeckers and the abrupt chick of Great Spotted Woodpeckers can be heard often across the city throughout the year. **Wrynecks** are now very rare migrants such as the bird seen near Newmarket Road in September 2016. In the early 1900s it bred regularly – the last possible breeding record was a pair in the Backs in 1968 (Bircham 1989).

Kingfisher

Kingfishers are regularly seen (and heard!) near the river and its immediate inflowing streams such as the Bin Brook There maybe three or four pairs nesting; four birds have been seen in a courtship chase at Riverside where they used to nest but this part of the river is now busy with rowing crews during the breeding season. Kingfishers are seen regularly at Milton Country Park and Hobson's Park; they can be seen flying under and over Silver Street Bridge.

Ring-necked Parakeet

The **Ring-necked Parakeet** is a rare wanderer north from of its expanding naturalised populations in the south and south-east of England; a single bird was seen in north Cambridge in September 2013 and a probable in Jesus college grounds in November 2019.

Corvids – crows and their relatives

In 1945 the number of **Rook** nests in rookeries in Cambridge City was 1197 nests in 30 rookeries; 90% of these Rookeries were in west Cambridge (Shipton 1961). By 1966 this had dropped to 220 nests in 21 rookeries (Easy 1967); in 2017, 2018 and 2019 numbers had reduced further to 108, 111 and 134 nests respectively in just six rookeries. The increase in number of nests in 2019 was due to an expansion of the rookery in Cherry Hinton Hall to nearby Walpole Road

The major losses were in west Cambridge where nesting Rooks were virtually eliminated. In 1945 a Rookery centred at the back of Queens College had 266 nests; by 1966 this had reduced to just nine (counts from: Sell, Raines, Darlington). This Rookery no longer exists. In the 1940s 77% of nests were reported in elms although Easy (1996) states that the loss of elms from Dutch Elm Disease has had no great influence on rookeries and Rook numbers. The rookery in Whitehouse Lane off Huntingdon Road probably moved up the road to Girton College when the elms died in Whitehouse

Figure 13.12 (top) Rooks by Hills Road, (bottom) New rookery 2019 in Walpole Road. (RJJ).

Lane. In the city persecution caused this decline due to grubbing for leather jackets on pristine college lawns, fouling and noise especially during revision time for exams (Jarman and Preston 2020).

In contrast to Rooks, **Carrion Crows** have increased in Cambridge; in 1986, 66 nests were counted across the city (Easy 1987) and in June 2017 84 individuals were seen on Parker's Piece. Their success may be due to lack of persecution, scavenging discarded takeaways and road kills, especially hedgehogs, and their habit of nesting discretely as individual pairs. **Jackdaws** are common across the NHC area and nest in redundant chimney pots; there are good numbers in the Mill Road area in the Victorian terraced properties. A significant pre-roost exodus of 400+ birds passes over north Cambridge most evenings during the winter months. **Ravens** are expanding eastwards across the country and several pairs now breed in Cambridgeshire including two pairs which nest just outside our NHC area; a pair was seen over farmland in the NHC area near Impington in February 2016.

Jays and **Magpies** are common across the NHC area. Jays are susceptible to failures in the continental acorn crop supply and this occasionally results in an influx during the autumn; a flock of nine was seen over Chesterton in October 2019. In many residential areas Jays are winter visitors although they become secretive in the breeding season. Pre-roost gatherings of Magpies of 18 to 25 are regular across the city and one of 26 was in Logan's Meadow in December 2016.

Crests
Goldcrests are widely distributed with active breeding groups even in isolated mature garden pines, as in Coldham's Lane, Roseford Road and Whytford Close. In winter, they forage more widely and also like dense ivy. In 2016 and 2017, there were several records of **Firecrest** from Girton but successful breeding was never confirmed. Elsewhere, there have been occasional and intermittent Firecrest records. This species is expected to breed in the near future; it likes Holly bushes in winter and Douglas Firs to nest.

Tits
Blue Tits and **Great Tits** are abundant and widespread resident breeding birds which are particularly helped by nest-boxes and garden bird feeders. **Coal Tits** are more local, often sharing

the same habitats as Goldcrests in isolated garden pines and ornamental conifers. **Long-tailed Tits** are common and widespread residents, often foraging in parties of 25+ in winter. **Bearded Tit** is a rare visitor; a male over-wintered at Trumpington Meadows and Hobson's Park in 2018/2019.

Larks

The NIAB's trials ground site on the north edge of the NHC area regularly has 16–25 singing male **Skylarks**, one of the highest concentrations of breeding Skylarks in the county. The advantage of this site is the variety of crops grown and the plot pathways give the birds ready access to ground feeding and nest sites. In winter, flocks of up to 60 birds assemble (e.g. winter 2018/2019). Much of this winter habitat has now been lost to the Darwin Green development.

Hirundines

Swallows are common summer migrants throughout the NHC area, especially along the river and over adjacent water meadows and arable fields; breeding status is unclear but regular sightings would suggest breeding thinly throughout the NHC area. A regular nest site is under the A14 river bridge near Fen Ditton. **House Martins** have a similar status; the colony at Addenbrookes Hospital is the largest breeding colony in the county (102 in 2017, 74 in 2018, 51 in 2019 of apparently occupied nests). House Martins often stay into November, as at Hobson's Park in 2018. **Sand Martins** are now uncommon birds of passage almost exclusively over water; they used to breed along Riverside up to the 1990s in drainage pipes that emptied into the river but these were removed.

Warblers

Chiffchaffs are common passage and breeding birds often in large city gardens; a few overwinter usually

near water – Cherry Hinton Lakes and Paradise Nature Reserve are regular sites. In December 2018/January 2019, birds of the Siberian race *Phylloscopus collybita tristis* were found at Milton CP in the orchard area and Logan's Meadow in December 2019. In 2016 a bird on Coldham's Common had mixed Chiffchaff/Willow Warbler song. **Willow Warblers** are uncommon on spring passage and can turn up almost anywhere, for example in the roadside trees in Ditton Fields in spring 2015. They may breed at Milton CP and in the willow copse near Cambridge North Station. This copse was being grubbed out in March 2019 to build an office block. There is a single recent record of a **Wood Warbler** from Milton CP in 2013. There are two remarkable records of **Icterine Warblers**, a very rare vagrant, singing in a birdwatcher's garden in Montgomery Road on 23th May 2012 and at Railway Street, Cherry Hinton on 30th August 2015.

Yellow-browed Warblers are rare migrants. Recent records are: Maids Causeway in 2013, Mount Pleasant in 2014 and Stourbridge Common (two records) in 2015. This matches an increasing number of records from coastal UK Bird Observatories and inland records in autumn, which is linked to a westerly shift in this species migration pathway and possibly an increase in observers familiar with its distinct call.

On 22nd November 2019, a **Pallas's Warbler** was found in Paradise Nature Reserve (Crosby 2020). It remained into early December and attracted about 150 birdwatchers. It was only the second county record and the first live one following a deceased bird found in Peterborough outside the Natural England offices in 1998 – it had struck a window. Similar to Yellow-browed Warbler, this species winters in south-east China.

Blackcaps are common summer visitors to large gardens, hedges and dense copses throughout the city and are now regular in winter (see below).

Figure 13.13 (left) Yellow-browed Warbler on Stourbridge Common, (right) Pallas's Warbler in Paradise LNR. (JH).

Garden Warblers are uncommon but present in large mature hedges along the margins of the riverside meadows and Coldham's Common. **Whitethroats** are common although the cold, late spring and northerly winds in 2018 considerably reduced the numbers arriving in our NHC area. They are adaptable and often nest in farm crops such as oilseed rape and winter beans. **Lesser Whitethroats** are thinly distributed on the edge of the NHC area, preferring overgrown hedgerows and dense scrub. In 2019, both Whitethroat species arrived in numbers; Lesser Whitethroats out-numbered Whitethroats and exceptionally established breeding territories across the NHC area.

Sedge Warblers are uncommon in the NHC area, though are present in suitable habitats along stream margins in the riverside meadows. **Reed Warblers** prefer larger areas of standing reeds, which are often found at the larger gravel pits and breed in Adams Road Bird Sanctuary and the Territorial Army pit near Cherry Hinton. On passage Reed and Sedge Warblers can turn up anywhere. Singing Reed Warblers in spring have been seen in the Asda car park at the Beehive Centre, Mill Road Cemetery and Romsey Road; and on autumn passage a Sedge Warbler frequented potted plants in a garden in Lovell Road. **Cetti's Warblers**, first recorded in Cambridgeshire in 1977, have made their way into the city and were recorded in 2017–2019 at Barnwell Pit, Coldham's Common and Cherry Hinton.

A female/first winter **Dartford Warbler** was found in a Cherry Hinton garden on 4th February 2001. This coincided with a sequence of warm winters and an increase in the Suffolk and Dorset populations and was the first Cambridgeshire record

Figure 13.14 Lesser Whitethroat in a north Cambridge garden. (JH).

During winter 2016/2017 over-wintering **Blackcaps** were recorded from 39 localities within the NHC area. Birds arrived in mid-November to early December (Chris Brown, pers. comm.) and moved into urban locations when rural temperatures fell. They often visited garden feeders. Some were seen vigorously defending low level berry-bearing clumps of female mistletoe in hawthorn and garden fruit trees. They also fed on *Mahonia* nectaries, honeysuckle, cotoneaster and pyracantha berries, fat balls and shrivelled grapes on vines. The overwintering birds left by the end of March and there was usually a gap of two to three weeks before the summer visiting Blackcaps arrived in the middle of April (Margaret Risbeth, pers. comm.). European Blackcaps, instead of migrating south-west in autumn, migrate north-west in increasing numbers. Ringing records suggest Blackcaps wintering in Britain come from eastern France, Austria, southern Germany and Slovakia.

Figure 13.15. Male Blackcap eating Pyracantha berries. (JH).

The Moustached Warbler: Britain's rarest bird that never was! In 1946 a breeding pair of Moustached Warblers was claimed at the Chesterton ballast pits which later became railway sidings, now Cambridge North Station. The adults and young were observed by the top ornithologists of the day and full records were submitted. Apart from a single record from the Channel Isles this was Britain's only record and was even more remarkable because it involved a breeding pair. The record remained for sixty years until 2006, when it was re-examined and then expunged from the records on the grounds that a key identification feature that distinguishes this species from similar Sedge Warblers was not noted in the original records.

Figure 13.16 (left) Waxwing at Cambridge Science Park, (right) Nuthatch in Girton College. (JH).

since 1870 (Bircham 1989). Another was seen just outside the NHC area on Magog Down in October 2017.

Waxwing

In irruptive years the NHC area has had its share of well watched groups of this remarkable and often very confiding bird. The most recent winter **Waxwing** influxes were 2012/2013 and 2016/2017. Berry-bearing *Sorbus*, *Cotoneaster* and *Rubus* trees and shrubs are often stripped bare before the birds move on. In November 2012 a flock fed next to the scoreboard during the University v Steele-Bodgers rugby match; in March 2017 a flock of 15 next to the guided bus way at Milton Road gorged on bramble and Mistletoe berries.

Treecreeper and Nuthatch

Treecreepers are thinly distributed over the NHC area with regular sightings in Logan's Meadow (birds singing in 2018 and 2019), Girton College, Paradise Nature Reserve, the Botanic Garden and Adams Road Bird Sanctuary.

Nuthatches bred in the Backs in 1989 and were present there and in the Botanic Garden in 1991. Bircham *et al.* (1995) describe the Cambridge population as centred around the Backs. There were sightings of single birds in Clare College garden in 2007 (Rob Pople, pers. comm.) and 2009. According to the *Cambridgeshire Bird Atlas 2007–2011* (Bacon *et al.* 2013), there were no breeding sites in Cambridge or the NHC area despite a specific search

in 2019. The most recent sightings include three at Girton College in November 2019 (Jon Heath, Stewart Rosell, pers. comm.), a dead Nuthatch found outside the Attenborough Building in Downing Street in July 2019 (likely a dispersing juvenile), regular sightings from St John's College gardens, Newnham in winter 2019 and Chaucer Road in winter 2020. The decline in breeding pairs is difficult to explain; the authors believe it could be due to the absence of mature oaks.

Wren

Wrens are widespread and common garden birds throughout the NHC area. They are the commonest UK breeding bird with an estimated 11,000,000 breeding pairs (Woodward *et al.* 2020).

Starling

Starlings are widely distributed breeding in the NHC area; from October onwards numbers are supplemented by annual winter visitors. Breeding is often associated with access to buildings and closely follows the distribution of nesting House Sparrows (Jarman, 2014). Occasionally, large murmurations can be seen towards the north of the city.

Thrushes

A survey of singing **Mistle Thrushes** in 2017/2018 counted 23 territories across the NHC area but they were strangely absent from Cherry Hinton; birds were commonly singing from mid-November 2017 to mid-April 2018. Mistle Thrushes may be partly

Figure 13.17 (left) Fieldfare in Longworth Avenue, (right) Spotted Flycatcher by Byron's Pool. (RJJ).

responsible for the large increase of Mistletoe; in Chesterton (see Chapter 6), and on Huntingdon Road they were seen vigorously defending berry-bearing female Mistletoe clumps from Blackbirds. The absence of Mistletoe in Cherry Hinton may be explained by the absence of Mistle Thrushes there.

Blackbirds and Song Thrushes are common throughout the NHC area. There has been an ongoing decline of breeding Song Thrushes in eastern England (Balmer *et al.* 2013); in winter numbers are boosted by migrants from the near continent.

The winter-visiting thrushes, **Fieldfares** and **Redwings**, appear in late October. Both species are shy and prefer berry-laden hedges and rural pastures; however, in cold harsh weather they enter urban areas in large numbers to feed in gardens. Redwings are prodigious night migrants and can be heard over Cambridge from the end of September onward (see Garden Birdwatching above); in spring, they often gather in numbers and begin a communal chorus – Paradise and Cherry Hinton Hall are good places to hear this pre-migration sub-song. **Ring Ouzels** are scarce but, probably, regular passage migrants. The earliest record was from Stourbridge Common on 3rd April 2016; other recent records are from Chesterton Fen and Trumpington Meadows and nocturnal sound recordings over Chesterton from 2017 (Gillings, pers. comm.).

Chats
Spotted Flycatchers are a greatly declining species that now rarely breed in the NHC area

(Holdsworth, pers. comm.). A pair used to breed in Whitehouse Lane, off Huntingdon Road but left when the elms died; the college gardens would appear to be ideal but there are no recent breeding records. Birds were seen at the western end of Byron's Pool in 2018 but breeding was not confirmed; a pair did breed at a site off Huntingdon Road in 2018. The reason(s) for decline are unclear but may include loss of elms, a decline in insect numbers and predation of eggs and young by Grey Squirrels. The best chance to see Spotted Flycatcher is in the passage periods, particularly early autumn; there was a record from a north Cambridge garden in August 2013, 2014 and 2015. **Pied Flycatchers** are rare passage migrants in the NHC area; in August 2019 there was an exceptional autumn passage in the county which included a record of one at Coldham's Common.

Robins are widespread and abundant residents throughout the NHC area; in winter numbers are supplemented by migrant visitors. In the 1930s it was suggested that along Trumpington Road there were more **Nightingales** per mile than any other stretch of road in England (Bircham 1989). There is a 1990s record of a bird singing in the shrubbery outside the public loos in Drummer Street but this declining species no longer occurs in the NHC area.

Black Redstarts are rare but regular in the NHC area. They can turn up at any time, usually around buildings; a singing male was present in the city centre from 26th May to 26th June 2017. Breeding was confirmed at a research park in our NHC area

Figure 13.18 Male Stonechat in Hobson's Park. (RJJ).

in 2018 and possibly two sites in 2019. **Redstarts** are easily overlooked and probably more common than records suggest, especially on autumn migration: recent records were one at Eddington in early October 2017 and in August 2018 and Cambridge Research Park in August 2019.

Whinchats are rare and occasional passage migrants to open fields and farmland. A regularly watched farm site in the north of the NHC area has 1–2 birds most autumns, three were seen at Hobson's Park in September 2016, two there in 2017, singles there in 2018 and 2019 and at Trumpington Meadows in 2017. **Stonechats** are uncommon winter visitors to open habitats with coarse standing weedy vegetation. They often appear in pairs which suggests potential breeding but by March they have gone. Hobson's Park and Trumpington Meadows have become regular wintering sites. In winter 2020/21 Stonechats were also seen at Storey's Field, Eddington and the NIAB's trials ground. **Wheatears** are uncommon but regular spring and autumn passage migrants to the open fields and farmland in the NHC area, often appearing in early March. Birds in late April to mid-May may be of the Greenland race and have one of the longest migratory flights in the bird world.

Dunnock (Hedge Sparrow)

The **Dunnock** is a widespread and abundant resident breeding bird throughout the NHC area. Pioneering work by Professor Nick Davies in the Botanic Garden using DNA analysis showed this bird to be polyandrous, rearing broods fertilised by more than one male (Davies 1992).

Sparrows

House Sparrows are members of the family of weaver birds. They are obligate colony nesters and nest in small colonies of three to four closely located nests; if nests are lost the colony will fail and the population declines. They are probably polyandrous and polygamous. Only 7–8 pairs were found in Newnham and the University gardens and buildings of west Cambridge. 'They were the sound of my childhood' said a former resident of the area. The highest breeding populations were in Cherry Hinton, Abbey and King's Hedges Wards. To nest they rely on access to roof space or beneath roof tiles, dense ivy growing on east-facing walls, or terraces of nest boxes. They are absent from recent housing developments with sealed and insulated roofs (Jarman 2014).

The **Tree Sparrow** has declined by over 90% since the late 1960s (Balmer *et al.* 2013) and was

> **House Sparrows** used to nest in hedgerows in loose colonies of untidy domed nests in north Cambridge before King's Hedges was built in the late 1960s to early 1970s. Up to the late 1970s foraging flocks of hundreds of birds would descend onto the ripening cereal trial plots at NIAB (now Darwin Green) and the Plant Breeding Institute (now Trumpington Meadows) to eat the ripening grains. The PBI had a dedicated sparrow killer but to no avail on numbers. These rural populations are now extinct and it has become an urban species. A survey in Cambridge City in 2013 and 2014 found 733 'active nests' and an estimated total population of 1000 pairs (Jarman, 2014).

Figure 13.19 Male House Sparrow in Longworth Avenue. (RJJ).

never a regular species in our NHC area. In Europe, it is a bird of open country not human habitations; in central Asia, the situation is reversed and House Sparrows are birds of open country and the Tree Sparrow becomes the bird of habitations (Inskipp and Howard, pers. comm.).

Wagtails, Pipits

Grey Wagtails are considered birds of fast-flowing waterways but they have become regular urban birds often seen (and more often heard) over residential areas and in the city centre well away from watercourses. From 2017–2019, a pair was heard feeding young on the roof of the Marks and Spencer store in Market Square. Birds used to roost on NIAB's greenhouses in Huntingdon Road but this site was demolished in 2009. The population in our NHC area is likely stable with possibly four to five breeding pairs (Robert Brown, pers. comm.).

Yellow Wagtails of the race *Motacilla flava flavissima* are almost entirely confined to Britain and near continent. There are perhaps 4–5 breeding pairs of this declining, Red Listed species, all on arable farmland in the north and south-east of the NHC area. **Pied Wagtails** are common and familiar waterside and urban birds; they can often be seen foraging in supermarket car parks. There used to be a winter roost of 100+ birds in the city centre outside the Lion Yard but this has now dispersed; recent roosts are about 100 at Cambridge Regional College, 85 near Homebase on the Cambridge Retail Park, 150 at Cambridge Leisure in November 2018 and 200–300 at the Clifton Estate in November 2020.

Meadow Pipits are local birds of the farmland on the edge of the NHC area. On the northern edge one to two pairs were regular breeders up to 2016 but since then there have been no breeding records. An adult was feeding young at Hobson's Park in 2017. On the NIAB site up to 2017 before the Darwin Green development there were winter flocks of up to 25, and 40 in Chesterton in March 2018. **Tree Pipits** are rare, though probably annual migrants (see Garden Birdwatching and noc-mig above); recordings of nocturnal flyover birds over Chesterton were made in 2017, 2018 and 2019.

Finches and Buntings

Bramblings are uncommon winter visitors and passage migrants, though their numbers vary from year to year; in some years singles may be seen with other finches visiting garden feeders. The Beechwoods is a regular wintering site where the birds feed on beech mast; up to 40 were recorded there in winter 2018/2019. **Chaffinches** are common breeding residents and winter visitors that readily come to garden feeders. On 23rd October 2016, 71 were counted on visible migration over Lovell Road. **Bullfinches** are uncommon residents; they like tall hedges and have been recorded around Storey's Way, Huntingdon Road and Eddington. **Greenfinches** are common breeding residents but nationally numbers are declining due to the disease Trichomoniasis which is readily spread between birds at garden feeders. Winter Greenfinch flocks include 120 in the Botanic Garden in January 2017, 35+ in Storeys Way in January 2018 and 65 in Fen Ditton/Horningsea in January 2018.

Siskins are uncommon winter visitors and occasional non-breeding summer visitors, often feeding with Lesser Redpolls on alder cones and at garden feeders; they have been seen singing in Cherry Hinton Hall in early April but no breeding was confirmed. Six visited a garden feeder in Chesterton daily over winter 2017/2018 but did not reappear in subsequent winters. **Goldfinches** are very common residents and winter visitors; they have become the familiar finch of urban England. Their abundance may be due to a liking for garden seed feeders, especially those containing sunflower seeds. **Linnets** are confined to farmland on the edges of the NHC area; in the north there are probably eight breeding territories but they are threatened by the Darwin Green development. At Nine Wells, 15 pairs of Linnets have been recorded (Meed 2021); about 200 were on sugar beet stubble close to the Histon Road/Huntingdon Road footpath over winter 2018/2019 and 200+ over winter 2019/2020.

Lesser Redpolls have vanished as breeding birds in the NHC area. This follows a national trend as the population has contracted northwards and westwards; it is a bird of cool temperate northern pine forests and woodlands. This range contraction may be due to climate change. In the 1980s and 1990s it bred regularly and the spring song flight of displaying males could be heard across the city. A male sang regularly from telephone wires across Ridgeon's wood yard in Cromwell Road. The last confirmed breeding was in Coleridge in 2002 but a singing male was heard over Carlton Way in April 2014. It is a winter visitor in declining number, often feeding on alder tree cones.

Figure 13.20 (left) Corn Bunting in Hobson's Park, (right) Meadow Pipit in Hobson's Park. (RJJ).

Crossbills are scarce post-breeding dispersal migrants, which are rarely seen other than as flyovers; most sightings are in mid-summer with records in recent years from north Cambridge and Chesterton. In October and November 2017 there was an exceptional influx of continental **Hawfinches** into Britain; birds were recorded in the Botanic Garden, over north Cambridge and from nocturnal sound recordings over Chesterton on four nights.

Corn Buntings suffered a 90% breeding population decline in Britain between 1970 and 2010 (Balmer *et al.* 2013). A singing male was present in the north of the NHC area in 2015 and 2016 but failed to find a mate; the stronghold is Nine Wells/Hobson's Park where 16 singing males were present in 2018 and 2020. We believe this is one of the best places in East Anglia to see and hear

this species! **Reed Bunting** are commonly recorded in farmland around the NHC area, especially where there are reed-filled ditches. They often nest in adjacent crops of oilseed rape. **Yellowhammers** are thinly distributed in farmland around the NHC area including Trumpington Meadows. A farm site in the north has 3–4 breeding territories. There are 15 breeding territories at Nine Wells (Meed 2021), and the NIAB's Trials ground had a flock of 56 in winter 2017/2018.

Black-headed Bunting is a scarce summer visitor to south-east Europe. Remarkably a first-summer male was found in an observer's garden at Fallowfields, Chesterton in May 1993 (Kirtland 1995). This was part of a mini-influx to Britain in early summer that year. To date this is the only record of this very rare vagrant in Cambridgeshire.

14. Mammals

Introduction

Mammals residing in cities attract attention by the effects they have on their environment and the public perception of the attractiveness of each species. It is only natural that one person's passion is another person's bête noire. So the increasing numbers of some of the more distinctive species has been met with opposing opinions amongst the local human population. **Badgers**, **Foxes** and **Muntjac** are prominent members of the Cambridge fauna and all of them have their supporters and detractors. The reaction of members of the public when faced with these garden visitors can vary from outright hostility to enthusiastic encouragement. Indeed one cause of the population increases may be food provided by humans. But to other people, problems caused by mammals are very serious and companies now exist to help solve wildlife issues. The rise in concern about diseases which have their origin in animals may change the public perception of wild animals in their back garden, but to date the possibility that these interesting garden visitors may be the next source of a disease transmitted by animals does not seem to be a significant public concern.

Two smaller species, **Grey Squirrels** and **Hedgehogs**, are also loved and hated by different people. Both are encouraged by food either left intentionally or put out for birds. A recent spate of Grey Squirrels entering the loft space of city houses has dented their reputation as interesting garden visitors. **Rats** and **House Mice** are generally not welcomed. Rats are everywhere and House Mice can become a serious problem. Nobody intentionally leaves out food to encourage them. But in some of the cemeteries and parkland formerly connected to countryside there survive populations of species which do not seem to belong in the city. **Wood Mice** and **Yellow-necked Mice** are both present in Cambridge and go about their business largely unnoticed. All of the smaller mammals are affected to a greater or lesser extent by another group of predators which certainly are encouraged by humans: domesticated dogs and cats.

Little is known about **Stoats** and **Weasels** in the city. There are few records, yet they are present in the more rural parts of our area. Along the river two larger members of the Mustelidae, **Otter** and **American Mink**, are known and their distribution has been well studied. **Polecats** are known to be present in Cambridgeshire in increasing numbers and they have been seen amongst road kill, but they have yet to be found in Cambridge.

There are 11 species of bats in Cambridge. Bat punt safaris on the river are popular, but bats, like other mammals, are disliked or feared by some people.

Larger mammals

Foxes

Sightings of **Foxes** *Vulpes vulpes* within the city have been reported during the project and there is a substantial population living within the NHC area. In one road alone we have 10 sightings, often at night and during the breeding season in daylight. Fox calls made during mating are very characteristic and are often heard. Other indications of their presence include footprints, particularly in fresh snow. Gardens which otherwise seem to be free of Foxes may carry the signs of a visit when they are searching for food on a cold, snowy winter's night. A number of dens have been found, and a common location is in tunnels under garden sheds whose floors provide a solid roof to the den. Unusual individuals have also been found, including a black Fox in the Science Park in 2019. This was not the first to be sighted in Cambridge but was the first for several years.

A number of national studies have attempted to estimate the size of the urban Fox population and concluded that it is growing but that there is considerable variation between cities. Nationally, it is estimated that there is one urban Fox for every 300 city dwellers. Our area has about 120,000 people occupying 30 km², which would imply 13 Foxes per km².

Fox populations have more than academic interest, because of the threat of rabies from illegally imported pets and the potential for transmission to wild populations. Except for one isolated case in Newmarket in 1970, Britain has managed to keep this disease out. **Fox tapeworm** *Echinococcus*

Figure 14.1 A Fox outside the Crown Court in East Road, Cambridge. (NRM).

multilocularis is present in European and Asian Fox populations and can be very harmful to pets and humans, but has not yet been found in Britain. Raids on the increasing numbers of chickens kept in gardens also gives Foxes a bad name as wasteful killers. On the positive side, Foxes are predators of rodents and help to regulate their populations. They are appreciated and enjoyed by many people.

Badgers

In recent years there has been a growing number of reports of **Badgers** *Meles meles* in Cambridge. Badger setts have appeared in several college grounds and also in private gardens. Newnham College has the biggest sett, with over 20 entrances. This seems to be one of the main setts in the city, with numerous outlier setts. In total there are six known setts within a mile of Market Square and a number of others further out from the centre. Badgers in urban areas have food sources that are not available in the wider countryside. Human-derived food sources, such as food put out for Cats and Hedgehogs, are readily consumed by Badgers. They also dig up flower beds and lawns in search of bulbs and invertebrates. The students of some colleges have been banned from feeding them. One of the effects of this abundance of food is an increase in size of urban badgers compared with their country cousins.

How Badgers get around the city is an interesting question. Camera traps have recorded them travelling along the passageways behind houses in Newnham, and they frequently tunnel under fences, creating their own routes through the urban jungle. Some college gardeners have expressed frustration when the Badgers create highways through flower beds on their way to the college next door. One garden owner gave up trying to live with Badgers and constructed a Badger-proof fence across the middle of her garden. The Badgers and their excavations were allowed to exist in her old orchard, while humans used the remainder of the garden. Unfortunately the Badgers do not always respect boundary lines, no matter how well constructed.

Originally, Badgers must have come into Cambridge from the surrounding countryside.

Figure 14.2 Badger strolling down a snicket in Newnham. (OW).

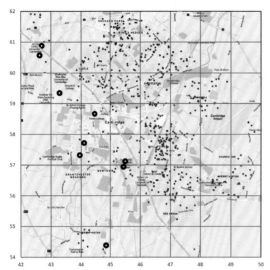

Figure 14.3 Map of Badger setts (black rings) and Hedgehog sightings (red circles and various triangles) in Cambridge. The pink line shows the historic main road through the middle of the city. Most Hedgehogs are found to the east of the line. Most Badger setts are found to the west of the line. (Map courtesy of bighedgehogmap.org, including data from the People's Trust for Endangered Species [red circles and triangles], the Suffolk Wildlife Trust [yellow triangles] and Project Splatter [purple triangles]).

Most reports are from the west side of the city, but sightings on the east side of the river are increasing. They have for example been seen in Jesus College and are starting to visit the more densely built-up parts of the city.

Hedgehogs

Hedgehogs *Erinaceus europaeus* are common night-time visitors to many gardens. They are encouraged by many households by the provision of food. A new trend is to make Hedgehog holes through fences, increasing the ease of Hedgehog movement between gardens. Some people even go as far as building hedgehog hotels with waterproof roofs and warm winter bedding.

There is concern about the national decline in numbers. One of the culprits for this decline has been suggested as Neonicotinoids (although three of the most significant chemicals were banned in 2018). Neonicotinoids have been used by gardeners to get rid of chafer grubs in lawns. These grubs are an important food for Hedgehogs and their removal can be detrimental.

Cream-coloured or leucistic Hedgehogs are more common than true albinos. They have

pigmented eyes and blonde coloration to their spines and belly. One example of this type was found in Trumpington during the study. It was quite young and living close to a large Badger sett, so its survival chances may be very dependent on whether the gardens it is using are also frequented by the Badgers.

Do Badgers hunt Hedgehogs?

Badgers are significant predators and Hedgehogs try to avoid contact with them, even showing avoidance behaviour to just their smell. Badgers have a strong sense of smell and claws which can penetrate the spiny skin and tear open an unfortunate Hedgehog. So clearly predation can occur, but there is discussion about how many are killed in this way. Cambridge has a growing Badger population. If you divide the city in half along the line of Huntingdon Road, through the middle of the town and out along Hills Road, the situations on the eastern and western sides of this line are very different (Figure 14.3). The eastern side is much more densely developed than the west. There are at least eight Badger setts on the western side of the line and one quite close to it. The Hedgehog sightings on either side of the line are: 331 Hedgehogs to the east and 32 to the west. One resident of Newnham reported that both Badgers and Hedgehogs visited their garden, but it was not long before three empty hedgehog skins were found on the lawn. The same story was repeated in a garden near Castle Hill, where the frequent camera trap records of Hedgehogs ceased completely after the first few visits by a Badger. So the Hedgehog is doing quite well in the eastern parts of Cambridge but badly in the west.

It is interesting how views on this matter have changed over time. Neal (1948) commented in his *New Naturalist* monograph about the Badger 'Hedgehogs are certainly a favourite food' but noted that Hedgehogs were eaten only occasionally. Morris (2018) was more definite, saying that 'The badger is undoubtedly the most important predator of hedgehogs'. He suggested that towns could provide the Hedgehog with a refuge from the Badger.

Otters

Otters *Lutra lutra* are present in Cambridge and are found along the line of the River Cam. They have also been reported following up the chalk streams of Hobson's Conduit, Cherry Hinton Brook and Bin Brook. Their presence has been detected by several methods. The location of spraint (droppings) left to scent-mark their territory can be monitored and it gives a good record of Otter activity. Direct observations from members of the public also indicate where they have been active. Recently camera traps which can record activity remotely have also been deployed successfully.

Sightings and signs of Otters have been reported to the NatHistCam survey. College night porters are the most likely to observe them. Darwin College is well placed beside the Mill Pool and the porters have reported a number of sightings. They have also found traces of dead fish. One member of the Leckhampton ground staff described riding along Grange Road, and hearing cries coming from the bank of Bin Brook. On investigating, he found a young Otter cub alone and apparently abandoned by its mother at a time when the stream was in flood. The cub was rescued and taken to an Otter sanctuary, where it was successfully reared and released. In the early part of the 20th century the Cambridge University otter hounds regularly caught Otters in Grantchester and there are numerous recent reports of Otters there. One well-known author and his wife had a Carp pond close to the river near Grantchester mill pond. The Carp were eaten and evidence in the form of footprints indicated that Otters were to blame.

In 2020 observations of Otters in the centre of the city declined, but there were sightings along the course of the Cherry Hinton Brook. The large fishing lakes beside the brook have suffered from raids by these efficient predators. The lakes hold many specimen fish between 10 and 15 kg. In all, eight fish were taken by Otters according to one member of the fishing club. One fish in excess of 10 kg was found half eaten in the largest of the Cherry Hinton lakes and the remains of a half-eaten 2 kg Pike have been seen beside Barnwell Pit. A report from one of the anglers indicated that Otters have been using the Territorial Army Lake for three years.

American Mink

American Mink *Neovison vison* are found close to fresh water in most instances. They are not native to Britain, having been released over a number of years since 1927 when they were first introduced in mink farms. Numerous escapes and releases have occurred including a large release in the 1980s by animal rights activists. The result has been an increasing population of these predators along Britain's waterways. Mink have had a deleterious effect on populations of waterfowl and especially on **Water Voles**, which were brought to low population levels. Mink are able to enter their holes. The smaller females in particular will eliminate Water Voles from long stretches of waterway in a very short time. By 2010 there were many Mink in the River Cam,

Figure 14.4 Otter investigating a garage used to store boats in Chesterton, 2016. (PJD).

and Water Voles had disappeared from their former habitats along the river. They survived in the upper parts of Hobson's Conduit, Cherry Hinton Brook and Bin Brook. They were also present in some isolated lakes and ponds.

In 2010, a programme of Mink control was started in the Bourn Brook and Upper Cam Catchment (Chapter 16). This eradication programme has allowed the Water Vole to return to the river, spreading out into areas such as Ditton Meadows and Byron's Pool. A much wider eradication programme has now been initiated, aiming to eliminate Mink from the whole of East Anglia.

Muntjac

This species of deer has been present in Cambridge since at least 1967 when one was regularly seen in a Newton Road garden. Its numbers have increased

Figure 14.6 Muntjac in a small Cambridge garden where it had taken up residence. A Magpie was seen to spend 10 minutes picking ticks and dead skin out of the deer's ears and fur. The deer seemed to enjoy the attention. (DJM).

greatly since 2014. It has now become very common across the city but is particularly abundant in Cherry Hinton, Newnham and the Botanic Garden. It has become well habituated to the presence of humans, and the only real threats come from domestic dogs and motor vehicles.

Muntjac *Muntiacus reevesi* can penetrate robust fences and cause havoc in gardens. Using camera traps, it has been estimated that the Botanic Garden has 26 of these deer living within the grounds, where they damage the plant collections. They have the ability to hide inconspicuously under vegetation and will dig themselves a shallow hole under the low-hanging branches of shrubs. In April 2019 one Muntjac was observed giving birth just a few feet from the observer, beside a path. Dead Muntjac are often seen at the side of roads as a result of accidents with vehicles. The number of these accidents has increased recently as the population of these deer has increased.

Roe Deer

Most records of **Roe Deer** *Capreolus capreolus* come from the fields around the margins of the city. They are regularly seen north of Fen Ditton and are mostly observed as solitary individuals. One Roe Deer came into Chesterton and there was a road kill near Trumpington. Roe Deer have not penetrated the city in the same way as Muntjac, but they are much more secretive and are most active at dawn and dusk, so some may have been missed.

Fallow Deer

Fallow Deer *Dama dama* are locally abundant in south and east Cambridgeshire. Some herds recently became so large that numbers have had to be reduced by culling. The Dullingham herd was more than 100 head before the cull. Despite being so common in the surrounding countryside, they have rarely been

Figure 14.7 Three Roe Deer near Horningsea in 2019. (DJM).

observed close to the city. The nearest record to Cambridge is between Trumpington and Shelford. Two deer parks with Fallow Deer are known to have existed in the past, one in Peterhouse and the other at the Leys School. It seems the Leys deer were removed in the late 19th century. The Peterhouse deer are reported to have gone after the First World War. There are no subsequent records of Fallow Deer in Cambridge.

Rabbit

Rabbits *Oryctolagus cuniculus* are common and widespread around the outskirts of the city. They are also to be found on many areas of waste ground within the city. In the University, 41% of colleges reported having Rabbits in their grounds. These populations have shown dramatic swings as first Myxomatosis and then Rabbit Haemorrhagic Disease have caused extensive declines. But the populations in the city now seem to be widespread and fairly stable. The Rabbit is capable of fast reproduction so recovery can be rapid. The increasing numbers of predators in the form of Badgers, Foxes and Buzzards may also affect population numbers. Rabbit populations do particularly well on derelict land and around the margins of farmland. As more brownfield land is developed, this habitat is becoming scarcer. Some former chalk pits near Cherry Hinton have been used for landfill and have not yet been developed. These areas carry substantial populations of Rabbits. There are also many records of Rabbits from the sides of the A14 and M11.

Brown Hare

Brown Hares *Lepus europaeus* are common on the agricultural land surrounding the city, but tend not to come into the more built-up areas. Their numbers have been fluctuating due to the European Brown Hare Syndrome Virus which is similar to but distinct from the Rabbit Haemorrhagic Disease Virus. It has been shown that these two diseases are caused by different viruses and they do not cross-infect the two species. Hare coursing is also a problem in Cambridgeshire, but it is not known if this happens close to the city.

Small mammals

Rodents

The **Brown Rat** *Rattus norvegicus* is ubiquitous in Cambridge and its environs. These adaptable animals have colonised every habitat present in

Figure 14.10 Brown Rat. (MH).

Cambridge and thrive in the presence of humans and have done so for a considerable period of time. They can utilise any type of habitat from woodland to fully urban areas. Despite being so numerous they are seldom seen except when they invade

> The **Black Rat** *Rattus rattus* was once common in Cambridge but now pretty much extinct in Cambridge as well as the rest of Britain. There are occasional sightings of one or a few individuals imported from the continent with goods and in lorries, but the rats have not persisted. They should not be confused with 'black' Brown Rats which occur occasionally in Cambridge.

domestic properties. The number of records is very small, probably because this species is considered a pest.

House Mouse *Mus musculus* is common in many habitats, particularly alongside human habitation. It is present in more rural areas but in lower densities. This species is under-recorded, probably because it is considered a pest, but it is very abundant in Cambridge.

Wood Mouse *Apodemus sylvaticus* is a very versatile species that has adapted to living in urban habitats as well as hedgerows, parks and gardens. It is very common and is encountered more regularly than the House Mouse in most parts of Cambridge.

Yellow-necked Mouse *Apodemus flavicollis* is primarily a woodland species so is scarce in Cambridge. In the autumn Yellow-necked Mice move from the countryside into urban areas and dwellings, so they may be encountered particularly in the outlying areas of the city.

Figure 14.11 (left) House Mouse, (right) Wood Mouse. (MH).

Figure 14.12 Harvest Mouse. (MH).

There are very few areas of suitable habitat for the **Harvest Mouse** *Micromys minutus* in Cambridge and most records are from the outskirts where small pockets of suitable habitat can be found, but even there they are uncommon. This was once a common species in hedgerows, but modern farming practices and urban habitat management are not compatible with their life cycle requirements.

Bank Vole *Myodes glareolus* is a very common species of parks, brownfield sites, scrubland, hedgerows and particularly gardens where it is commonly encountered. This species likes to feed on fruits and seeds, coming into conflict with gardeners. Bank Voles can be found almost

everywhere in Cambridge apart from the most densely urbanised parts.

The **Field Vole** *Microtus agrestis* is more restricted in its habitat requirements than the Bank Vole, preferring areas of long grass and cover, but it is fairly adaptable and the areas of habitat can be quite small. It is found all over Cambridge in parklands, river banks, grassy scrub areas, hedgerows and large gardens.

The **Water Vole** *Arvicola amphibius* is a real success story. It was reduced to a few sites in the Cambridge area in the late 1990s and early 2000s and extinction in the area seemed imminent. But following the eradication of the American Mink, the small relict populations have expanded and

Figure 14.13 (left) Water Vole, (right) Bank Vole. (MH).

Water Voles are now present in good numbers in almost every waterway in our area and are often seen in the city centre. Some individuals can be quite confiding and they are popular photographic subjects on social media.

Red Squirrels *Sciurus vulgaris* were once common in Cambridge but started to decline once the introduced Grey Squirrels reached the area. They were outcompeted by them and the Squirrel Pox Virus that Grey Squirrels carry is more dangerous to the Red Squirrels than the Greys. Red Squirrels have not been seen in the Cambridge area since the 1980s and are unlikely to return.

Eastern Grey Squirrel *Sciurus carolinensis* was introduced from North America in the 1870s and is now the most commonly seen mammal in Cambridge. Grey Squirrels are present in most habitats and are particularly common in woodland, parks, scrub and hedgerows. They are quite bold and take advantage of bird-feeders in gardens which is where most people encounter them.

Insectivores

Common Shrew *Sorex araneus* is the most common and widespread of the shrews and is found in almost any green space that has suitable cover, including woodland, hedgerows, gardens and areas of scrub. They are often encountered in gardens when people move objects under which they reside. They are found widely within the city as well as the rural surroundings where they are very common.

Pygmy Shrew *Sorex minutus* is probably under-recorded as it can be difficult to separate from the Common Shrew without close scrutiny. Pygmy Shrews are present in Cambridge in very similar places and habitats to the Common Shrew; which adds to the difficulty of identification. They are commoner in the rural outskirts of Cambridge.

Water Shrew *Neomys fodiens* is a very elusive Cambridge resident, recorded at only two sites in the city but is present in outlying areas where it particularly likes ponds, small streams and other water bodies. It is probably more common than we think as it is hard to observe it or see evidence of its presence.

Black Squirrels are the melanistic form of the Eastern Grey Squirrel not a separate species. Their core area is Cambridgeshire, Bedfordshire and Hertfordshire, where they are frequent, but outside this area they are scarce. They are widely distributed within Cambridge itself and sightings come from a variety of habitats. In Girton the majority of squirrels are black but most areas have relatively few black individuals.

Figure 14.14 Black Eastern Grey Squirrel. (MH).

Figure 14.15 (left) Common Shrew, (right) Mole. (MH).

Mole *Talpa europaea* is common in Cambridge and is found in many central areas particularly where there are green spaces, verges or gardens. Their mostly subterranean existence means that they are hardly ever seen, but their presence is easy to detect by the characteristic molehills. They are extremely common in the surrounding rural areas.

Carnivores

Polecat *Mustela putorius* has recolonised East Anglia over the last 10 years. The first Cambridgeshire record for over 100 years was of a Polecat live-trapped during the Mink eradication project in 2010. Cambridgeshire Polecats derive partly from expansion of their natural range, together with some limited reintroductions further west. They are now quite common in Cambridgeshire but have not really penetrated the city and all sightings have been in the rural surroundings.

Weasel (*Mustela nivalis*) is the smallest of our mustelids. Its main prey are mice and voles so this

Ferret *Mustela furo* is a domesticated Polecat. Feral Ferrets are present in Cambridgeshire, derived from escaped pets. Some individuals are very similar to Polecats but others are very different in coloration, usually a sandy colour which has been selectively bred. However, since the return of the Polecat there has been some interbreeding and the paler colour forms are declining. It is expected that they will revert to the wild coloration and be absorbed into the Polecat population. Feral Ferrets are only likely to be seen at the edge of the city.

predator is present in many parts of our area where prey are present. Weasels inhabit parkland, scrub, woodland, and pockets of green space. They are not very common in Cambridge itself, being much commoner in the outlying areas.

Stoat (*Mustela erminea*) is found in the rural outskirts of Cambridge where it is fairly common. It has not really penetrated the city very much. Stoats are largely diurnal, but are not often seen despite their relative abundance.

Figure 14.16 (left) Stoat, (right) Weasel. (MH).

Bats

Introduction

Most people will have seen bats flying around at dusk, usually as they walk the dog or sit out in the garden on a summer's evening. Many people will likely be co-existing with bats that roost in houses, knowingly or otherwise. Love them or hate them, bats are fascinating mammals that have inspired folklore and gothic tales in cultures across the globe. They are the only mammals able to undertake powered flight; they give birth to young and nurture them until they are weaned; they are not blind, nor do they purposely fly into people's hair; and, perhaps most interesting of all, for such small mammals, bats are amazingly long-lived, and their DNA may hold clues to help humans stay healthier for longer (Dietz & Keifer 2018; Teeling 2019).

Of the 18 species of bat that are resident in Britain, Cambridgeshire is home to 11 – potentially 12 if the presence of **Brandt's** *Myotis brandtii* is ever confirmed (Hows *et al.* 2016, Cambridgeshire Bat Group 2020). Records of these species within the county reflect their habitat preferences and abundance, and it was a pleasant surprise during the collation of bat records to discover that a total of 10 species have been recorded within the NHC area. These species are as follows, in no particular order: **Common Pipistrelle** *Pipistrellus pipistrellus*, **Soprano Pipistrelle** *Pipistrellus pygmaeus*, **Nathusius' Pipistrelle** *Pipistrellus nathusii*, **Brown Long-eared Bat** *Plecotus auritus*, **Barbastelle** *Barbastella barbastellus*, **Noctule** *Nyctalus noctula*, **Serotine** *Eptesicus serotinus*, **Natterer's Bat** *Myotis nattereri*, **Daubenton's Bat** *Myotis daubentonii* and **Whiskered Bat** *Myotis mystacinus*.

Whilst all bats in the UK are afforded statutory protection, some species are of particular interest for the conservation of biodiversity. Soprano Pipistrelle, Brown Long-eared, Noctule and Barbastelle are listed as Priority Species under Section 41 of the Natural Environmental and Rural Communities (NERC) Act (2006).

Species distributions

Records may have originated from bat group or other public activities, such as the Bats on the River trips in summer 2017 and 2018 along the River Cam, and the recorded presence of several bat species during annual field surveys of Cambridge Botanic Garden, part of a national monitoring programme run by the Bat Conservation Trust

(BCT). The distributions of all bats within the NHC area are presented in Figures 14.17, 14.18 and 14,19, with a total of 164 records.

River trips and bat surveys produce most of the records, but several records have come from bat carers who receive calls from members of the public after discovering injured or exhausted bats. It was through a bat carer that we have a single record of a **Whiskered Bat** in the NHC area, north of the River Cam near Chesterton in 2019. Barty, named by his carer, was brought in by a cat and had been bitten near the shoulder joint, had a big tear in his tail membrane, and had heavily bruised legs. He responded well to treatment and was released 10 days later near to where he had been found. This record is a great surprise as Whiskered Bats are associated with woodland, and are not very common in the county.

From the distribution maps it is immediately obvious that certain species are much more frequently recorded than others. **Common Pipistrelle**, **Soprano Pipistrelle** and **Noctule** are the most frequently recorded, correlating with their habitat preferences. These species are happy to forage and commute across more open habitats and are better adapted to urban environments than other species. **Daubenton's** have also been frequently recorded along or near to waterbodies, of which there are plenty within the NHC area; they are distinctive in flight as they forage close to the surface of water, catching insects in their tail membrane. **Brown Long-eared Bats** have a few scattered records throughout the NHC area, but as this delicate-looking bat has very quiet echolocation calls and does not emerge from roosts until much later than other bats, it is probably under-recorded.

As with the single record of the Whiskered Bat, there are also only single records of **Barbastelle** and **Natterer's** within the NHC area. The Barbastelle record south-west of the city is not so far away from Wandlebury Country Park where this species is often heard on detectors during walked transects, so it is likely that their foraging range may take them closer to the city. Like Whiskered bats, Natterer's are usually associated with more wooded landscapes so the record of this species in the Newnham area is unexpected.

The **Nathusius' Pipistrelle** is quite a rare and special bat in Britain, and while they are present at several sites across Cambridgeshire there is only

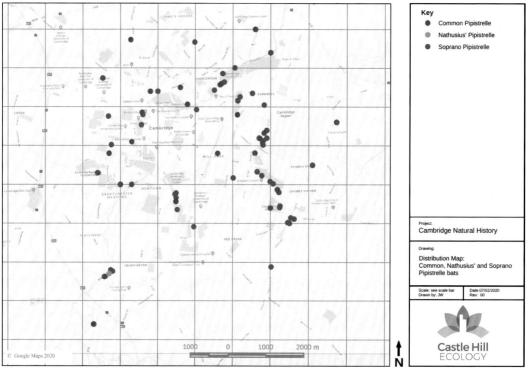

Figure 14.17 Distribution of Common Pipistrelle, Nathusius' Pipistrelle and Soprano Pipistrelle.

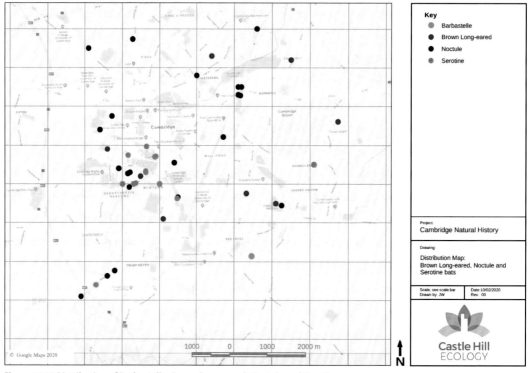

Figure 14.18 Distribution of Barbastelle, Brown long-eared, Noctule and Serotine.

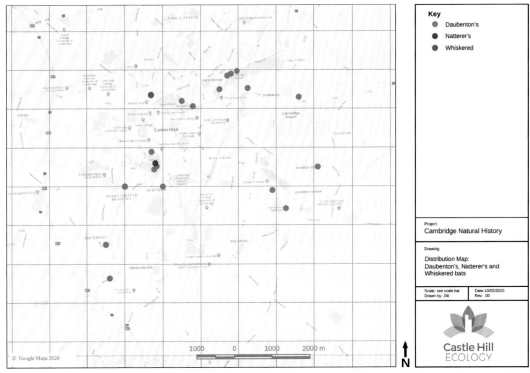

Figure 14.19 Distribution of Daubenton's, Natterer's and Whiskered.

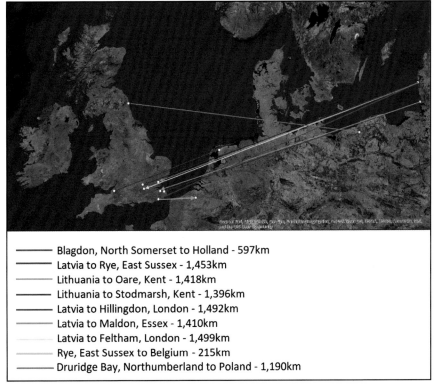

Figure 14.20
Nathusius' Pipistrelle **migration routes.**
(Source: Bat Conservation Trust 2020).

——— Blagdon, North Somerset to Holland - 597km
——— Latvia to Rye, East Sussex - 1,453km
——— Lithuania to Oare, Kent - 1,418km
——— Lithuania to Stodmarsh, Kent - 1,396km
——— Latvia to Hillingdon, London - 1,492km
——— Latvia to Maldon, Essex - 1,410km
——— Latvia to Feltham, London - 1,499km
——— Rye, East Sussex to Belgium - 215km
——— Druridge Bay, Northumberland to Poland - 1,190km

one record of this species within the NHC area. Ringing projects here and on the continent have shown us that this species migrates vast distances. Individuals ringed in Latvia have appeared in London, a distance of 1,499 km (Figure 14.20), while individuals ringed here in Britain have turned up in Belgium, Poland and Holland.

While there are species that are rarer, either nationally or just within Cambridgeshire, the presence of **Serotine** is of particular note, with most records concentrated south-west of the city around Grantchester Meadows. Serotine has often been recorded in south-west Cambridgeshire but seems to be less frequent across the rest of the county. It may have been under-recorded in these areas, but the records we do have suggest roosts may exist close to the city.

Concluding remarks

Many of the older buildings within Cambridge have potential to support roosting bats; Pipistrelles may roost under old clay roof tiles, or Brown Long-eared may roost within old timber-framed roof voids. It is likely you will not even know they are there! Buildings that may not be commonly associated with bats, such as new structures and high-rise flat-roofed buildings, may in fact provide valuable areas to hibernate. Research has shown this to be the case in the Netherlands (Korsten *et al.* 2016), so it is possible that Pipistrelles in particular may hibernate in taller buildings within Cambridge city centre.

Similarly, older trees throughout the NHC area, especially within the Cambridge colleges and the Botanic Garden, are likely to contain holes, cracks and splits where a bat may snuggle in to roost. The extent to which the built environment is used by bats will depend on the species; bats such as the Pipistrelles and Noctule are better adapted to urban areas and higher levels of light pollution in comparison to the *Myotis* bats and Barbastelle. Roosting habits aside, Cambridge has large areas of well-connected habitat that are suitable for foraging bats, thanks in part to the River Cam and the Cambridge commons and parks. This perhaps helps to explain how such a variety of species have been recorded within the NHC area.

There will always be more to learn about bats in Cambridge, whether it is finding new roost locations, discovering popular foraging areas and important habitat corridors, or gaining a better understanding of the distribution of some of our species. One species notable for its absence is **Leisler's Bat** *Nyctalus leisleri*. One of the least common bats in the county, Leisler's may simply not be present in great numbers, have a patchy distribution, or be under-recorded. The challenge going forward is to continue collating reliable confirmed records of our bats, with perhaps more focus on under-recorded areas.

15. Interesting sites

College gardens
College garden survey 2017–2019

The University of Cambridge is made up of 31 constituent colleges, which provide living accommodation for students amongst other functions. Many are of great antiquity and have extensive grounds, thereby providing a very large area of relatively undisturbed habitat for wildlife. Some sites have been unchanged in layout and function for several hundred years. Besides the more public gardens, there are often smaller areas of private garden, set aside for the Master, Fellows or Scholars. Since the River Cam flows through the city, many of the Colleges have some access to water.

The distinctive types of habitat which are found within the colleges include:
- Tall buildings, often built of limestone or ancient masonry, with opportunities for secure nests and roosts for insects, birds and bats
- Large parkland spaces with mature trees and few obstacles to movement of wildlife
- More formal areas with closely cut grass and well-tended flower beds
- Playing fields often surrounded by trees and less intensively managed habitats
- Old orchards with mature fruit trees
- Areas specifically set aside for wildlife and informal gardens
- Water frontage onto the River Cam
- Large mature ponds or ditches with emergent vegetation
- A wide variety of trees including some veteran specimen trees
- Student vegetable patches with compost heaps.

Between 2017 and 2019, all colleges were contacted and the Head Gardener (where possible) was asked about the wildlife in the college grounds. Questions included:
- What is the area of the gardens and are you on more than one site?
- What birds, mammals, amphibians and reptiles have you seen in your garden over the past two years? Please comment on problem mammals.

- Is there an active programme of natural history observations?
- Do you have a pond, compost heap, vegetable patch, bird feeder(s), bird boxes, wild-flower meadow?
- Do you use metaldehyde slug control, if so, to what extent?
- Are you partially or wholly organic?
- What are your worst weeds?

Problems in collecting data

Occasionally, it was found that the Head Gardener had retired or had been replaced by contractors, so historical records were difficult to obtain. Some colleges had multiple sites, ideally requiring individual data on each. Sports grounds were included when they were adjacent to the college, but not otherwise. While the main colleges were contacted, the theological colleges and other smaller institutions were not, neither were schools. Outside the 'official questions', much other information was volunteered and may not have been systematically recorded.

Findings

Data was available for 32 sites. The total area of college gardens (as reported) was 147 ha, i.e. about 2.3% of the total NHC area. However, the actual area of open space under college and University control is much greater than this, as only the main sites were included, omitting many smaller sites, faculty sites and the most of the sports grounds, which are at least 40 ha in total.

Provision and management for wildlife

It was clear that many of the gardeners (also other staff, especially in the Porters' Lodges) were interested in wildlife and keen to enhance it. Several mentioned involvement and interest from the whole college community of students, staff and fellows. Student ecology projects have been encouraged and are helpful to gardeners. Besides bird boxes, present at 28% of sites, several mentioned bee hives, log piles, insect hotels and pollinator borders. Increasing numbers of colleges were setting aside land for wildflower meadows and

Figure 15.1 Leckhampton Meadow. (PAR).

one site, at Leckhampton, had abandoned formal borders altogether. This proved particularly good for butterflies.

Moth trapping was carried out at four sites and regular bee and butterfly counts at one. At Peterhouse and Jesus, full illustrated records of all vertebrate and invertebrate fauna sightings have been compiled since 2017 and 2014 respectively. Ecological management included avoidance of hedge cutting during the nesting season and rotational cutting of pond and riverbanks to avoid disturbance to **Water Voles** and birds. At one site, concrete bank reinforcement to the brook had caused **Fox** and **Hedgehog** casualties, so the banks were returned to softer and more rounded outlines.

About half the colleges had some area devoted to vegetables and three had beehives. Most had extensive composting arrangements. Of the 27 sites where information was available, one was wholly organic and three said they used only minimal glyphosate, with no pesticides. Five used metaldehyde slug bait occasionally (one only in the greenhouse), two used it more freely, while 20 did not use it at all.

Rivers, ditches and ponds

The majority of sites (84%) had some water – either access to the Bin Brook, or River Cam and its ditches, or contained one or more ponds, some of considerable size. Several obtained water from

Figure 15.2 Darwin College bee hives. (PAR).

Figure 15.3 Darwin College bug hotel. (PAR).

Figure 15.4 **Trinity College fake coyote.** (GCK).

Hobson's Conduit. Ditches and ponds, with emergent vegetation, enhanced insect populations and were beneficial to amphibian, fish, bird and mammal populations. There were comments about bats, dragonflies, damselflies, **Grass Snakes**, **Otters** fishing for **Swan Mussels**, **Water Voles**, **Kingfishers**, **Common Frogs**, **Common Toads**, **Eels** and other fish – including some very large fish. **Canada Geese** were previously discouraged along the Backs by oiling the eggs and subsequently by deploying a fake coyote – apparently effective!

Trees and plants

The larger sites had many mature trees including some massive **Plane**, **Willow** and **Yew** trees. The huge **Chichester Elms** *Ulmus* × *hollandica* at Queens' are described in detail in chapter 4. Robinson College claimed a total of 800 trees, while another had a booklet devoted to its notable tree collection. Churchill College had an exceptional amount of **Mistletoe** and many had areas of woodland garden. Nine sites had received a detailed botanical survey; all had plant species that were unique to them and all had species that are on the Cambridgeshire Register of Plants of Conservation Concern (Shanklin 2020). Most had old lawns, dating back to when they were grazed pasture. In Trinity College, there was a large area of **Goldilocks Buttercup** *Ranunculus auricomus*, more typical of shady places such as woodland or copses.

Gardeners were asked which were their two worst weeds. Of 26 replies, **Bindweed** was mentioned by 18 and **Ground Elder** by 10. Others included **Nettles** (2), **Giant Hogweed** (2), **Yarrow** in lawns (2), **Willowherb** (2) and a miscellany of 12 other species.

Figure 15.5 **Huge Chichester Elms at Queens' College.** (PAR).

Mammals

Although the Head Gardeners were asked for information, it was sometimes the case that the Night Porters were much better informed about mammals, especially those whose grounds had CCTV. 'No, we don't see **Otters** ever' turned into 'Oh, yes, they come up onto the lawn with **Swan Mussels** and leave the shells around'! Reports of footprints, spraints and half-eaten fish have come from several riverside colleges including Clare, Darwin, Trinity and St John's.

Similarly **Badgers** were rarely seen in the daytime, but were present in 44% of college grounds, one having an enormous sett with more than 20 entrances. **Rats** (88%), **Fox** (88%) and **Muntjac Deer** (91%) were very common. Muntjac are intrepid, seen day and night, and can get through all but the very smallest gaps in hedges and fences. It is almost impossible to keep them out. **Grey Squirrels** were almost ubiquitous (97% of sites), with black ones reported from four sites – this melanic form is concentrated mainly in Hertfordshire, Bedfordshire and Cambridgeshire.

Hedgehogs were reported at 63% of sites, but rarely where Badgers were active. **Water Voles** had been seen at 25% of colleges, which indicated an encouraging recovery following the successful programme of removing **Mink** from the whole of the Cambridge water system. Other mammals mentioned were **Rabbits**, **Moles**, **Mice** and **Voles**. Moles were surprisingly scarce (6%).

Given the presence of water, it was not surprising that 75% of sites had **Common Frogs** and 53% **Common Toads**. **Smooth Newts** and **Grass Snakes** were present in 31%. **Slow Worms** were absent however, as in Cambridge generally.

Birds

The bird survey (by questionnaire) proved difficult, as some Head Gardeners were much more aware of their avian neighbours than others. Table 15.1 shows the reported prevalence of various birds, 43 species in total. Notable was the frequency (28% of colleges) with which the **Peregrine Falcon** was observed,

nesting on a nearby University building and hunting **Pigeons** in the Market Square and college gardens. **Sparrowhawks** (75%) and **Kestrels** (56%) were also flourishing.

A quarter of colleges reported **Blackcaps**. Perhaps surprising was the prevalence of **Pheasants** (69%) in the centre of the city, reflecting the availability of habitat for surplus birds released into the surrounding countryside. **Tawny Owls** may be under-recorded (as gardeners are not present during

Table 15.1 More frequent bird species reported from 32 college gardens according to a survey of staff between 2017 and 2019. Counts exclude birds that had not been seen for two years.

Species	Total	Species	Total
Blackbird	31	Swallow	22
Blue Tit	31	Swift	22
Magpie	31	Long-tailed Tit	22
Robin	31	Pheasant	22
Green Woodpecker	29	House Sparrow	21
Jay	29	Goldfinch	20
Mallard	29	Goldcrest	20
Woodpigeon	29	Black-headed Gull	19
Jackdaw	28	Tawny Owl	19
Wren	28	Moorhen	19
Feral Pigeon	27	Coal Tit	18
Great Tit	26	Kestrel	18
Collared Dove	26	House Martin	16
Pied Wagtail	25	Greenfinch	15
Carrion Crow	24	Blackcap	13
Chaffinch	24	Redwing	13
Sparrowhawk	24	Bullfinch	12
Great Spotted Woodpecker	24	Chiffchaff	12
Grey Heron	24	Fieldfare	12
Song Thrush	24	Mute Swan	10
Starling	23	Peregrine	9
Dunnock	22		

Figure 15.6 Adult and young Tawny Owls in Queens' College. (RKW).

the night) so when reported from 59% of sites, they would seem to be very successful. More owl boxes are needed! **Great Spotted** (75%) and **Green Woodpeckers** (91%) were in extraordinary numbers for the city, showing that they really like college life, especially the mature trees for nesting.

Swallows 69%, **Swifts** 69% and **House Martins** 50% were regularly noted, the college buildings sometimes providing nest sites for them, as with the House Martins under the main entrance arch of Trinity College Great Court. Swifts are not known to nest in the colleges, so an effort to provide boxes for them would be worthwhile.

Nuthatches, generally rare in Cambridge, were regularly sighted along the Backs. The presence of mature **Oaks** within their breeding territories may be important, but their main threat when nesting is probably the ubiquitous **Grey Squirrels**.

Grey Herons and **Mallards** were regularly noted along the watercourses. There is a heronry less than a mile from the city centre, in Newnham.

The Thrush family was well represented, with **Blackbird** (97%), **Song Thrush** (75%), **Redwing** (41%) and **Fieldfare** (38%), as was the **Robin** (97%). **Grey Wagtails** were rarely reported. There was one report of a **Common Sandpiper**.

Conclusion

Inevitable conflicts arise between the impact of wildlife and the demands of garden maintenance. Badgers, present in many of the colleges, have dramatic effects which are not always welcome –

the college with the biggest sett had planned that area for a croquet lawn! Crows, in their search for Cockchafer grubs, can do extensive damage to lawns. Foxes may discover human-derived food sources which lead to unwelcome activities in the dead of night. Unwanted Canada Geese foul the lawns! The use of pesticides and herbicides makes gardeners' lives easier, but may harm wildlife.

Many of the University and college garden staff are knowledgeable about wildlife – often, one or more can be considered an expert or enthusiast. They are all aware of both the effects of wild creatures on their gardens and also the effects of their management on biodiversity. Many are taking active steps towards conservation and wish they could devote more time and effort to this issue. The colleges are also becoming aware of the benefits that wildlife can bring to the wellbeing of students. The large area of University and college grounds, the great diversity of habitats and this positive approach all contribute to a huge diversity and abundance of plant and animal species.

Cambridge University Botanic Garden

Covering just over 16 ha, located between Trumpington Road and Hills Road and linked via a wildlife corridor to Sheep's Green and Coe Fen, CUBG curates a scientific collection of over 8000 plant species from around the world. The site hosts over 1600 trees, extensive ornamental plantings, areas of lawn, a large lake, a stream, areas of wildflower meadow, a miniature fen

Figure 15.7 An example of one of the ornamental beds called the Bee Borders showcasing a display of plants attractive to bees. (CUBG).

Figure 15.8 Aerial photograph of the glasshouses, rock garden and lake. (CUBG).

Figure 15.9 View of the Ecological Mound showcasing natural habitats in the East of England in miniature. (CUBG).

garden, a small chalk bank, several rockeries (some of which include imported rock with an entirely different geology and its own fauna), and large log piles, along with some wilder areas around the boundaries.

Hobson's Conduit runs along the western boundary and feeds the stream and lake. Although small and isolated, the areas in the Garden representing natural habitats in the East of England, such as the Fen Display and the Ecological Mound, provide patches of habitat that are known to attract a number of habitat specialists.

The Botanic Garden is listed as a Grade C site in the JNCC Invertebrate Site Register owing to the diversity of Diptera recorded there in the 1970s and 1980s and some earlier records for aculeate Hymenoptera. Many of the Diptera were associated with rot holes and sap runs of mature trees. The site was also listed as a site of major importance for bryophytes by Newton (1986). Combined, these qualify the Garden as a County Wildlife Site.

The Garden has a long history of wildlife recording and has recently databased many of the wildlife records received over the years, allowing for some interesting analyses of the levels of recording effort in the Garden across different taxonomic groups. Records have been provided by staff and by local natural history groups and amateur naturalists, as well as through regular bioblitz events run in collaboration with the Museum of Zoology, where local experts are invited to survey for as many different groups of organisms as possible over a defined period of time. Combined, this level of recording effort has made the Botanic Garden one of the best-recorded sites in Cambridge for a number of species groups.

The wildlife database currently holds over 22,000 records, of which 66% are bird records,

Figure 15.10 Gorse Shieldbug *Piezodorus lituratus* photographed during a bioblitz event at the Garden. (GO).

Figure 15.11 Feathered Thorn *Colotois pennaria* caught in the Robinson moth trap. (WMB).

16% insect records (Table 15.2), 6% fungi, and 4% flowering plants (those not part of the accessioned collection). The most under-recorded groups are the Annelids and Scorpion Flies *Mecoptera*, with only one record each, followed closely by Booklice *Psocoptera*, Alderflies *Megaloptera*, Earwigs *Dermaptera* and Caddisflies *Trichoptera*, all with fewer than ten records each. Moths are the best-recorded insect group in the Garden as a result of weekly moth trapping for the Garden Moth Scheme, undertaken by volunteers since March 2018, using a Robinson moth trap.

At the time of writing, 2932 taxa have been recorded in the Garden (Table 15.3). Just over 45% of these are insects, 21% are plants (including

Table 15.2. Total number of insect records in the CUBG wildlife database as of Dec 2019.

	1950–1999	2000–2009	2010–2019	Total
Alderfly			5	5
Beetle		3	430	433
Booklouse			2	2
Butterfly	11	37	142	190
Caddisfly			9	9
Dragonfly	1	7	94	102
Earwig			6	6
Hymenopteran	59	40	405	504
Lacewing			12	12
Mayfly			7	7
Moth		63	1440	1503
Orthopteran			16	16
Scorpion Fly			1	1
True Bug		7	451	458
True Fly	27	9	236	272
Total	98	166	3256	3520

Table 15.3 Counts of species recorded in the CUBG wildlife database compared with those known to occur in Cambridgeshire, together with the numbers of CUBG taxa with conservation designations.

Taxon Group	CUBG	Cambs	CUBG% of Cambs	Conservation designations
Slime mould	12	74	16%	
Fungus, fungoid, lichen	615	2225	28%	3
Moss, liverwort	141	316	45%	1
Vascular plant	464	2545	18%	42
Annelid	1	26	4%	
Mollusc	80	144	56%	1
Moth	358	1750	20%	27
Beetle	284	2304	12%	4
Wasp etc. *Hymenoptera*	158	614	26%	15
Bug *Hemiptera*	261	714	37%	5
Fly *Diptera*	198	2687	7%	5
Other insects	74	263	28%	
Non-insect arthropod	123	588	21%	1
Bird	137	375	37%	90
Mammal	18	52	35%	11
Fish, amphibian, reptile	8	48	17%	3
Total non-animals	1232	5160	24%	46
Total insects	1333	8332	16%	56
Total animal non-insect	367	1233	30%	106
Total all taxa	2932	14725	20%	208

flowering plants, mosses, ferns and liverworts not part of the accessioned collection) and 17% are fungi. Over 26% of the insect taxa recorded are moths, 21% are beetles and 19% are bugs.

The number of species recorded at any site is a function of both recording effort and the availability of suitable habitat, as well as connections to nearby species-rich sites. Even with regular moth trapping since 2018, only 20% of moths known to occur in Cambridgeshire have been caught at CUBG, indicating that it may not be a particularly good site for moth species diversity – surprisingly so given the large number of different plants and habitats.

It is clear that no effort has been made to record annelids in the Garden, despite earthworms being encountered daily by the horticultural staff. Future bioblitz events may well focus on this group and others which have received limited past recording effort. On the other hand, amphibians and molluscs have been well recorded. There was no evidence of the protected Great Crested Newt on site. An interesting diversity of molluscs was found to be associated with imported rocks in the rock garden and unique habitats provided by the heated glasshouses.

Plant diversity is moderately high, with 420 species out of the monad total of 481 noted in Chapter 4. This total is lower than that for the Backs monad (676 species) and may reflect the high levels of maintenance of the plant collections undertaken by horticultural staff. Bird recording in the Garden has historically been extensive, less so in recent years. Only one reptile species has been recorded in the Garden – the **Grass Snake** regularly seen in the lake and Fen Display.

Historical recording effort, the high diversity of plant species as host plants, and the many different habitats at CUBG combine to provide a site that supports a large number of species not recorded

in other areas nearby, including four bee species recorded nowhere else in Cambridgeshire *Andrena bucephala*, *Coelioxys quadridentata*, *Colletes similis* and *Lasioglossum lativentre*.

Two-hundred and eight (7%) of the species recorded in the CUBG wildlife database have a conservation designation at the international, national or county level (Table 15.3).

Six species of bats **Noctule**, **Soprano Pipistrelle**, **Common Pipistrelle**, **Brown Long Eared Bat**, **Serotine** and **Daubenton's Bat** have been recorded through National Bat Monitoring Programme annual surveys. Other species of conservation importance include the **Five-banded Weevil-wasp** *Cerceris quinquefasciata*, a UK BAP species last recorded in 2017 and often associated with **Goldenrod** *Solidago* sp. in the Systematics Beds and the **Red-tailed Mason Bee** *Osmia bicolor* recorded in 2018 on **Green Alkanet** *Pentaglottis sempervirens*.

The weekly moth trapping undertaken in the Garden using the Robinson moth trap has caught 358 moth species to date, 25 of them BAP species including **Knot Grass** *Acronicta rumicis*, **Blood Vein** *Timandra comoa*, **Mouse Moth** *Amphipyra tragopoginis*, **Dot Moth** *Melanchra persicariae*, **Mottled Rustic** *Caradrina morpheus*, and **Ghost Moth** *Hepialus humuli*.

Of birds with conservation designations spotted on site, **Hawfinch** and **Turtledove** were recorded in 2017. **Tree Pipit**, **Tree Sparrow**,

Figure 15.12 Grass Snake, a regular sighting in the lake and Fen Display. (PC).

Cuckoo and **Spotted Flycatcher** were last seen in 2008. **Great Spotted Woodpeckers** frequently breed in holes in mature trees in the Garden and a pair of **Sparrowhawks** sometimes nest in the New Pinetum. **Swift** parties of over 30 screeching individuals are also common in the skies over the Garden in summer enjoying the plentiful supply of insects. **Kingfishers**, **Little Egrets** and **Herons** frequent the stream and lake. **Tawny Owls** roost in the tall trees by day.

In addition, there are 51 'notable' species (species without conservation designations that are recorded in only a limited number of UK hectads). These include the ant *Lasius brunneus* which nests in **Oak** *Quercus* sp. trees; *Chyliza extenuata*, a Psilid fly that is reputed to feed on the underground stems of **Broomrape** *Orobanche* spp. and was last recorded in 2011; the nationally scarce beetles *Platyderus depressus* recorded during the 2019 bioblitz and **Adonis' Ladybird** *Hippodamia variegata* recorded in the last few years near the Systematic Beds; the notable gall mite *Aceria tristriata*, a very local species and one of only a very few records made in Cambridgeshire, found on **Walnut** *Juglans regia* in 2018. Bees are another group that has been well recorded in the Garden and notable species include the nationally scarce **Hill Cuckoo-bee** *Bombus rupestris*, **Large Yellow-faced Bee** *Hylaeus signatus*, *H. cornutus* and a ground-nesting bee *Macropis europaea*.

The Garden also had one of the largest examples of **Giant Elm Bracket** *Rigidoporus ulmarius* ever recorded and the sole remaining population of **Frizzled Crisp-moss** *Tortella tortuosa* in Cambridgeshire.

There is a main **Badger** sett on the mound at the centre of the lake which has established relatively recently. Badgers are often seen around the site at night with multiple latrines marking the boundaries between neighbouring clans. Unfortunately, due to the high density of Badgers, no **Hedgehogs** have been seen in the Garden since 2013. **Muntjac Deer** are abundant. A recent camera trap study has revealed a population of 23 Muntjac, which at 1.4 deer per hectare is one of the highest densities on record. The Muntjac gorge themselves on the unrivalled variety of plants growing in the Garden. This is a serious problem for the horticultural staff; indeed several plant species cannot be planted out as a result. **Foxes** are resident in the Garden and often breed. Regular small mammal trapping surveys have recorded **Wood**

Mice and **Bank Voles**. **Rabbits**, an increasingly rare sight, are sometimes spotted on wildlife cameras placed around the Garden.

In 2019 for the first time, Nature Metrics, a company monitoring wildlife through environmental DNA, sampled five areas in the Garden's waterbodies during the bioblitz event in April that year. (Environmental DNA is DNA left behind in the environment by organisms living there. It is a new way to detect the presence of different species in an environment.) The analysis revealed the presence of three fish species which had not previously been recorded on the site, **10-spined Stickleback**, **Stone Loach** and **European Bitterling**.

Several wildlife monitoring projects have been started over the past few years, with students using the data to answer a range of questions. For example, Cambridge zoology students have been studying the genetic diversity of a moth parasite, *Wolbachia*, found on the moths caught through these weekly moth trapping surveys. *Wolbachia* is a genus of bacteria that infects moths (and many other arthropod species) potentially causing sex-ratio distortions by killing males, with obvious potential impacts on populations. This is a great example of how wildlife monitoring in the Garden can link to University student teaching and practical sessions.

Currently we are setting up a bat monitoring project in the Garden. This involves placing static bat detectors in trees overnight which can record the ultrasound that the bats use for echolocation. These recordings can then be analysed to determine the species of bat present and obtain an index of activity levels. Students are being trained in bat sound analysis to help with the monitoring efforts. Each year the Garden runs a number of bat walks after normal closing hours, giving attendees a unique opportunity to visit the Garden after dark and learn about the fascinating ecology of these nocturnal hunters.

There are thousands of beneficial insect species in the Garden, but also others that adversely affect plant health. Recently the Garden has joined a national monitoring programme to keep an eye out for the arrival of the **Brown Marmorated Stink Bug** *Halyomorpha halys*. Hanging from one of the *Sorbus* trees you may spot a sticky trap with a pheromone stick attached to a branch. This is part of a research project undertaken by the National Institute of Agricultural Botany (NIAB EMR) and is an early warning mechanism for the arrival of this invasive shield bug from East Asia. Its arrival could decimate fruit trees in Britain. It has recently been detected in Essex, and monitoring the trap weekly will improve our chances of detecting it if it spreads to Cambridge.

The Garden is an urban biodiversity hotspot, forming a significant part of the green space network across the city of Cambridge and an important resource for researchers trying to understand the impacts of urbanisation on wildlife populations. However, its core focus is on the maintenance of the scientific plant collection for the University of Cambridge, for teaching and research. At times this may result in some disturbance of the wildlife that has been attracted to the site as a result of the available habitat and food **resources**. Plant pests and diseases are not often welcomed, but the ultimate aim is to manage the collections in as wildlife-friendly manner as possible.

Spotlight on Paul Rule's garden

On 19 October 2016, the NHC garden survey team carried out a survey of our garden and found 85 plant species. My own meagre records of animals recorded in the preceding years brought the grand total up to 130 species.

It was at this point I decided to carry out a longer-term detailed survey with a particular emphasis on nocturnal invertebrates that up to this point had been largely overlooked. Initially planned to be a finite project to run alongside the main NHC project, it has now been extended indefinitely, with the results recorded here covering

observations up to the end of 2020. The Covid-19 lock-down was a particularly productive period due to the amount of time that I was forced to spend in my own garden.

The garden and surrounding area

Situated in Langham Road, our garden is typical of the rows of semi-detached houses that were built on former agricultural land in the 1930s. The north-facing rear garden is long and narrow (38 × 8 m) and is mainly laid to lawn with good numbers of mature trees and shrubs. There is also a small wildlife pond. There are 15 similar gardens to the east, 11 to the west, and these all back on to a matching arrangement of gardens belonging to the houses in Radegund Road, placing our garden in a green space of approximately 1.6 ha. With the exception of the occasional use of slug pellets to protect pot plants, no chemicals have been used for pest control. Apart from mowing, the lawn has been left to its own devices, resulting in a rich diversity of plants including common wildflowers such as **Slender Speedwell** *Veronica filiformis*, **Cowslips** *Primula veris* and the star of the show, **Bee Orchid** *Ophrys apifera* which throws up flowering spikes most years.

Some of the more mature trees were planted by previous owners including an apple and pear tree, but others such as a large **Sycamore** *Acer pseudoplatanus* and a **Silver Birch** *Betula pendula* are self-sets.

There is also a small front garden which is mainly laid to block paving with a small area of shrubs to attract bees and other pollinators.

Figure 15.13 (left) Bee Orchid, (centre) Slender Speedwell, (right) Cowslip. (PAR).

In the last three years we have also ripped out a hedge of non-native species and replaced it with mixed native species including **Hazel** *Corylus avellana*, **Bird Cherry** *Prunus padus*, **Hawthorn** *Crataegus monogyna* and **Dog Rose** *Rosa canina* which are more attractive to native invertebrates.

At the time of writing the total number of species recorded had increased to 783. Most of the new records were obtained by running a light trap year-round to capture nocturnal insects, particularly moths. Table 15.4 shows a breakdown of species by types.

Table 15.4 Counts of species in Paul Rule's garden

Non-insects	No.	Insects	No.
Fungi	10	Dragonflies	9
Lichens	19	Mayflies	1
Mosses and liverworts	26	Earwigs	2
Vascular plants	75	Crickets and grasshoppers	4
Microscopic animals	11	Barkflies	3
Worms	3	True bugs	62
Molluscs	8	Beetles	53
Millipedes & centipedes	4	Lacewings	7
Crustacea	7	Ants, bees, wasps & sawflies	31
Harvestmen & mites	5	Butterflies	13
Spiders	26	Moths	292
Springtails	6	Caddisflies	11
Birds	44	True flies	43
Mammals	5		
Amphibians	3		
Total Species			783

The above numbers only include species actually found within the garden and exclude birds and bats only observed in flight over the garden. In the following pages I describe some common and notable species observed over the last five years to give an idea of the hidden wildlife that can be found in a typical Cambridge garden. Apart from a couple of notable fungi, I have concentrated on my main field of interest, invertebrates, and in particular on species that have not been covered in other sections of this book.

I hope this will encourage our readers to explore their own gardens and discover some of the secret wildlife hiding there.

Fungi

The garden is not rich in fungus species, but there were a couple of interesting finds. The first was *Illosporiopsis christiansenii* – a tiny species that would go unnoticed but for its unusual pink colouring. It is parasitic on the lichen *Physcia tenella* which grows in abundance on all our mature trees and shrubs. The second was **Nettle Rust** *Puccinia urticata*. This species has a five-stage life cycle in which it infects two hosts, **Stinging Nettle** *Urtica dioica* and sedges, but it is only during the nettle phases that these rather spectacular galls are produced.

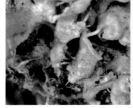

Figure 15.14 (left) *Illosporiopsis christiansenii* among *Physcia tenella*, (right) Nettle Rust on Stinging Nettle. (PAR).

Crickets and grasshoppers (Orthoptera)

The **Common Field Grasshopper** *Chorthippus brunneus* is an occasional visitor to the garden, but bush crickets are common. Nymphs of the **Speckled Bush-cricket** *Leptophyes punctatissima* are often seen on plants from May onwards and the

Figure 15.15 (left) Common Field Grasshopper, (right) mating Speckled Bush-crickets. (PAR).

Figure 15.16 Female Southern Oak Bush-cricket. (PAR).

mature adults from midsummer. Although they feed on leaves and flowers their numbers are not large enough to do any noticeable damage.

The **Oak Bush-cricket** *Meconema thalassinum*, and **Southern Oak Bush-cricket** *Meconema meridionale* are arboreal species. They are both carnivorous, feeding on small invertebrates in the tree canopy. The Oak Bush-cricket is a native species but its southern cousin is a relative newcomer to Britain. First recorded in Surrey and Berkshire in 2001, it is now common across southern England. As nymphs, these two species appear identical, but in adults only the native species develops a full set of wings capable of flight. Southern Oak Bush-crickets have tiny residual wings.

Moths (Lepidoptera)

Until starting to use the light trap, I had only recorded a handful of moth species, but this has grown to 292 in 3 years. Moths have their own chapter in this book, but I have included a couple of regular garden visitors of particular interest to me.

The first is the **Toadflax Brocade** *Calophasia lunula*. The first specimen was a caterpillar rather than an adult and I was quite excited to read on the UK Moths website that 'this moth is restricted to the south-east and central southern coasts of England, and appears to be in decline'. Since then, significant numbers of adults have turned up in my light traps each year and I have also found caterpillars on our small patch of **Purple Toadflax** *Linaria purpurea* every year. Other local moth recorders have also recorded this species in significant numbers. So, far from being in decline it seems to be thriving and expanding its range well away from the coast.

The second moth is the **Tree-lichen Beauty** *Cryphia algae*. This small moth is a migratory

Figure 15.17 Toadflax Brocade, adult and caterpillar. (PAR).

species which until 1991 only turned up in Britain in very small numbers, but now shows up in large numbers in south-east England and East Anglia. It is now not unusual to record more than 20 individuals in a single night between mid-July and early September. The large numbers indicate that it has become a resident breeding species, but so far no caterpillars have been observed in the wild, so there is an opportunity to be the first person to do so.

Figure 15.18 Tree-lichen Beauty. (PAR).

Figure 15.19 (left) *Chrysopa perla*, (below) Common Green Lacewing larva. (PAR).

Lacewings, dustywings and spongeflies (Neuroptera)

The most common species of lacewing to be found in any Cambridge garden will be the **Common Green Lacewing** *Chrysopa carnea*. Although there are several very similar species, this is the only green lacewing that hibernates as an adult, so any found over winter in sheds, garages and other outbuildings will be this species.

Lacewing larvae are sometimes spotted in pursuit of aphids and some carry shed skins and other detritus on their backs as a defence against predation.

The distinctive blue-green lacewing *Chrysopa perla* is a species that prefers scrubby grassland and woodland edge, but the occasional specimen does turn up in mature gardens.

Brown lacewings are mainly nocturnal and are regularly attracted to light traps. Three species have been recorded in our garden, *Hemerobius lutescens*, *Wesmaelius nervosus* and *Micromus variegatus*.

Dustywings, also known as Waxy Lacewings, are very small insects that often go unnoticed due to their small size, but when they are noticed, they are easily mistaken for whitefly, which is unfortunate as they are actually predators of whitefly and other aphids. Adults and larvae of *Conwentzia psociformis* are regularly seen on our hedges and trees.

Spongeflies resemble a brown lacewing. However their larvae are aquatic and feed on freshwater sponges (see Microscopic aquatic animals). There are just three British species, the commonest being *Sisyra nigra* which I have recorded on just two occasions.

Figure 15.20 *Wesmaelius nervosus.* (PAR).

Figure 15.21
(left) *Conwentzia psociformis*, (right) *Sisyra nigra.* (PAR).

Figure 15.22
(left) *Graphopsocus cruciatus*,
(right) *Ectopsocus* sp. (PAR).

Barkflies (Psocoptera)

Barkflies are small mainly overlooked insects found on trees and shrubs. They feed on algae and lichen. Three species have been found in the garden: *Graphopsocus cruciatus* and two only identified to genus level, *Ectopsocus* and *Loensia*. Some Psocoptera species can be found inside damp houses, where they feed on mould or the starch sizing in the bindings of old books. These species are commonly known as booklice, but thankfully none of those have made my list.

Arachnids

As well as spiders, our gardens (and houses) are home to several other families of arachnids including harvestmen and mites. Harvestmen *Opiliones* look superficially like spiders *Araneae* but there are major differences between them. The first is the difference in body shape: spiders such as the crab spider *Ozyptila praticola* have obvious separation between head and abdomen, which is lacking in harvestmen. Harvestmen also lack fangs and do not spin silk.

Both **Opilio canestrinii** and **Paroligolophus agrestis** are common garden species but only the latter is native to Britain. *O. canestrinii* was first discovered in Britain as recently as 1999 and is now widespread though southern England. The species has been expanding northwards from Italy, Austria and Switzerland and in parts of northern Europe it has displaced the other two *Opilio* species; this may also happen in our area.

Mites are our smallest arachnids and most, like the **House Dust Mite** *Dermatophagoides pteronyssinus*, go unobserved. Those that are seen can be difficult to identify. Compost may contain thousands but so far I have not been able to identify any that I have found in our compost bin.

Figure 15.24 (left) Red Velvet Mite, (right) Walnut Leaf Gall. (PAR).

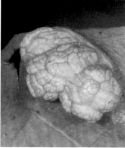

Figure 15.23 (left) *Ozyptila praticola* (spider), (right) *Paroligolophus agrestis* (harvestman). (PAR).

The **Red Velvet Mite** *Trombidium* sp. is an exception due to its colour and relatively large size. The presence of some mite species can be detected by the unique signatures they produce on a host plant. **Walnut Leaf Gall Mites** *Aceria erinea* can only really be observed under a microscope, but they live in a very distinct leaf gall that they create on **Common Walnut** *Juglans regia*.

Moth trap intruders

Moth traps attract a lot of species other than the intended target. Some are just pulled in by the UV light, while others like our resident **Common Frog** *Rana temporaria* are attracted to the possibility of a free meal.

Figure 15.25 *Ophion obscuratus.* (PAR).

Figure 15.26 *Macrocentrus bicolor.* (PAR).

Figure 15.27 Western Yellow Centipede. (PAR).

Parasitic ichneumon wasps are regular visitors with the large, rather spectacular ***Ophion obscuratus*** being the most common. This wasp parasitises moth caterpillars and has a very short ovipositor. Another impressive ichneumon wasp that occasionally turns up is ***Macrocentrus bicolor.*** It parasitises the larvae of various wood- and stem-nesting solitary wasps and females are equipped with a very long ovipositor to reach their victims in their burrows.

The **Common Brown Centipede** *Lithobius forficatus* is often seen hunting around the trap but I have only once seen the **Western Yellow Centipede** *Stigmatogaster subterranea* out of its hiding places while moth trapping. At up to 70 mm long and equipped with between 77 and 83 pairs of legs, it is Britain's longest centipede and normally resides under leaf litter, stones or in soil.

At half the size of the **Common Earwig** *Forficula auricularia*, the **Lesser Earwig** *Labia minor* mainly goes unnoticed in our gardens. It likes to spend its time hidden away in warm places like compost heaps, but is attracted to UV light and can turn up in the moth trap on warm summer nights in significant numbers.

Figure 15.28 Lesser Earwig. (PAR).

Figure 15.29 *Tephritis divisa.* (PAR).

Figure 15.30 (left) Twin-spot Centurion, (right) Common Stiletto Fly. (PAR).

Figure 15.31 (left) *Macrocera phalerata,* **(right) female** *Chironomus plumosus.* (PAR).

Tephritis divisa is the rarest species I have recorded: this fruit fly was first recorded in Britain in 2004, and the specimen that visited my trap in 2018 is the first, and as far as I know, the only record from Cambridgeshire. It lays its eggs in the flower heads of **Bristly Oxtongue** *Helminthotheca echioides* where the larvae develop inside a gall. Over half of the 43 species of true flies *Diptera* recorded in the garden have been moth trap visitors. One of my favourites is the **Twin-spot Centurion** *Sargus bipunctatus.* This soldier fly *Stratiomyidae*

is one of the easier flies to identify with distinctive white spots between the eyes. The **Common Stiletto Fly** *Thereva nobilitata* does not seem to be common in the NHC area. The one night-time visitor to our garden was the only reported sighting of this species during the project.

Macrocera phalerata is classified as a fungus gnat, although species of this genus are predatory. Their larvae spin a web with droplets of acid fluids, which kill their small invertebrate prey. At up to 12 mm long *Chironomus plumosus* is our largest non-biting midge. Adults are common visitors to the moth trap and it is likely that they also breed in the pond where large unidentified midge larvae have been found.

Crustaceans

Like almost all Cambridge gardens, ours contains Britain's four most common woodlice **Common Shiny** *Oniscus asellus,* **Common Rough** *Porcellio scaber,* **Common Striped** *Philoscia muscorum* and **Common Pill** *Armadillidium vulgare.* In addition

Figure 15.32 Common garden woodlice (from left to right) Common Shiny, Common Rough, Common Striped, Common Pill. (PAR).

to these we also have **Ant Woodlouse** *Platyarthrus hoffmannseggii*. This small white species spends its entire life underground within ant nests and I have observed them after accidentally disturbing a **Yellow Meadow Ant** *Lasius flavus* nest.

Our pond is home to large numbers of tiny aquatic crustaceans which, although just big enough to be seen with the naked eye, require a microscope for identification. The most numerous of these are water fleas *Cladocera* which on sunny days form large swarms near the water surface. The two species so far identified are *Daphnia curvirostris* and *Chydorus sphaericus*. The two other crustaceans found are Ostracods of the genus *Cypidopsis* and Copepods of the genus *Cyclops*.

Figure 15.33 (left) *Daphnia curvirostris*, **(right)** *Chydorus sphaericus*. (PAR).

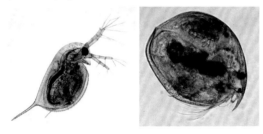

Figure 15.34 (left) *Cypidopsis* sp., **(right)** *Cyclops* sp. (PAR).

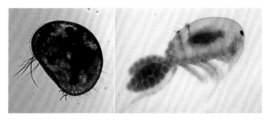

Springtails (Collembola)

Springtails form the largest of the three lineages of modern hexapods that are no longer considered insects. The main differentiation is that unlike insects they have internal mouth parts. They are present in very large numbers in soil, among foliage, in leaf litter and compost, but are mainly overlooked because of their very small size.

Springtails come in two basic shapes; globular and elongated. The globular springtail *Dicyrtomina saundersi* and *Tomocerus minor* are the most abundant species in the garden and are found among foliage, leaf litter and compost. *Entomobrya intermedia* is another common species, which I have found in large numbers among leaf litter.

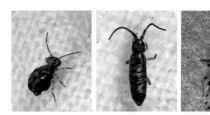

Figure 15.35 (left) *Dicyrtomina saundersi*, **(centre)** *Tomocerus minor*, **(right)** *Orchesella cincta*. (PAR).

Orchesella cincta is one of our largest species, growing to 4 mm in length, and unlike the previous two is large enough to identify by the naked eye. These are far less numerous, with just the occasional individual being found under stones and plant pots.

Microscopic aquatic animals

As well as in the pond, many of these tiny creatures can be found in temporary sources of water such as bird baths, gutters and planters. Some can also be found among damp soil and moss.

Of the single-celled animals observed, the most numerous are the Ciliates. This large and diverse group of protozoa are all characterised by the presence of hair-like organelles called cilia which they use for feeding and propulsion. At up to 2 mm *Stentor coeruleus* is by far the largest of these and the one visible to the naked eye. The bell-shaped *Vorticella* use their 'stalk' to attach themselves to aquatic plants or other suitable substrates.

Figure 15.36 (left) *Stentor coeruleus*, **(right)** *Vorticella* sp. (PAR).

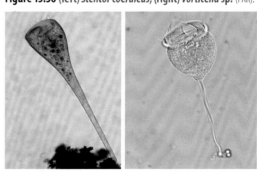

Figure 15.37 (left) *Arcella* sp., **(right)** *Actinophys* sp. (PAR).

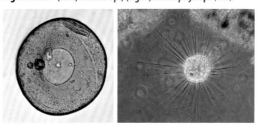

Amoebae and the closely related Heliozoa (sun-animalcules) are common finds although identifying to species level is difficult. So far I have only been able to identify one genus of amoeba, the distinctly doughnut shaped testate amoeba *Arcella*, and one Heliozoa genus, *Actinophys*.

Among the multitude of multicellular animals to be found in a single drop of water are tardigrades (water bears), nematodes (roundworms) and rotifers (wheel animals). Identifying tardigrades and nematodes is beyond my skill set, so although I often find them none have been included in my list of garden species.

Rotifers are a little easier and so far three genera have been found: *Rotaria*, *Keratella* and *Euchlanis*. Rotifers are characterised by a ciliated corona located at head. Under the microscope the movement of the cilia gives the illusion that the coronas are rotating, hence their name.

There are five species of freshwater sponges Spongillidae found in Britain, the most common being the **Pond Sponge** *Spongilla lacustris* and the **River Sponge** *Spongilla fluviatilis*. The small colony in the following photograph was found in our pond so is likely to be *S. lacustris*, which is only found in the still waters of lakes and ponds.

Figure 15.38 Pregnant *Rotaria* rotifer. (PAR).

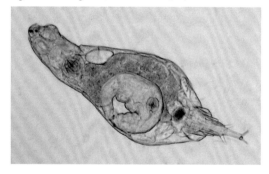

Figure 15.39 (left) *Euchlanis* rotifer, (right) *Keratella* rotifer. (PAR).

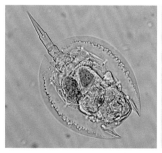

Figure 15.40 Pond Sponge. (PAR).

Although individuals are microscopic, sponges form large colonies living on rocks and aquatic plants so a microscope is not required to observe them. Their coloration ranges from white to green. The green coloration is found in colonies receiving plenty of sunlight and is produced by symbiotic algae living within the sponge.

Summary

For me, this project within a project has been an eye opener to just how many species a fairly ordinary garden can be home to, especially one that does not have manicured lawns or make liberal use of pesticides or herbicides. One of the biggest challenges to a project of this type is identifying what you have found. Many of the 783 species identified have only been done so with the help of others. I certainly would not been able to identify many of the plants, especially the grasses and mosses, without the expert help of Monica Frisch and Mark Hill, and the online community of invertebrate specialists has also been invaluable.

Finding a species you have never seen before is quite thrilling and to find it in your own garden is even more so. The highlights have to include finding invertebrates that have rarely or, in the case of the fruit fly *Tephritis divisa*, never previously been recorded in Cambridgeshire. It has also been satisfying being a part of a wider network of recorders who are helping to map the changes in abundance and distribution we are seeing both in our native species and those new to these shores.

Although the main NHC project has ended, my garden survey goes on. There are many more species to be discovered and by making changes such as adding bat boxes and setting aside part of the lawn for wild meadow flowers I hope to attract yet more.

Cemeteries and churchyards

'God's Acre' provides a haven for wildlife as well as for people. The grass of churchyards has rarely suffered the 'improvement' of farmed pasture or the eutrophication and neglect of road verges, so retains a window on what might formerly have been present in the surrounding landscape. The NHC area has churches of several denominations and public cemeteries that are shared by the differing faiths. Some churchyards are 'closed' for burials, and these, along with the public cemeteries, are managed by the City Council. Others are usually, but not always, managed on a local basis. Several have 'friends' groups that input into the management.

Several churchyards and cemeteries are designated as City Wildlife Sites (CiWS), usually on the basis of botanical surveys, but occasionally based on the presence of other nationally scarce species. The rationale of using plants as indicators is that they are often easy to identify and if there is a good diversity of plant species, particularly when some are of county significance, then the diversity of other taxa will be good as well. Most of the churchyards and cemeteries are open to all, but a few keep their gates locked.

Indicator species

To help with deciding whether sites qualify for designation as either City or County Wildlife Sites there is a set list of species that indicate different types of good habitat. These are mostly vascular plant species, which are usually more readily identified by Wildlife Trust surveyors than are fungi or lichens. Another advantage is that unlike animals, plants stay put for detailed examination. In addition to the indicator species, any that are regarded as Nationally Rare (found in 15 or fewer hectads), Nationally Scarce (16–100 hectads) or of county importance, are likely to help qualify the site.

In the past, many of these churchyards and cemeteries were either managed for amenity, with the grass kept short and nothing out of place, or were left in a state of neglect with the consequent growth of scrub and rank grass. Because of the growing understanding of the importance of biodiversity, the City Council has declared a biodiversity emergency and because churchyards and cemeteries are centres for biodiversity, their management has begun to change. Increasingly a middle course is being steered in order to provide a range of habitats and to suit a range of management views.

Around 500 vascular plant species are known from city churchyards, with 100 of these being 'axiophytes'. These are species that are neither very common nor very rare and generally indicate good habitat.

In the next section some of the larger or more diverse churchyards are discussed, with an emphasis on the vascular plants.

Churchyards and their cemeteries
Cambridge, St Bene't

St Bene't's churchyard is one of those that are mostly managed for amenity, with neatly cut lawns, though nevertheless it has interest. To enter the churchyard you have to descend steps or circle down a ramp from the street level. Over time, the street level has risen due to infilling and the churchyard represents the original soil level. In the grass it is still possible to find species such as **Lady's Bedstraw** *Galium verum*, which have managed to survive the regular mowing. The chest tombs, many constructed from oolitic limestone, support ferns such as **Wall-rue** *Asplenium ruta-muraria* and one has acquired a population of **Tussock Bellflower** *Campanula carpatica* – one of only two sites for it in the county. Butterflies often overwinter in the church tower, where the roof beams have a few **Deathwatch Beetles** *Xestobium rufovillosum*. The larvae largely feed in a newer block of oak supporting a roof-hatch and the architect regards this as a sacrificial block that keeps them out of older beams. Bats are actually rare in city belfries, with few specimens ever seen.

Cambridge, Little St Mary's

The churchyard is very much a wildflower garden. It was designated a CiWS for the presence of what was at the time thought to be a Nationally Scarce moss, **Curve-stalked Feather-moss** *Rhynchostegiella curviseta*. It is now known that the moss is rather more frequent in southern England. The introduced species of wildflower include plants such as **Birthwort** *Aristolochia clematitis* and **Yellow-flowered Teasel** *Dipsacus strigosus*.

Cherry Hinton, St Andrew

Enthusiastic volunteers regularly mow most of the churchyard, which is a CiWS, but there are now plans to provide more space for nature. Particular foci for this are the provision of insect hotels and habitat for **Hedgehogs**, which should ensure that there are flower-rich areas with longer grass in future. A spring plant of note in the churchyard is **Goldilocks Buttercup** *Ranunculus auricomus*, which grows under trees near the entrance. A plant that signifies long-established grassland is **Hoary Plantain** *Plantago media* and its flat-leaved rosettes are still found in the churchyard. In the wider countryside it is slowly disappearing, so is classed as Near Threatened in England.

Chesterton, St Andrew

This is another churchyard that was originally designated as a CiWS for the presence of what was at the time thought to be a Nationally Scarce moss, **Lesser Screw-moss** *Syntrichia virescens*. It does however still qualify on account of its neutral grassland, although the necessary indicator species are in low abundance. As a closed burial ground it was for many years managed by the City Council on the 'cut and drop' principle, which acts to suppress wildflowers and increase coarse grasses. Despite this, many interesting species have survived and the management has changed to allow a varied sward height with cuttings collected where possible. It has the largest botanical list of any of the city's churchyards. A winter visit will reveal **Mistletoe** *Viscum album* in a Lime tree along the road boundary. In summer the rosettes of **Hoary Plantain** can be seen in the closer mown species-rich grass outside the church, and occasionally it gets the chance to flower, showing its purple anthers. In late spring the less desirable and invasive **Alexanders** *Smyrnium olusatrum* is in flower at the back of the church. Originally brought into the country by the Romans as a pot-herb, it is normally a coastal plant but in recent years has spread significantly. You may see the fiddle shaped leaves of **Fiddle Dock** *Rumex pulcher* in this area. It is one of several plants, such as **Wild Clary** *Salvia verbenaca* and **Yew** *Taxus baccata*, which are often associated with churchyards.

Fen Ditton, St Mary the Virgin

Fen Ditton church is on a bluff overlooking the River Cam, and is often known as the rowers' church. The churchyard is fairly species-rich at the front, with **Rough Hawkbit** *Leontodon hispidus*, **Field Wood-rush** *Luzula campestris*, Hoary Plantain and Wild Clary, though the back is shaded and neglected. The churchyard walls provide a home for **Mexican Fleabane** *Erigeron karvinskianus*, which has escaped from a nearby garden. There is a separate cemetery a few hundred metres from the churchyard. This still has **Field Scabious** *Knautia*

arvensis, one of many once common species that are now threatened in England due to ploughing of old meadows and eutrophication of waysides.

Grantchester, St Andrew & St Mary

Viewers of the TV crime series will have seen the vicar scything the churchyard, though sadly this practice ended in most churchyards around the time that the series was set. The benefits of scything to biodiversity are significant: the grass and flower stems are cut at the base and left intact. As they are raked off, seeds fall, providing the next generation, and removal of the cuttings both prevents a dense thatch from building up and reduces nutrient input – both of which benefit wildflowers. Any insects in the grass simply drop to the ground. When a rotary mower or strimmer is used a fine mulch is deposited and very often any insects in the sward will be macerated. The churchyard has an interconnecting series of graveyards, with one enclosed by high walls. The varying aspects provide good habitat for insects. On a CNHS visit during a New Year's Day walk there was a cluster of 68 **Seven-spot Ladybirds** *Coccinella septempunctata* on a church bench. On visits later in the year the group saw **Hairy-footed Flower Bee** *Anthophora plumipes* and its cuckoo the **Common Mourning Bee** *Melecta albifrons*, with **Harlequin Ladybird** *Harmonia axyridis* and **European Hornet** *Vespa crabro* amongst other insects.

Figure 15.41 St Andrews churchyard and cemetery in Chesterton. (PAR).

Teversham, All Saints
Teversham is isolated from most of the Cambridge conurbation by the city airport, and so is infrequently visited by city naturalists as it is not on the way to anywhere. For some the interest will lie not in the churchyard, but in Airport Way, part of which is a protected road verge for its botanical interest. If the churchyard lay within the city boundary it would probably qualify as a CiWS for its neutral to calcareous grassland, as many of the standard indicators are present. Along with many churchyards, ferns such as **Wall-rue** *Asplenium ruta-muraria* and **Hart's-tongue** *A. scolopendrium* grow in the churchyard wall.

Trumpington, St Mary & St Michael
Trumpington churchyard was a frequent destination for Botany School bryophyte excursions in the 1950s and 1960s, especially to admire **Anomalous Bristle-moss** *Orthotrichum anomalum* and **Thickpoint Grimmia** *Schistidium crassipilum* fruiting on the wall by the road. Since that time these two species have increased enormously in the city, and Trumpington churchyard (34 species since 2009) has been left behind by Cherry Hinton (39 species) and Chesterton (35 species). A nice little plant found in the churchyard is **Rue-leaved Saxifrage** *Saxifraga tridactylites*, which flowers at the base of an old stone cross in the spring. There is also a small cemetery at the junction of the Hauxton and Shelford Roads.

Other churchyards
Some particularly notable species occur in other churchyards. **Rustyback** *Asplenium ceterach* grows on the churchyard wall of St Andrew the Less on Newmarket Road. **Dwarf Thistle** *Cirsium acaule* grows in St John's churchyard on Hills Road. St Mark's churchyard on Barton Road hosts **Perring's Comfrey** *Symphytum × perringianum*, which is a Cambridge endemic. Most churchyards have little oases of green, so are worth visiting. The continually changing fauna and flora of the city means that something new may be found at any time.

The public cemeteries
Ascension Parish Burial Ground CiWS
This small burial ground, found down a lane off Huntingdon Road, was established in 1857 to serve the parishes of St Giles and St Peter's. It qualifies as a CiWS for its neutral grassland, but there are also a few indicators for calcareous grassland.

Dark avenues of Yew at the southern end suppress much wildlife on the ground, but do provide a source of berries. Next to the former chapel you might find **Deadly Nightshade** *Atropa belladonna* and depending on the time of year see the purple tinged flowers or the glossy black berries. Do not be tempted to eat them! Because of its reputation, it is in decline in England and is significantly so in Cambridgeshire.

City Cemetery, Newmarket Road
The City Cemetery is the largest of all the public cemeteries and is still open for burials. It is built over areas of both sandy and chalky ground, providing differing habitats. Traditionally herbicides were used to keep many of the graves weed-free, with mowing to keep a short sward across the entire site. Today herbicide use is much reduced and the mowing regime changed to allow longer areas of vegetation. Importantly however, relatives who wish to keep the grass short around their grave are allowed to do so. As a consequence of the change in management, **Pyramidal Orchid** *Anacamptis pyramidalis* flowered for the first time in 2020 on the grave of Captain J.L. Stuart. An uncommon plant on one of the areas of more sandy ground is **Hoary Cinquefoil** *Potentilla argentea*, the English and Latin names referring to the colour of the underside of the leaves. In the sector adjacent to Newmarket Road there are patches of **Strawberry Clover** *Trifolium fragiferum*, which has pale pink flowers that produce globose seed-heads vaguely reminiscent of strawberries.

Histon Road Cemetery
The cemetery was established in 1843 to serve the nonconformist community, but it came to serve the local community as well. Designed by the horticulturist J.C. Loudon, it is of architectural significance. The tradition of being a 'garden cemetery' continues today, with new beds of wildflowers being sown to confuse the botanists and provide nectar sources for pollinators. Some of the introductions occasionally cross-breed, and the planted **Silver Ragwort** *Jacobaea maritima* has hybridised with native **Common Ragwort** *Jacobaea vulgaris* to produce the hybrid *Jacobaea × albescens*.

Mill Road Cemetery CiWS
The cemetery was consecrated in 1848 for use by 13 of the city parishes. It was built on what was partly grazing land and partly the 1820s' University

Figure 15.42 Mill Road Cemetery. (JDS).

cricket ground, and the latter part retains many of the original species from the area. It has been closed for burials since 1949 and is maintained by the City Council. The cemetery is designated as a CiWS for its neutral and calcareous grassland. Management used to be a mix of frequent cutting of some grassland areas and neglect of much of the rest. This has resulted in a species-poor sward at the north end (the grazing land), but a more species-rich sward in the more frequently cut areas (the cricket ground). With a move towards biodiversity management the cutting regime has changed, with previously frequently cut areas left to flower. It remains to be seen whether this produces a sustainable improvement in biodiversity, but future management will be proactive rather than prescriptive.

As a CiWS the cemetery has many of the indicator species expected, including Hoary Plantain, Field Scabious and **Yellow Oat-grass** *Trisetum flavescens*. It has at least eight different **Bramble** species in it, including the cultivar **Himalayan Giant** *Rubus armeniacus*, which is invasive and can become dominant. An unusual species in the southern part is **Ivy Broomrape** *Orobanche hederae*, which is parasitic on **Ivy** *Hedera* spp. Over 40 species of birds, 20 species of butterflies and many other insects are known from the cemetery. **Rabbits** *Oryctolagus cuniculus* used to help graze the grass, but have been driven off by the increased presence of dog walkers who let their dogs off lead as soon as they enter the cemetery.

Hobson's Brook: A Cambridge chalk stream

Hobson's Brook (Figure 15.43) is a tributary of the River Cam that flows through southwest

Figure 15.43 Map of the Hobson's Brook corridor showing the main sites of interest. (Howard Slatter, Hobson's Conduit Trust).

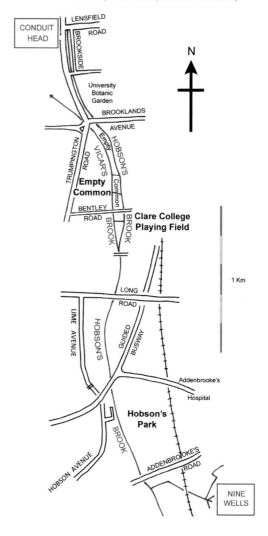

Cambridge, where it forms an important wildlife corridor within the urban fringe. It rises from Nine Wells springs, where water issues from the Totternhoe Stone, a hard and fissured band in the Chalk bedrock, at the foot of the Gog Magog Hills. Nine Wells provides unusual springhead and chalk stream environments, where the water emerges at a constant 10.2°C.

Hobson's Brook flows north from Nine Wells near Great Shelford in a wide shallow valley, just 4 km south of central Cambridge. Geological investigations by the author suggest that this valley was occupied by the River Cam during the last glacial period.

The brook was canalised in 1614 to supply Cambridge with clean water, with a system of subterranean pipes emanating from the Conduit Head on Trumpington Street (Bushell 1938). The artificial watercourse (Hobson's Conduit) is now a Scheduled Ancient Monument. The old course of the stream, known as Vicar's Brook, runs roughly parallel for more than 1 km before entering the River Cam near Newnham. The Hobson's Brook system drains about 12 km², but is fed by a much more extensive chalk aquifer.

Ecological history of Nine Wells and Hobson's Brook

Two ecological studies of Hobson's Brook and Nine Wells were carried out by E.A. Gray in the 20th century (Gray 1974, 1977a, 1977b). In the 1940s Hobson's Brook was a healthy free-flowing chalk stream full of animal life including beetles *Coleoptera*, mayflies *Ephemeroptera*, caddisflies *Trichoptera*, blackflies (Simuliidae), **Freshwater Shrimp** *Gammarus pulex* and molluscs such as the **Freshwater Limpet** *Ancylus fluviatilis*.

In the 1970s Gray found a marked decline in flora and fauna and concluded that this was the result of increased abstraction and the expansion of intensive agriculture in the catchment. Gray documented a reduction in average annual flows from 50 l/s in 1949, to 12 l/s in 1965 and almost zero in the summer drought of 1976. The rare relic flatworm *Crenobia alpina* and caddisfly *Agapetus fuscipes* were lost from the site, and in 1981 its SSSI status was revoked. The importance of Nine Wells as the principal source of water for the entire Hobson's Brook system was keenly apparent.

Nine Wells was surveyed again in 1985 by Fiona MacCallum (MacCallum 1986). Although she did not find the rare relic species, other springhead endemics such as flatworms *Polycelis felina* and *P. nigra* were abundant at the site. In 1989 I conducted a study of macro-invertebrates in the Hobson's Brook system. Although the water quality was judged to be generally good, the average flow from Nine Wells was just 10 l/s and several of the key taxa identified by MacCallum were apparently absent (Boreham 1990).

In a 2002 survey of Nine Wells, I found the caddisfly *Agapetus fuscipes* present again at Nine Wells (Boreham 2002b). The summer flow rate peaked at about 60 l/s, but despite this, the abundance of flatworms (*Polycelis* spp.) was low, especially around the springheads. Later that year the flow from the springs was very low and the presence of the **Rat-tailed Maggot** *Eristalis tenax* in the stream channel indicated anoxic environments and poor water quality due to decomposing organic material.

In summer 2002 Nine Wells and Hobson's Conduit showed the scars of an amenity site close to a large suburban population. The springheads and stream channel had been disfigured and partly filled in, bridges and hedging had been damaged, and there were abandoned vehicles and dumped rubbish. This, coupled with the overgrowth of woody vegetation and consequent deep shade, threatened to reduce the site to a plot of scrubby wasteland.

Despite this, the potential for Nine Wells, if rehabilitated, to be a suitable recipient site for the reintroduction of rare relic aquatic invertebrate species was recognised. A management plan for Nine Wells was drawn up in 2004 in consultation with Natural England and in 2005 the site was declared a Local Nature Reserve (LNR), and qualified as a County Wildlife Site because of its chalk stream habitat. In winter 2005 the springheads were cleaned out, and several dangerous trees were felled, opening-up the centre of the site. In 2006 the future of Nine Wells as part of the 'Hobson's Conduit Open Space' in the Cambridge Southern Fringe Development became part of the planning process. Originally a large wildlife area with Nine Wells at its centre was proposed to create a 'Greater Nine Wells Reserve'.

Unfortunately, low flow rates from the springs continued to blight Hobson's Brook and Nine Wells. In 2008/9 Cambridge Water determined that abstraction at Babraham pumping station had a direct and profoundly adverse effect on flow rates at Nine Wells. Ecological studies in 2009 and 2016 by the author failed to find the rare relic aquatic invertebrates, or indeed even the flatworms *Polycelis* spp. In 2010 the Environment Agency began discussions with Cambridge Water (now South Staffs Water) about supporting low summer flows at Nine Wells by abstracting water at Babraham and pumping it *c*.8 km to Nine Wells for discharge through boreholes close to the springheads.

In 2017 the Hobson's Conduit Trust carried out bioblitz events centred on Nine Wells and further down the Hobson's Brook valley at Empty Common, near the Botanic Garden in Cambridge. These were followed in 2018 and 2019 by bioblitz events at Hobson's Park and Clare College Playing Field, also in the Hobson's Brook corridor. On each occasion forty experts and volunteers ran hour-long identification sessions, covering mosses, vascular plants, small mammals, birds, bats, amphibians and reptiles, small mammals, moths, bugs, beetles and other insects, fish and freshwater invertebrates. More than a hundred people participated in
each event.

During 2019 Nine Wells and Hobson's Brook suffered one of the worst droughts since 1976, with very low flows throughout the system for an extended period. Finally, in 2020 the flow support system came into operation, and flows at Nine Wells remained at about 20 l/s throughout the summer. This was probably the first time this had happened since 2002, and represents a significant environmental improvement for Nine Wells and the whole Hobson's Brook system.

In the same period, the Cambridge Southern Fringe Development at Clay Farm and the Addenbrooke's Biomedical Campus adjacent to Hobson's Brook valley have created special challenges for the management of surface water. The issue of flooding and poor water quality has been largely dealt with using a series of large balancing ponds throughout the system, and the implementation of sustainable urban drainage schemes (SUDS).

Nine Wells LNR
The 1.2 ha site (it is only 225 × 75 m) is jointly owned by Cambridge City Council and the University of Cambridge. Nine Wells is within South Cambridgeshire, but control is delegated to Cambridge City Council. The site straddles a break in slope between the rolling chalklands to the south, and the flatter claylands to the north.

Unusually for a springhead, it is located at the end of a promontory (White Hill). The site offers heritage, landscape, geological, archaeological, wildlife and amenity aspects at the urban fringe. The site is a small copse of mature **Beech trees** *Fagus sylvatica* with **Ash** *Fraxinus excelsior*, **Maple** *Acer campestre*, **Elder** *Sambucus nigra*, **Spindle** *Euonymus europaeus*, **Holly** *Ilex aquifolium*, **Dogwood** *Cornus sanguinea* and **Hawthorn** *Crataegus monogyna*.

It contains four main springheads linked by a chalk stream. The woodland, hedgerows and chalk stream are all identified as priority habitats under the Cambridgeshire Local Biodiversity Action Plan 1998. Management of the site has had a number of clearly defined objectives under the Local Habitat Action Plan (LHAP) for Cambridgeshire, addressing water quantity, increased nitrate levels in the groundwater, and the accumulations of organic debris causing anoxic conditions harmful to wildlife.

Common Frogs and **Common Toads** have been recorded at the site, and the mammals present include **Fox**, **Rabbit**, **Hare**, **Muntjac Deer**, **Grey Squirrel** and **Badger**.

The site is an important refuge for birds with **Sparrowhawk**, **Green Woodpecker**, **Long-tailed Tit**, **Bullfinch** and **Redwing** recorded regularly, as well as a variety of finches, tits, thrushes and warblers. **Kingfishers** are regular visitors, where they feed on the **Bullhead** *Cottus gobio* and **Three-spined stickleback** *Gasterosteus aculeatus* that live in the springheads and chalk stream.

The 2017 bioblitz at Nine Wells identified 166 different taxa (mostly to species level). The highlights included breeding **Tawny Owls**, **Elephant Hawk-moth** *Deilephila elpenor*, **Soprano Pipistrelle**, **Common Twayblade** *Neottia ovata* and **Deadly Nightshade** *Atropa belladonna*.

Hobson's Park
Downstream of Nine Wells, Hobson's Brook has an open aspect where the flowing water is fringed by **Water-cress** *Nasturtium officinale*, **Water-starworts** *Callitriche* spp. and **Common Duckweed** *Lemna minor*. Other plants in the stream channel include **Common Reed** *Phragmites australis*, **Unbranched Bur-reed** *Sparganium emersum* and **Water-plantain** *Alisma plantago-aquatica*. Birds frequently recorded feeding in Hobson's Brook include **Grey Heron**, **Moorhen**, **Mallard**, and of course **Kingfisher**.

Figure 15.44 Nine Wells. (SB).

Figure 15.45 Hobson's Park looking south. (SB).

Hobson's Park, Trumpington, which was created from former agricultural land, borders Hobson's Brook and a development of new-build housing. The 2018 bioblitz at Hobson's Park produced 203 different taxa. The highlights were **Buzzard**, **Great Crested Grebe**, **Little Grebe**, **Privet Hawk-moth** *Sphinx ligustri*, **Noctule Bat**, **Wood Mouse** and **Water Vole**, with **Cottongrass** *Eriophorum angustifolium*, **Cyperus Sedge** *Carex pseudocyperus* and **Lesser Bulrush** *Typha angustifolia* growing in wetland habitats.

Clare College Playing Field
Northwards along the Hobson's Brook corridor is the tree-lined riparian habitat of Clare College Playing Field, off Bentley Road, Cambridge. Its woodland includes **Ash** *Fraxinus excelsior*, **Black Poplar** *Populus nigra*, **Elm** *Ulmus minor*, **Lime** *Tilia × europaea*, **Scots Pine** *Pinus sylvestris* and **White Willow** *Salix alba*. The 2019 bioblitz produced 205 different taxa. Bioblitz highlights were the **Great Spotted Woodpecker** and **Little Egret**; the **Poplar Hawk-moth** *Laothoe populi* and **Spectacle Moth** *Abrostola tripartita*; the **Serotine Bat** and **Mole**; the **Water Scorpion** *Nepa cinerea*;

the **Lesser Water-parsnip** *Berula erecta* and **Stinking Iris** *Iris foetidissima*. **Tawny Owls** and **Kingfisher** were also recorded at the site.

Empty Common
Further downstream near the Botanic Garden is Empty Common, a tree-lined area of allotment gardens between Hobson's Brook and Vicar's Brook. The wooded areas here include Ash, **Black Poplar** *Populus nigra*, **Elder** *Sambucus nigra*, **Rowan** *Sorbus aucuparia*, **Sycamore** *Acer pseudoplatanus* and Hazel. The 2017 bioblitz at Empty Common identified 233 different taxa. The highlights were **Common Pipistrelle**, **Bank Vole**, **Grass Snake**, a **Flatworm** *Polycelis nigra* and **Water-violet** *Hottonia palustris*.

The Conduit Head, Brookside and the Botanic Garden
Further downstream north of Brooklands Avenue, Hobson's Conduit takes on the form of a 'linear pond', with excess flowing water being diverted into Vicar's Brook. This reach is important for dragonflies and damselflies including the **Emperor** *Anax imperator* and **Banded Demoiselle**

Calopteryx splendens. Recently (summer 2020), silt has been cleared from the Botanic Garden stretch to' facilitate bank repairs. Water Violet has increased greatly here in the last 20 years and flowers abundantly in May.

Conclusion

Taken together, the four bioblitz events along the Hobson's Brook corridor identified 517 species (Table 15.5). Each bioblitz site produced between 166 and 233 unique species, demonstrating the biodiversity of habitats close to the built environment, and showing the importance of the Hobson's Brook 'green corridor' in preserving wildlife in the City of Cambridge.

It is clear that maintaining a strong year-round flow of high-quality chalk water in Hobson's Brook is essential for the continued success of these ecosystems, which offer considerable benefits to the people that live close by. It is only by careful protection and management of these wildlife resources that we can guarantee these ecosystem services for future generations. The augmentation of flow at Nine Wells is a significant and welcome step in the right direction, with benefits for the whole Hobson's Brook system. The ongoing challenge is to create a management plan and scheme of works that will monitor, maintain and improve all habitats along the whole Hobson's Brook corridor from Nine Wells to the Conduit Head.

Table 15.5 Species recorded at Hobson's Brook bioblitz events 2017–2019.

Bioblitz	Birds	Mammals	Fish	Herptiles	Moths	Other inverts	Plants	Total
Nine Wells 2017	35	5	2	0	30	20	90	182
Hobson's Park 2018	34	5	2	2	42	33	85	203
Clare College Playing Field 2019	36	8	1	0	48	23	89	205
Empty Common 2017	17	4	2	1	39	67	103	233
All sites 2017–19	62	12	2	3	103	140	198	517

16. Nature Conservation

Introduction

Many people in Cambridge value its wildlife and support conservation charities. Some are active conservation volunteers. Cambridge City Council plays a major part in nature conservation, described below. The Wildlife Trust for Bedfordshire, Cambridgeshire and Northamptonshire (hereafter called the Wildlife Trust) manages two major sites and several smaller ones. The Cam Valley Forum (CVF) campaigns for the River Cam and organises work parties. The Countryside Restoration Trust is active on the Bourn Brook. The Environment Agency protects both fish and water quality. In addition, Cambridge Past, Present & Future manages two large sites close to Cambridge: Coton Countryside Reserve, of which a small part is in the NHC area, and Wandlebury Country Park, just outside it.

There are many other local initiatives, ranging in scale from small wildflower plantings by roads to the large meadow now established on the back lawn of King's College. Private individuals construct hedgehog passes and feed birds. There is a small private bird sanctuary by Adams Road. These activities and places are mentioned elsewhere in our pages. In this chapter we concentrate on the main wildlife sites and describe some notable conservation activities in our area.

Wildlife sites are given various designations under the planning system, which allows them greater to lesser protection against undesirable development. In the NHC area the highest level of protection is that of Sites of Special Scientific Interest (SSSI), which are of national importance. Cambridge has two SSSIs that have been designated for geological reasons and two for mainly biological reasons. Next come Local Nature Reserves (LNR), which have a statutory designation, but are of local importance. Most of these sites are owned by the City Council. One LNR is also a County Wildlife Site (CWS), a designation which gives no statutory protection, but is a factor that does need to be seriously considered when planning applications are made. The final levels of designation are City Wildlife Sites (CiWS) and Protected Road Verges (PRV). These are often smaller features, though some county PRVs are also CWS. The designation will help to inform their management, but does not always stop development or prevent degradation.

Wildlife sites in Cambridge

Wildlife, both flora and fauna, can be found throughout Cambridge and the city provides a wide range of habitats. Sites that are managed specifically for nature conservation and other locations that are good for wildlife are listed below, with information on the habitats which characterise them and notes on their management. For each site, there is a list of designations, together with an indication of whether the site is managed by the Wildlife Trust (WT).

Cambridge City Council has designated eleven sites as Local Nature Reserves, which are managed for both people and wildlife, providing opportunities for people to study, learn about and enjoy nature on their doorstep. All are open access.

Cambridge's many churchyards (Chapter 15) provide a variety of habitats, though they vary greatly in size and natural history interest. Two (Little St Mary's and St Andrews, Chesterton) are City Wildlife Sites as are the Ascension Burial Ground and Mill Road Cemetery. Histon Road Cemetery is listed as of historical importance, with an active Friends group who help manage both the historic features and the natural history interest. Mill Road Cemetery is well studied by Anglia Ruskin University students and has a Friends group.

Almost any park or public open space provides habitat for some creatures. Many of the newer developments around Cambridge incorporate open spaces, including wildflower meadows and lakes, which are being managed to provide habitats and benefit biodiversity. A list of 25 of the more notable wildlife sites follows. The name is followed by the conservation designation(s) of the site (if any), its area and its Ordnance Survey grid reference.

Barnwell East (LNR/WT; 2.6 ha; TL478581)
Grassland and scrub with a pond. Pond-dipping platform near entrance on Barnwell Road. Common Toads breeding.

Barnwell West (LNR; 3.8 ha; TL477584) Scrub and woodland. Coldham's Brook runs alongside this woodland reserve. Water Voles, Kingfishers.

Beechwoods (LNR/WT; 9.8 ha; TL484545) Woodland and chalk grassland. Beech trees planted on chalk slope in the 1840s. A new area of woodland was planted to the west in 1992.

Botanic Garden (CWS; 16 ha; TL454571) Grassland, woodland and lake. Owned by Cambridge University, with a charge for entrance. Active wildlife monitoring. See chapter 15.

Bramblefields (LNR; 2.1 ha; TL472606) Grassland and scrub with ponds. Site of former allotments, now dominated by scrub. Some habitat creation.

Brook Leys (18 ha; TL422601) Parkland and lake by M11 near Eddington. New developments include green spaces sown with wildflower mixes. Lake to encourage wildlife.

Byron's Pool (LNR; 4.4 ha; TL437546) Mixed deciduous woodland; four ponds; fish pass; meadow. Adjacent to the River Cam.

Cherry Hinton chalk pits (SSSI/CWS/WT; 11 ha; TL484558) Former chalk quarries. East Pit was worked until the early 1980s. Chalk cliffs; rare chalk grassland plants; scrub. Limekiln Close is now largely wooded.

Cherry Hinton Hall (12 ha; TL481564) Parkland, woodland and lakes. Managed by the City Council primarily for leisure. Specimen trees with tree trail. Includes a small woodland nature reserve and several lakes.

Coe Fen and Sheep's Green (LNR; 17 ha; TL446575) Grassland and riverside. Grazed by cattle. Many ditches; also a fast-flowing stream leading to a fish pass. Wetland plants, veteran willows, rare invertebrates.

Coldham's Common (LNR; 49 ha; TL474586) Grassland with pockets of scrub and woodland. Big site with some chalk grassland. Streams, soakaways and scrub favoured by breeding birds.

Ditton Meadows (16 ha; TL475601) Riverside meadows between Cambridge and Fen Ditton. The area is mainly grassland, criss-crossed by ditches, with streams and small areas of woodland.

Gog Magog Golf Course (SSSI; 88 ha; TL490541) Calcareous grassland with a rich flora. Access to members only.

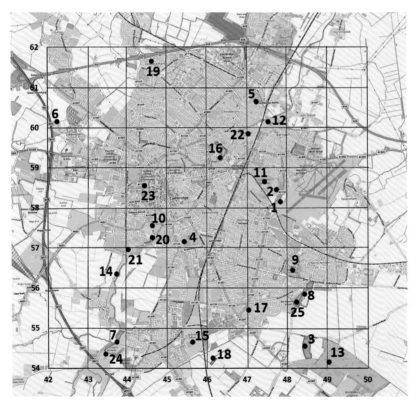

Figure 16.1 Map showing Cambridge wildlife sites: 1 Barnwell East; 2 Barnwell West; 3 Beechwoods; 4 Botanic Garden; 5 Bramblefields; 6 Brook Leys; 7 Byron's Pool; 8 Cherry Hinton chalk pits; 9 Cherry Hinton Hall; 10 Coe Fen and Sheep's Green; 11 Coldham's Common; 12 Ditton Meadows; 13 Gog Magog Golf Course; 14 Grantchester Meadows; 15 Hobson's Park; 16 Logan's Meadow; 17 Nightingale recreation ground; 18 Nine Wells; 19 Orchard Park; 20 Paradise; 21 Skaters' Meadow; 22 Stourbridge Common; 23 The Backs; 24 Trumpington Meadows; 25 West Pit.

Grantchester Meadows (40 ha; TL437563)
Extensive riverside meadows along W bank of River Cam between Cambridge and Grantchester.

Hobson's Park (41 ha; TL456546) Parkland created as part of the Clay Farm development between Trumpington and the railway line. Lake with bird reserve. Hobson's Brook runs along west side.

Logan's Meadow (LNR; 1.1 ha; TL463592) Wet grassland. Two ponds and a mosaic of open and closed habitats on north bank of River Cam in Chesterton. Formerly a grazing marsh.

Nightingale Recreation Ground (2.3 ha; TL470554) Park and community garden. The recreation ground includes sports facilities but areas are being managed for biodiversity and a community garden has been created.

Nine Wells (LNR; 1.2 ha; TL461542) Woodland and springs. Source of Hobson's Brook, a chalk stream which runs into central Cambridge. Deadly Nightshade. See chapter 15.

Orchard Park (0.6 ha; TL446616) Parkland. Small site on a housing development. Wildlife area, wildflower bank, orchard.

Paradise (LNR/CWS; 2.2 ha; TL446572) Wet riverside woodland, dominated by willows, with a central lake and marshy area. Site often floods in winter.

Skaters' Meadow (CWS/WT; 2 ha; TL440569) Wet meadow with ancient hedges. No public access but visible from the road along its north-western edge.

Stourbridge Common (LNR; 20 ha; TL470598) Floodplain grassland, which is seasonally wet and grazed by cattle in summer. Scrapes and wet woodland have been created.

The Backs (18 ha; TL444585) Riverside, grassland, gardens. Mostly owned and managed by various Cambridge colleges. The richest wildlife site in Cambridge. Public access along Queen's Road.

Trumpington Meadows Country Park (WT; 58 ha; TL434543) Grassland, hedgerows, ponds, woodland. Created on former agricultural land since 2008. The reserve abuts the River Cam and Byron's Pool. The Wildlife Trust have an office and run various events.

West Pit (LNR; 4.3 ha; TL482556) Former chalk quarry, now a caravan site. Species rich chalk grassland near top of site; woodland.

Reserves and City wildlife sites

City Council management

Cambridge City Council's Streets & Open Spaces Team is responsible for the designation, management and monitoring of the City's LNRs. Management plans are in place for the majority of sites, the delivery of which is overseen by a Local Nature Reserve officer, primarily working with a team of volunteers. Friends' groups are encouraged and have been established for some of the LNRs to facilitate local community involvement. The LNR officer is able to provide guided walks, presentations and practical volunteer activities.

Cattle summer-graze the three Common Land reserves. The council hold the graziers' rights and advertise annually for local graziers. The livestock are selected to be of a temperament suitable for public sites and the council Operations Team assists the graziers with stock monitoring and management. When required, large scale cutting is undertaken by the Operations Team with guidance from the LNR officer to ensure that species and habitats are considered.

Trees are inspected by council Arboriculture Officers on a three-year programme, with specified work being undertaken by contractors approved by the Arboriculture Association.

The Council work closely with the Wildlife Trust who run volunteer work parties on some sites including Coldham's Common, Barnwell East and West Pit.

Conservation volunteering on the LNRs

The LNR volunteer group has been running for nearly ten years, with some of its members having been involved from the start. The group not only tackles day to day management tasks, for example keeping paths clear from overhanging branches, litter-picking, bench renovations etc., but they are also vital in developing the reserves' habitat potential while maintaining what is already thriving.

Here are some examples of the volunteers' tasks.
- Seasonal cutting and raking of grassland/ meadows/marsh
- Creation of wildflower areas
- Pond clearance/installation
- Reed bed maintenance/creation
- Stream/ditch maintenance and enhancement
- River bank restoration
- Tree planting

- Coppicing
- Hedge laying and planting
- Scrub removal/creation
- Building of solitary-bee banks
- Surveying and monitoring of species.

Figure 16.2 Volunteers working on the Sheep's Green Rush. (VS).

Three examples show how volunteers contributed to habitat enhancement. This valuable work relies on volunteer input and makes the reserves become more complex and diverse habitats.

Volunteering example 1. Reed bed extension at Logan's Meadow LNR

Volunteers planted reeds and marginal aquatic plants along the side of a newly created stream. This work has now been rewarded with a very healthy reed bed, which boasts Wainscot moths, Water Vole and Water Rail.

Figure 16.3 Volunteers planting reeds by hand. (VS).

Figure 16.4 Logan's Meadow reed bed, Year 1. (VS).

Volunteering example 2. The recycled crushed ceramic mound at Bramblefields LNR

This reserve had previously been connected to an extensive brownfield area which was lost due to the building of Cambridge North rail station. To compensate for this, a project was devised to

Figure 16.5 Creating the mound at Bramblefields reserve. (VS).

Figure 16.6 Summer growth year 1 on the mound at Bramblefields. (VS).

try and recreate some of the lost conditions. This came in the form of a mound which was covered in recycled crushed sinks and baths. Such a feature may seem an unlikely basis for a thriving habitat, but this substrate has the low-nutrient and heat-retentive qualities characteristic not only of brownfield sites but also of chalk grassland. This project was seen as an experiment to investigate ideas around 'ecomimicry' (mimicking the natural world in the technological world) and the issues faced by fragmented urban nature sites. The volunteers made this experiment possible. They shifted 20 tonnes of this recycled substrate and then helped with seeding, creating different conditions within the mound by altering the topography. As the plants grew, the volunteers helped with the weeding and they monitored invertebrates and reptiles.

Volunteering example 3. Cherry Hinton Brook restoration

Cherry Hinton Brook is a chalk stream running from its source in Cherry Hinton, through Coldham's Common and then out to the river via Stourbridge Common. To enhance the flow of the brook in a section in Cherry Hinton the volunteers incorporated large amounts of gravel into the stream. This also helped to increase oxygen levels and create feeding and spawning grounds for fish and invertebrates. Again, this project could not have happened without the volunteers' hard work and dedication.

Figure 16.7 Shovelling gravel into Cherry Hinton Brook. (VS).

Trumpington Meadows Country Park

Trumpington Meadows Country Park, managed by the Wildlife Trust, is a 58-hectare (143 acre) area of meadows, woodlands and ponds set beside the River Cam and within the Cambridge green belt. The site is an important and diverse part of our local cultural and natural heritage, shaped by its geology, history and previous land use, and is part of a string of open spaces linking the centre of Cambridge to the surrounding countryside.

The area has a long history of human occupation and is the site of a Romano-British settlement. A seventh century Saxon grave site was uncovered during the archaeological works conducted before the development at Trumpington Meadows. Thereafter the land was mainly used for agriculture, except for a prisoner of war camp during the Second World War. In 1955, the Plant Breeding Institute conducted research into and breeding new crop varieties. This activity continued under various ownerships until 2004 when the current owners purchased the site to create the Trumpington Meadows development.

Since 2008 the Wildlife Trust has been working with the site owners to design and create a new landscape with new habitats, while retaining the remaining features such as hedgerows and coprolite ponds. These ponds were created through the excavation of coprolite, phosphate-rich nodules used as fertiliser in Victorian times (see Chapter 2). The new habitats include flower-rich meadows, new copses, ponds, new hedgerows and field margins across the farmland.

The mixture of old and new grasslands, dry and damp meadows, river and ponds, old trees and new woodland provides a rich mosaic of habitats. The reserve is already rich in wildlife, and will continue to change over the years as newly created habitats mature. There is still much to learn about the wildlife and plenty of opportunities for visitors to contribute to recording new species.

The Wildlife Trust manages the site through a mixture of extensive agricultural techniques that are sympathetic to wildlife, such as hay cutting, low intensity grazing, pollarding of riverside willows, and coppicing or limited intervention within the small woods. Wildlife Trust staff, contractors and volunteers manage the reserve so that present and future generations of visitors can enjoy the open space.

Trumpington Meadows is a place where local people can enjoy the countryside and wildlife just

Figure 16.8 Trumpington Meadows Country Park; the southern half lies outside the NHC area. (Google ©2021).

Figure 16.9 Flower-rich lowland meadow established at Trumpington Meadows on former arable land; yellow flowers are Rough Hawk's-beard *Crepis biennis*, white Oxeye Daisy *Leucanthemum vulgare* and pinkish Quaking-grass *Briza media*. (MOH).

a stone's throw from Cambridge. Nature lovers, walkers and cyclists can explore paths, enjoying the sights, sounds and smells of this beautiful reserve. A programme of events, guided walks and educational activities ensures that visitors, young and old, are able to find out more about the reserve and its wildlife.

River

The River Cam flows along the western boundary of the reserve towards Cambridge city. The river supports a range of fish species including Minnow, Gudgeon, Dace, Chub, Roach, Pike, Bullhead, Perch, Spined Loach, Stone Loach, European Eel and Brown Trout. Above Byron's Pool, the river has a more natural pool and riffle form with shallow gravel shoals, where Brown Trout have bred. The 2009 river restoration project by South Cambridgeshire County Council added gravel shoals, bank protection and backwaters for fish protection.

Kingfishers regularly nest in the river bank. Grey Heron and Mute Swans are seen along the river. Otters are present and evidence of breeding has been found in the past with the observation of mother and cub footprints.

A range of aquatic invertebrates can be found from dragonflies and damselflies to mayflies, caddisflies, stoneflies, water beetles and snails.

Meadows

Over 98% of flower-rich lowland meadows were lost from England in the twentieth century. At Trumpington Meadows we have re-created nearly 30 hectares of new flower-rich meadows. These support a range of wild flowers and grasses including Bird's-foot Trefoil, Salad Burnet, Oxeye Daisy, Kidney Vetch and Cowslip. In turn these will provide a home for a wide range of insects including butterflies, grasshoppers, crickets and beetles. They also provide habitats for ground nesting birds such as Skylark and feeding areas for Grey Partridge. In 2018 the first Small Blue butterfly was seen on site, a species that had been absent from Cambridgeshire since about 2004. As of 2020 a good-sized population could be found there.

Two flood meadows at the southern end of the site were originally described as 'fen' but were drained for agriculture in the 1970s. They were restored to flood meadows in 2003 and sown with a native wildflower seed mix. Meadow plants such as Ragged-Robin, Common Knapweed and Lady's

Bedstraw can be found. They are both cut for hay and grazed during the summer.

Woodland

Cambridgeshire is one of the least wooded counties in England. Approximately eight hectares of new native woodland has been created at the reserve with other small copses planted throughout the adjacent farmland. These will provide habitats for badgers, deer and a range of breeding birds.

Ponds

The ponds across the site, from the historic coprolite pits to the recently created lake (a balancing pond), provide homes for wetland birds including Little Grebe and Moorhen. Common Toads have been seen by the coprolite ponds as well as various dragonfly species. The clear water of the lake supports a range of aquatic plants including stoneworts, which are reliant on clean water. As the lake (figured in chapter 10) matured, taller plants of pond margins such as Common Reed and Yellow Iris increased. In the summer a variety of dragonfly and damselfly species can be seen around the ponds, including the first Willow Emerald Damselfly in 2019.

Farmland

The areas of arable farmland adjacent to the country park with their new hedges and copses provide habitat for a wide range of farmland wildlife including Brown Hare, Grey Partridge, Corn Bunting and in winter flocks of Golden Plover.

The Pennywort Project, Cam Valley Forum 2016–2019

The invasive weed, **Floating Pennywort** *Hydrocotyle ranunculoides* is steadily spreading through Britain, after its release in 1999 into a river in Essex. This is an invasive species which grows rapidly to clog watercourses. It harms biodiversity and water quality, impedes recreational use, increases flood risk and clogs filters. Because even a 1-cm length of stem can spread the infestation, it is readily spread by the flow of the river and the wind, by river craft and fishing equipment, or very occasionally by waterbirds.

By 2015 the infestation was becoming a noticeable problem on the Cam above Cambridge. Cam Conservators tried tackling it using glyphosate, but the need for repeated applications made the process expensive and of limited effectiveness. Cam Valley Forum and the Wildlife Trust ran a few volunteer working parties trying to remove it using rakes and nets. However, by December 2016 the river at Grantchester Meadows was clogged with pennywort from side to side. Despite more intensive volunteer activity in 2017, from the bank, from canoes and from punts, it was frustratingly clear that the battle was being lost.

By autumn 2017 the upper Cam was blocked in two places on Grantchester Meadows with many tonnes of Floating Pennywort between Cambridge and its upstream extent on Bourn Brook, just above Grantchester. A big infestation, hidden in the private section of Grantchester Mill Race, was discovered by Cam Valley Forum and then cleared by the Environment Agency in October 2017.

It was clear that something needed to be done, so Cam Valley Forum decided to coordinate an attempt to systematically eradicate it from the upper Cam.

During 2017 volunteer 'Pennywort Pullers' had been getting frustrated because the drooping branches of the riverside willows were trapping pennywort fragments, making clearance extremely difficult and time consuming. Stimulated by the offer of a small grant from Cambridge Water's PEBBLE fund, Cam Valley Forum decided to engage contractors to prune back these branches.

It was a challenging project, because there is no easy river access for powered craft between Cambridge and Grantchester, and the extremely wet conditions in February 2018 prevented vehicle access along the bank. Instead it was decided to operate the project entirely from two large ferry punts, kindly lent by Scudamore's.

Initially the focus for the contractors was on a 0.6-km stretch of the upper Cam at Grantchester Meadows, but following an inspection and the award of additional funding from the Environment Agency and others, this was increased to 2.8 km: all the way from the confluence with Grantchester Mill Stream to Lammas Land car park in Cambridge. Over seven weeks, despite occasional pauses due to floods, strong winds and snow, the contractors cleared the drooping branches and remaining winter pennywort from the full stretch.

At intervals, guided by the Wildlife Trust, twelve 'Habitat Refuges' were created. These were protected from potential pennywort infestation by floating booms. Following the tree works, volunteers continued to monitor for re-emergence. Cam Valley Forum arranged two follow-up working parties during 2018. One in partnership with Cambridge Canoe Club in July aimed to 'seek and destroy' any fragments, while a second in November cleared a previously unnoticed infestation in Swan Island Ditch, Newnham.

Figure 16.10 Cambridge Canoe Club clearing a passage through the Floating Pennywort, Grantchester Meadows, Nov 2017. (ATM).

Figure 16.11 Tree works in progress February 2018. The cleared area is on the right, uncleared on the left. The light green patches to the left are Floating Pennywort. The three contractors are just visible in the middle of the image. (ATM).

Figure 16.12 Working party clearing Swan Island Ditch, Newnham, November 2018. (ATM).

At the time of writing (mid 2020), the project appears to have successfully eradicated Floating Pennywort from the whole 4.5 km of the upper Cam between Cambridge and the M11. This required about £30,000 in grant funding, £10,000 in pro-bono support and 1000 volunteer hours.

Although the project is apparently successful, vigilance remains vital. This was demonstrated in 2020 by the discovery of infestations in the neighbouring Great Shelford Award Stream (which flows into the Cam via Hobson's Brook) and at an unused punt mooring station in Central Cambridge.

Learnings

- Manual removal can be easier, more effective and less damaging than glyphosate.
- Partnership working is key. Motivated volunteers will willingly regularly monitor and remove pennywort from the rivers they love, but agencies or contractors need to do the heavy work.
- It is important to be systematic and persistent. Start at the upstream end. Start early in the year. Remove every shred. Put it somewhere dry to die. Check regularly for re-emergence.

Mink and Water Voles

Invasive non-native species can have severe impacts on native wildlife. The **American Mink** *Neovison vison* is one of Europe's most damaging invasive species, and in Britain it has been clearly demonstrated as the number-one cause of the decline in **Water Voles** *Arvicola amphibius*. Mink have negative impacts on other species, and Water Voles have other factors which impact them negatively, but this close negative relationship is very powerful and the spread of Mink has led to the Water Vole earning the title of 'The UK's fastest declining native mammal'. Here in Cambridgeshire, Jefferies *et al.* (2004) wrote of the Water Vole's catastrophic 99.8% crash between 1989 and 1997. The Game and Wildlife Conservation Trust (GWCT) undertook research and developed a system of catchment-based Mink control which proved highly successful at removing Mink from river systems, and they demonstrated that, in the absence of Mink, Water Voles could be successfully reintroduced.

Trapping Mink on the Bourn Brook

In 2010, I started a project at The Countryside Restoration Trust (CRT) to apply this catchment-level control to the Bourn Brook, the stream which flows eastwards from the village of Bourn, much of it through CRT farmland, to join the River Cam at Byron's Pool. The lower reaches of the Bourn and the area of Byron's Pool are in the south-western corner of the NHC area. Although most of the Mink trapping work took place outside the project recording area, the benefits have certainly been seen in the Water Vole population within the city.

The CRT Mink trapping was done as part of a partnership project with the Wildlife Trust, under the name of Bourn Free. This project aims to reduce the impact of various non-native species on the Bourn Brook. It relies on support from all the landowners along the watercourse, Farming and Wildlife Advisory Group, Cam Valley Forum and volunteers from the Cambridgeshire Mammal Group, The Cambridge Conservation Volunteers, CRT volunteers, local people, and various other visiting groups of volunteers. It has been a long ten years at the time of writing, with plenty still to do, but the results as far as Water Voles are concerned have been spectacular. This is one of the most successful conservation projects I have been involved with and a blueprint for Mink eradication which we are hoping to roll out regionally across

East Anglia. If that proves successful and viable, we will be pushing to start a GB-wide eradication of Mink within the UN 2021–30 'Decade of Ecosystem Restoration'.

The main method of trapping Mink is the use of a GWCT Mink raft, a floating platform with a tunnel on top. The tunnel tempts Mink to explore inside. Their natural curiosity is sufficient with no requirement for bait or lure. The tunnel can hold one of two things: a smooth clay surface where Mink leave their footprints, or a cage trap which closes when the treadle is trodden on. In standard GWCT mode, the clay is checked for footprints every ten days or so, and if Mink tracks are seen the trap is deployed for a ten-day period, during which visual checks have to be made on the trap every 24 hours. If a Mink is found in the trap, it is shot (using a method that is as humane as can be), and

Figure 16.13 A Mink raft on the Bourn Brook. (VL).

Figure 16.14 Mink (left) and Water Vole (right) tracks on the clay surface of a monitoring cartridge from a Mink raft tunnel. (VL).

the trap is replaced for another ten days. If no Mink are caught during the ten-day trapping period, the raft is reverted to clay-based tracking mode and the next check is done ten days later. The advantage of this system compared to previous random trapping operations is that the time-consuming daily trap checks are only made when a Mink is thought to be around, while the regular checking of the clay gives a less time-consuming means of assuring the operator that Mink remain absent.

Results
The Mink population of the Bourn Brook was removed in the first winter of 2010–11 – just over 50 Mink. As far as we know, none bred in the 2011 summer, or any subsequent years, but juveniles returned from elsewhere and required continuous, reduced, efforts to remove them. The reduced effort allowed more time to deal with the source of incomers: it became possible to expand the operation to other rivers in the Upper Cam Catchment, and this network gradually expanded with the result that numbers of Mink returning to the Bourn Brook declined quite rapidly to around four per year. Prior to this project, the gamekeeper on the lower reaches of the Bourn and the area around its confluence with the Cam had been catching about 20 Mink per year, every year. After five years of catchment-scale Mink control in the Upper Cam, he stopped catching Mink and put his traps away!

More efficient Mink trapping elsewhere in the Cam catchment
An even more time-efficient system became available during this project: Trap Alarms. The first system to come onto the market was the Mink Police Unit. Our first Mink caught with one of these was in December 2014, and as funds have allowed, we have gradually increased the number of such alarms available. The box sits on the back of the trap, and has a magnet which activates an alarm when it is pulled off; the magnet is connected to the trap door so when the door shuts, the magnet is pulled off and the alarm system sends a text and email to the trapper to alert them of the activity. The system also sends twice-daily 'heartbeat' messages so that you have confidence that the unit has charge in the batteries and is in reach of a phone signal. Any trap alarm or failure to operate is alerted to the trapper, who can attend the trap straight away to deal with it.

The advantage of this system is that it will catch Mink when they become rare; many of our volunteers drifted away as Mink captures declined and checking the clay pads returned negative results, but Mink can return from far distant populations and repopulate a river quite quickly. Dispersing Mink will explore many kilometres of river (up to 60 km dispersal distance) and will keep travelling if they do not encounter a mate; a permanent trap will intercept these individuals before they meet members of the opposite sex! Use of this system allows me as an almost lone operator to maintain traps at a wide range of remote locations with only occasional visits required to deal with trapped animals or faults on the equipment. Once the Upper Cam was more or less dealt with, trapping started to expand into the lower Cam north of Cambridge, and out into Fenland, with the aim of joining up Cambridgeshire operations with other projects underway in Norfolk and Suffolk. There has been a strong partnership in East Anglia for nearly 20 years, and our work is now part of that.

One trapping location on the River Cam in Chesterton has been in operation, on and off, since 2016, and only one Mink was caught there (Feb. 2018). Apart from that, no trapping has been done within the city boundary, and it seems that deleting Mink from the wider countryside has created a vacuum which has pulled Mink out of the city and into the areas where trapping is generally easier to undertake. Prior to this work, Mink were regularly seen on the Cam in the city; I recall seeing one in the 1990s attacking a brood of Mallards while I was on a punting trip with friends – several of the ducklings came onto the punt for safety while the attack was underway! Others have told me of sightings of Mink repeatedly taking Moorhen chicks. In summer 2020 a Mink was seen on Grantchester Meadows (taking Moorhen eggs), but this seems to be a wandering individual rather than a breeding animal, as no further sightings have been reported and no juvenile Mink have been caught in autumn 2020.

Outcome for Water Voles and Otters
Sightings of Water Voles across Cambridge have become commonplace in the last 5 years. The Bin Brook at TL4257 used to be a well-known place to see Water Voles, but sightings declined in the early 2000s. Trapping there has only ever caught two Mink, just outside the NHC area, a male and female in short succession in 2011. Subsequently no

Mink have returned. Hopefully in time the Water Vole population there will return.

The Wildlife Trust role in the Mink-Water Vole aspect of Bourn Free has mainly been concerned with monitoring the results. It undertook the first complete survey of the Bourn Brook in 2011 after the first winter of Mink removal, giving us a picture of the baseline Water Vole population. Surveyors also searched for signs of Mink and Otters, giving us a picture of their status, and monitored invasive plants. This survey was repeated in 2014 and again in 2017. A partial survey was undertaken in 2019 but that one did not reach the NHC area. All surveys were conducted by Ruth Hawksley plus volunteers, giving a strong element of consistency to the data. The 2011 survey revealed just 32 Water Vole signs on the whole Bourn Brook, with none in the NatHistCam area. By 2014 there were 171 field signs, including a few records in both TL4254 and TL4354, while by 2017 there were 608 field signs, and a continuous distribution of records upstream of the M11 in TL4254, and good numbers in TL4354.

Water Voles have made a remarkable recovery and are now part of the natural food chain, as they should be – having been seen in Barn Owl prey caches, and disappearing down the beak of a Grey Heron, for example. They are regularly sighted on the Bourn Brook, and are starting to modify the riparian habitat through their grazing efforts, creating a more diverse vegetation structure and, no doubt, converting some of the excess nutrients that are flowing through the Bourn Brook into vole meat for their many predators to take a share of.

In addition to the benefits to Water Voles, increases have been noted for Mallard and Moorhens breeding along the brook and in the number of Otter spraints; reduced competition for food has undoubtedly benefited the Otter. Mink are quite varied in their diet, taking about one-third each of fish, mammal and bird prey (plus invertebrates and amphibians if available). The **Signal Crayfish** *Pacifastacus leniusculus* population seemed to increase shortly after Mink were removed but has subsequently declined again now that Otters are crunching them up! Otter spraints have increased on the Bourn Brook survey with 11 records in 2011, 35 records in 2014 and 90 records in 2017. A dip in 2019 signs may reflect the shorter survey length covered or natural reduction now that Otters have eaten many of the larger fish in the Bourn Brook, but hopefully future full surveys will reveal a healthy population of this welcome returning native top predator.

17. Cambridge's natural history in a wider perspective

In this book we have looked closely at many aspects of Cambridge's natural history. The aim of this concluding chapter is to step back from the intense focus of previous chapters and draw out some of their main themes, putting them in a slightly broader context.

Naturalists have always made observations in cities. Indeed, the chronicler who noted the pair of **White Storks** that nested on St Giles Church in Edinburgh in 1416 was writing long before anything we would regard as modern natural history. Gerard (1597) knew **Navelwort** *Umbilicus rupestris* at Westminster Abbey, 'over the doore that leadeth from Chaucer his tombe to the olde palace', a site from which it had gone by 1633, and his successors saw how **London Rocket** *Sisymbrium irio* came up in abundance on the rubble around St Paul's Cathedral after the Great Fire of 1666 (Ray 1670). The latter was an early example of the tendency of alien species to colonise urban sites. **Ivy-leaved Toadflax** and others were listed by John Sibthorp on the walls of Oxford in 1794. These individual observations were gradually replaced by more detailed studies of urban habitats, a few broad in scope, such as Storrie's *The flora of Cardiff* (1886) and Hudson's *Birds in London* (1898), others much more detailed, including (amongst many such publications) Burkill's study of the plants distributed by the Cambridge dustcarts (1893) and Horn's list of the fish of the London docks (1923).

Despite this tradition of urban natural history, it was only after the Second World War that the numerous individual studies cohered into the distinct discipline of urban ecology. There is no suggestion in the 900 pages of A.G. Tansley's *The British Islands and their vegetation* (1939) that ecologists had any interest in towns. However, in Britain, as elsewhere in Europe, the rapid wartime recolonisation of bombed sites by wildlife, especially plants, surprised observers and sparked an interest in urban ecology (Sukopp 2002). Richard Fitter's book *London's natural history* was commissioned in 1943 and published as the third volume in the Collins *New Naturalist* series in 1945; it emphasised the richness and resilience of London's wildlife (Marren 1995). However it was in West Berlin that the discipline was developed by ecologists in the post-war years, and in particular by Herbert Sukopp

Figure 17.1 Ivy-leaved Toadflax growing against Queens' College Wall. (PAR).

of the Technische Universität Berlin (Kowarik 2020). Their academic studies of urban ecology were combined with an interest in landscape planning and the conservation of urban wildlife habitats.

Even after the boom in studies of urban wildlife by academic ecologists and amateur naturalists after the War, urban habitats in Britain were undervalued for several decades. They did not meet the criteria by which Sites of Special Scientific Interest were judged, which reflected Tansley's outlook and emphasised the presence of rare native species in natural and semi-natural habitats. David Goode (2014) identified a public inquiry into the development of Gunnersbury Triangle in west London, a secondary woodland on abandoned allotments, as the turning point in Britain. Against all expectations, the development of this site, regarded by officialdom as of little wildlife value, was prevented in 1983 because of its importance as woodland to local residents, who had mounted a vigorous campaign for its preservation.

The complexity of habitats in cities

One of the general features identified by urban ecologists is the complexity of habitats in cities. This is certainly true of Cambridge. The habitats in the NHC area, listed in Chapter 1, include built-up areas, brownfield and semi-industrial sites, water and wetlands, grassland, woodland and arable land. This range of habitats in a small area is an obvious contrast with the more uniform landscape of the surrounding county of Cambridgeshire. In the county as a whole 75% of the area (and 82% of the land in the low-lying north of the county) is arable land (Preston & Hill 2019). Passengers for Cambridge travelling by train from Peterborough pass through the county and for much of the journey see homogeneous countryside with just one major landmark, the parallel rivers of the Ouse Washes. It is only when passing through Ely and approaching Cambridge that the environment begins to vary.

The variety of urban habitats is perhaps surprising as the effect of building development on natural habitats is usually seen as destructive. The main habitat that was destroyed during the growth of Cambridge was arable land, and this continues to be built on in the current phase of expansion. More distinctive habitats in the NHC area have been lost, but in general these were not destroyed for building. The drainage of Hinton Moor, an astonishingly rich wetland by modern standards, was undertaken as part of the general agricultural improvement which followed Parliamentary Enclosure in southern Cambridgeshire in the early 19th century. However, the nearest of several small sandy areas to the town, the Hill of Health, became partly occupied by a 'gentleman's house' after enclosure (Preston 2018).

Despite their shared characteristic of habitat complexity, towns and cities vary in their history and this is reflected in their habitats and wildlife. Many grew to prominence during the Industrial Revolution, sometimes (like Manchester) from small townships, and these are characterised by their industrial heritage. Others became prominent because of their cathedrals (Ely), spas (Bath), naval facilities (Portsmouth), railways (Swindon) or as national capitals (London). Cambridge is (with St Andrew's and perhaps Oxford) one of only two or three towns in Britain and Ireland with a history which has been dominated since the Reformation by a university. In Aberdeen, Dublin, Edinburgh and Glasgow, the long-established university is clearly one component of a much more varied whole.

The varied wildlife habitats of Cambridge have been explored in detail in this book. The most urban of its habitats are the buildings, with their surrounding walls and nearby pavements and streets. Buildings have often been described as artificial cliffs, and this impression is certainly strengthened by the sight of a **Peregrine Falcon** plucking its prey on a pinnacle or ledge high above the city centre. However, occupied buildings are largely inaccessible to recorders and although older buildings, in particular, might potentially have a varied and interesting fauna, the only ones likely to be surveyed adequately are those with resident entomologists. The recent trend for 'green roofs' provides a habitat which is more visible, but scarcely more accessible. Buildings are otherwise of little interest to botanists, except where mosses and lush ferns colonise areas where water drips down from broken gutters or leaks out of downpipes. Smaller stone or brick structures such as boundary walls and gravestones are much richer and support the wide range of mosses and lichens described in Chapters 6 and 7.

In many towns post-industrial wastelands can support rich assemblages of plants and significant communities of invertebrates (Goode 2014). Alongside its university, Cambridge has an industrial history which has included aviation, electronics and railways. As the nature of industry and transport has changed in the post-war period, some firms have expanded whereas others have ceased to occupy their former premises. However, such 'brownfield' sites are less significant in Cambridge than might have been expected as they were rapidly converted to other uses in the late 20th and early 21st centuries. Many of the areas occupied by the Pye electronics company were taken for housing with almost indecent haste. A large area of railway sidings at Chesterton was progressively abandoned by British Rail from *c.* 1990. After a decade or so it had acquired a remarkably rich flora and associated butterfly fauna (Easy 2001a,b; Napier 2001; Tribe 2001). However, this area was redeveloped during the course of the NHC project as a railway station (Cambridge North), with associated hotels and other buildings. The station opened in 2017 and now (2021) only a few fragments of the sidings with their calcifuge lichens remain (Chapter 7). However, sandy soils introduced in recent developments are some compensation for the loss of the natural sandy outcrops and support many of the same species (Chapter 5).

Encapsulated and fringing countryside: the dynamics of urban expansion

As towns grow, some of the countryside onto which they spread is developed and converted to purely urban use, but other areas, although engulfed, nevertheless retain something of their former character. These engulfed areas have been called 'encapsulated countryside' and often such green spaces are as important as its buildings in giving the city its character. Around the edge of the town lies what might be called 'fringing countryside'. As towns expand the fringing countryside becomes increasingly influenced by the dense urban population until eventually it is itself built over or encapsulated. In many cities the most obvious examples of encapsulated countryside are woods, but this is not the case in the NHC area, a reflection of the very sparsely wooded nature of the surrounding county. The named woods are all plantations towards the edge of our area. The river and its adjoining commons are our examples of encapsulated countryside and these are discussed in more detail below.

Brick, chalk and gravel pits may have an even more complex history. Originally industrial sites, they can after abandonment be incorporated into the countryside then engulfed by the town. These processes are particularly evident in Cambridge in the complex of former chalk quarries at Cherry

Hinton. Cherry Hinton Lakes are former chalk quarries, now flooded and encapsulated. Lime Kiln Close, a long-abandoned chalk pit, has lost its post-industrial character and is largely dominated by trees and scrub, its industrial origin now scarcely more apparent than its earlier history in the shallow Cretaceous seas. The adjacent East Pit, quarried until 1984, still retains its character as a recently abandoned chalk quarry, thanks to active programmes of scrub clearance by the Wildlife Trust. Both are at the very edge of the current town.

One consequence of our decision to choose as our study area an 8×8 km square including the city, rather than the city itself, is that we have included a good representation of the fringing countryside. Much of this is arable land, but this has been rapidly shrinking as the city expands on to it. The loss of the birds of arable farmland in the area is described in Chapter 13. It is a consequence of the local reduction of arable habitat and a severe decline in farmland birds nationally. Specialist woodland birds have also declined both nationally and in the study area. By contrast, woodland plant species have proved to be rather resilient, and are not amongst the groups showing a marked decline nationally. The distribution of woodland and shade plants in the NHC area is not closely tied to the plantations around the southern fringe, as they occur in other shaded habitats, especially along the Backs and in other areas of low building density on the west side of the city. One notable woodland, Beechwoods LNR, has in fact rather a low concentration of woodland plants, as it has a sparse ground flora characteristic of beechwoods on chalk soils.

Encapsulated countryside along the river

The watercourses and associated habitats along the River Cam represent encapsulated countryside, but they have been greatly modified by the canalisation of the river and the drainage of the surrounding land by a network of ditches. Some of this modification has been a direct consequence of the proximity to a growing town, notably the systematic levelling of the commons by rubbish dumping in the Victorian period. These changes have led to a gradual loss of numerous aquatic and wetland plant species from the area over a period of several centuries. **Marsh Thistle**, **Frogbit**, **Fine-leaved Water-dropwort** and **Fan-leaved Water-crowfoot** are listed in Chapter 5 as species occurring in the county but absent from the NHC area – all were formerly found here, but are amongst the losses. Such gradual degradation is a feature of encapsulated countryside, which is isolated and subject to a range of urban pressures. A particularly well documented example is the Singapore Botanic Gardens' Jungle, an isolated fragment of tropical rain forest which lost half its native species in a century (Turner *et al.* 1996). Closer to home, many of London's numerous commons were heathland when they were saved as public open spaces in the 19th century, but they have often become 'little more than town parks' (Goode 2014); even those such as Hampstead Heath which have retained some semi-natural vegetation have lost many of their rarer species (Bellamy *et al.* 1986).

The riparian commons of Cambridge show a similar spectrum of modification to that of London's commons. They range from Jesus Green, now no more than a town park, to Coe Fen or Stourbridge Common, which have lost many species but still retain much of interest. It is, however, impossible to imagine that the Cambridge commons would have retained their rich range of aquatic plants even if they had been miles from any human settlement; such sites have not survived intact anywhere in the county. Indeed the riparian grassland of Grantchester Meadows has been largely reduced to a species-poor sward because it has been treated in the same way as its rural equivalents. Its post-war agricultural management is not documented, but it presumably involved the application of herbicide and fertiliser in the 1950s. The wildlife habitats alongside the Cam have been particularly vulnerable as the river is a relatively minor waterway with a small catchment area, and lacks an extensive floodplain. The contrast to Oxford is particularly striking. Oxford is on the River Thames, the second longest river in Britain, and it retains a series of species-rich flood meadows including Port Meadow, which is close to the city, extends over 120 hectares and is regularly flooded in winter.

The riparian habitats retain their importance as a habitat for birds, even though breeding species such as **Redshank** and **Snipe** have been lost. We would very much like to be able to compare the history of the aquatic and wetland flora with that of the invertebrate groups characteristically found in the same habitats, but this is not easily done. Duncan Mackay's research for this book has failed to unearth any comparable documentation for dragonflies and damselflies. However, the current dragonfly fauna is a rich one and although it is possible that species such as **White-legged**

Figure 17.2 Newly emerged male White-legged Damselfly. (PAR).

Damselfly have declined, there are certainly species which have colonised the area in recent years (Chapter 10). This reflects national trends in a group which has benefitted from a warming climate in recent decades. Until the post-war period molluscs were a more popular group than dragonflies, and there is very clear evidence for the loss of aquatic species from the NHC area (Chapter 11). The historical records for caddisflies need to be interpreted with caution, as the historical records are less detailed than those of plants and molluscs, and the recent survey is not exhaustive. However, species of predominantly northern and western distribution in Britain, more acidic waters and stony or gravelly substrates, are disproportionately represented amongst the species which have not been refound in the current recording period (Chapter 8). This suggests a decline similar to that of flowering plants.

Parks and gardens

Parks and gardens occupy a large area but assessing their wildlife presents considerable problems. A few public parks are open and accessible, and can be studied by those natural historians who are prepared to practise their fieldcraft in full public view. The larger institutional gardens, notably those of Cambridge colleges, can generally be visited and studied with permission; the thousands

Figure 17.3 *Amblyteles armatorius.* A large and quite distinctive Ichneumon wasp, one of a very few Ichneumon species recorded from our parks and gardens. (PAR).

of private gardens are largely invisible and inaccessible.

The special survey of 60 ordinary gardens presented in Chapter 5 has given us a record of the commoner lawn plants, garden weeds and bryophytes, as well as the planted trees. The plant species recorded were rather a mundane group, with no rarities.

It is only the long and detailed study of his own garden by Paul Rule that has revealed the wealth of the invertebrate life that might be found in the average garden (Chapter 15). This comes as no surprise. Jennifer Owen carried out the most famous study of garden wildlife, recording the species in her Leicester garden between 1972 and 2001 (Owen 2010). Her garden, like Paul Rule's, was fairly typical of the gardens of houses built between the wars; it was certainly not special in any way. She recorded 2673 species over the thirty years of her study, compared with the 744 species recorded by Paul between 2016 and 2020. Clearly the longer the period of study, the higher the total will be, as many species are only rare visitors. In the Leicester study, for example, 12% of the 94 hoverflies, 18% of the 282 macro-moths and 29% of the 421 beetles were recorded only once. Short studies of invertebrates lasting a few weeks record very much lower totals in gardens (Smith *et al.* 2006). The individual garden, though the natural unit of study, is perhaps too small to document the diversity of garden landscapes efficiently. Moreover the total number of

recorded species is not just a function of the length of study but is to a large extent determined by the number of taxonomic groups included in it, which itself depends on the number of experts who can be called upon to identify material. The most species-rich group in Owen's study were the ichneumons, a group which presents formidable identification problems. Owen managed to obtain the services of a leading world authority who identified 533 species caught in just three years (1972–74) in her garden. We have not had access to such specialist help, and only 30 species of parasitic Hymenoptera were recorded in the entire NHC area during the course of our project (Chapter 10).

The species total for the Botanic Garden in Cambridge, 2932 (excluding the cultivated plants), exceeds that for Jennifer Owen's Leicester garden. Although it has not been the subject of such an intensive study, the Botanic Garden has benefitted from its accessibility to a range of specialists and the encouragement given to recorders in recent years (not least on the regular bioblitzes). A garden of its size would be expected to have a much larger species total than Owen's domestic garden, especially as it deliberately sets out to recreate a range of habitats and grows such a large number of plant species. Although it is commonly believed that native plants support more species of invertebrate than introductions, Owen found no strong evidence that 'native is best' when she looked at the food plants of moth larvae in her garden. Whatever the relative frequency of species on native and alien hosts, alien hosts undoubtedly support additional specialist invertebrates that would otherwise be absent from the Cambridge area. **Box Bug**, **Juniper Shieldbug** and **Toadflax Brocade** are native species that have expanded their range by colonising cultivated and naturalised foodplants, whereas **Horse Chestnut Leaf Miner** and **Knopper Gall Wasp** are introductions that are dependent on introduced plants. The powdery mildews are perhaps an extreme case as 25% of the species recorded in the area are confined to non-native hosts (Chapter 7). Alien species are discussed in more detail below.

Despite the problems, or perhaps the impossibility, of documenting their wildlife adequately, it is clear that the innumerable gardens of the city make an enormous contribution to its biodiversity.

Habitats created for wildlife

The NHC project has provided an early opportunity to assess a new group of habitats in the city, those associated with modern housing developments. Whereas the houses of the interwar years were well-spaced and surrounded by sizeable gardens, the largest recent developments have been high-density flats surrounded by landscaped areas planned as a combination of recreational space and wildlife habitat. These developments include Eddington, Hobson's Park (associated with the Clay Farm estate) and Trumpington Meadows.
The relative contribution to wildlife of the two types of landscape will be difficult to evaluate, but the new areas provide a few large lakes and extensive grassland swards, which were absent from the earlier housing estates. They are certainly much easier to study, as they are publicly accessible. Botanists have recorded those plants which have been deliberately or accidentally introduced to these areas, but they are still working through the problem of their attitude to such species. The sight of a flourishing stand of **Common Cottongrass** in Trumpington Meadows (Chapter 4), a species usually associated with the bogs of the north and west, is certainly disconcerting. When first seen in 2014 this was described as an 'an unfortunate deliberate introduction' (Leslie 2015), illustrating the widespread botanical view that planted species are of less value than those accidentally introduced and of much less value than those which have arrived by unassisted dispersal. It may be that some mental adjustment will be required to cope

with the plants of these new habitats. Naturalists interested in more mobile groups, which are much more capable of reaching the new habitats without human assistance, are much less troubled and have welcomed the sight of **Small Blues** on Trumpington Meadows and breeding **Black-headed Gulls** (and, for a couple of years, **Common Terns**) in Hobson's Park.

Species in flux

Cities have always been regarded as restless places. The daily migration of commuters, the weekly binges of the young on Friday and Saturday nights, the termly, annual and triennial rhythms of the universities and the influx and departure of summer tourists are all apparent to the Cambridge resident. Less apparent, but no less significant, are longer term patterns of human immigration, settlement and dispersal. The wildlife of the city is also in a constant state of flux, at a range of spatial and temporal scales. Our ability to detect these changes depends on the availability of historic records, which varies greatly from group to group. Predictably, birds and flowering plants have been well recorded but other groups differ, and sometimes the differences appear to be influenced by chance events. Cambridgeshire's current tradition of bryophyte recording dates back to Paul Richards who, when he arrived as an undergraduate in 1927, had already written a bryophyte flora of his home county (Glamorgan). There is no such sequence of records of fungi and lichens, even though mycology was one of the research strengths of the University's Department of Botany for much of the 20th century. When historic records allow changes to be identified, a surprising number of them can be seen to be a reflection of national trends rather than a response to changes particular to Cambridge. This is true for a range of animal and plant groups, although they have responded to different environmental factors.

Persecution and pollution

One trend over the last century, and especially over the last few decades, has been the recovery of some conspicuous animal species from persecution. Birds of prey, which were formerly shot on sight or trapped by gamekeepers and then further reduced in numbers by the effects of pesticides such as DDT in the post-war years, have spread eastwards from their western redoubts (**Buzzard**, **Peregrine Falcon**), have been introduced to sites within their former

Figure 17.4 Mating Common Frogs in a garden pond. (PAR).

range (**Red Kite**) or have recovered their numbers (**Sparrowhawk**). **Greylag Geese** and **Canada Geese** have expanded from feral populations but their current abundance must similarly reflect a tolerance which would not have been extended to them until recently. The same tolerance is doubtless the reason for the large numbers of **Mallard** on the river. This species was uncommon in Cambridge in the early years of the 20th century when 'a tame and confiding duck … would have been in considerable danger of finding its way into the pot' (Keynes 1976). The only **Mute Swans** on the Cam then were kept as pinioned birds by St John's College and Keynes records the public interest when a pair nested on a small island by Silver Street Bridge in 1942. Similarly the **Badger**, which Marr & Shipley (1904) describe in Cambridgeshire as 'a very occasional wanderer, though possibly still breeding near Wimpole'; it is now not only tolerated but often encouraged by feeding. Even surreptitious persecution of these species is unlikely to be attempted at all frequently in a city where all land is potentially overlooked. Our commonest amphibian, **Common Frog**, was once reduced to a relative rarity by the collection of animals for dissection in biology classes. At the start of the 20th century the price paid for Frogs had increased from a halfpenny to a penny and 'the purveyors have had to extend their raids further and further a-field' to meet an 'incessant demand' (Marr & Shipley 1904).

Another rather less conspicuous trend, but one that has affected many more species, is the recovery of many moss and lichen species from air pollution (Chapters 6, 7). Nationally this has been a striking change (Pescott *et al.* 2015), albeit one which is under-appreciated as it does not feature the most popular organisms, birds, butterflies and flowering plants. Species such as *Cryphaea heteromalla*, previously excluded by high levels of atmospheric sulphur dioxide, and the consequent effect on their substrates of 'acid rain', have colonised Cambridge and continue to do so. Mosses and lichens growing on trees and on stonework were more adversely affected than those in other habitats and the changes in these habitats have been remarkable. Some may have spread into the city from less polluted sites in the surrounding region, but others must have arrived by long-distance dispersal. The moths with larvae that feed on mosses and lichens, such as **Buff Footman** *Eilema depressa* and **Orange Footman** *E. sororcula*, have shown a corresponding increase, and **Tree-lichen Beauty** *Cryphia algae*, only known as a very rare migrant in Britain until 1991, is now established in our area. A few species, notably the moss *Dicranoweisia cirrata* and the lichen *Lecanora conizaeoides*, favoured by highly acidic conditions, reached artificially high levels of abundance during the years of pollution and have since retreated to the acidic habitats from which they had spread.

One form of pollution that has favoured some flowering plants is the spread of salt as a de-icer on roads. Some coastal species have spread inland along the roadside habitats that are themselves salted, or which receive water draining from the salted roads (Chapter 4). Although the large populations of halophytes such as **Danish Scurvygrass** and

Reflexed Saltmarsh-grass only occur by major roads, seed sometimes spreads from them and hence small groups of plants, or single individuals, can be found even on the sides of minor roads.

Climate change

The long-term records of Cambridge's weather clearly indicate that since 1980 we have experienced warmer winters with few prolonged periods of freezing temperatures, warmer summers and more sunshine (Chapter 2). The temperature changes are a local symptom of global climate change. The effects of this on different groups of plants and animals have been a recurrent theme in this book, and reflect the well-documented national trend for southern species to spread northwards in recent decades (Mason *et al.* 2015).

Some of the species we now see in Cambridge were formerly rather scarce in Britain and known only from warmer counties in southern England. I was particularly interested in plants with Mediterranean affinities in the late 1970s and travelled to Cornwall to see **Early Meadow-grass** *Poa infirma*, **Four-leaved Allseed** and **Musk Storksbill** *Erodium moschatum*. I can now see all of them on the streets of Cambridge, just a few minutes' walk from home. Naturalists of my age with other interests could all provide their own examples – citing species such as **Bee Wolf** (a wasp), **Jersey Tiger** moth and **Hornet Hoverfly**. Other southerly species with ranges which were not quite so restricted have also spread northwards and can now be seen in our area, including **Marbled White** butterfly, **Pale Pinion** moth *Lithophane socia* and **Tortoise Shieldbug**. Most notable of all the additions are the flying animals which colonised Britain from mainland Europe. These include bees and wasps (**Median Wasp**, **Violet Carpenter Bee**), birds (**Cetti's Warbler**, **Little Egret**) and dragonflies (**Willow Emerald Damselfly**, **Small Red-eyed Damselfly**). Other less mobile species have had to rely on human assistance to reach our island and these are dealt with under the alien species below.

Whether and to what extent climate change has caused the loss of northern species is a surprisingly difficult question to answer. In contrast to the many examples of increasing southern species, few recent examples of declining northern species have been highlighted during our study of Cambridge. The best examples come from the aquatic habitats along the Cam, discussed earlier in this chapter. Species expansions are more apparent than declines – the first appearance of a species in an area is a notable event, whereas the last sighting can only be recognised in retrospect, sometimes decades later. This is particularly true of less conspicuous species in groups which lack a history of continuous recording. However, there are other more fundamental reasons why any effect of climate change on northern species would be difficult to detect. Northern species tend to be associated with a range of habitats, such as fens, moors and bogs, characterised by nutrient-poor, sometimes acidic soils and waters. These habitats have long been in decline in southern England; many such sites and their specialist species were eliminated by agricultural improvement in the 19th century. Surviving fragments will be affected by climate change but also by other factors which would also have an impact on northern species (such as eutrophication of wetland and reduced grazing of grassland). Disentangling the possible role of climate change from that of other factors therefore requires detailed analysis rather than a broad-scale survey (Hill & Preston 2015). In addition, towns have a more southerly fauna and flora than their hinterland, as the characteristic urban habitats favour species of warm, dry places. Cambridge is therefore not a suitable place for charting any loss of northern species in the 21st century.

Expansion of alien species

It is clear from the accounts in this book that alien species (species accidentally or deliberately imported into Britain by human beings, as opposed to those arriving naturally) are familiar and well-established members of most plant and animal groups. Furthermore, many species are particularly associated with human settlements, and are therefore much more frequent in towns. The link is particularly clear for flowering plants, where more alien species have been introduced as garden plants than in any other way. Some of these, such as **Butterfly-bush** and **Green Alkanet**, are now thoroughly established and self-sustaining. However, the gardens of Cambridge provide a source of fruits and seeds of many other species that spread into the nearby streets where they often give rise to offspring with a precarious and rather transient existence. Vigorous perennials, dumped outside gardens, also become established. In an analysis of the distribution patterns of the Cambridgeshire flora, the biggest single group of species comprised garden escapes concentrated

Figure 17.5 Green Alkanet. (PAR).

around Cambridge (Hill *et al.* 2020). Recording such species gives rise to the very large plant totals which have been recorded by botanists from Cambridge and other urban areas. Along with these garden plants come their associated invertebrates, such as the **Japanese Maple Leafhopper, Scarlet Lily Beetle** and **Western Conifer Seed Bug**. Woodchips spread as a mulch in gardens support a suite of alien fungi including **Redlead Roundhead**. The zoological equivalent of the garden plants are the captive animals that have escaped or been released into the wild. These are much less numerous, but include **Canada Goose, Grey Squirrel, Muntjac** and **Red-eared Slider**. Unlike the plants, both Grey Squirrel and Muntjac were released in groups in the British countryside in a deliberate attempt to establish them in the wild (Yalden 1999). Cambridge's **Midwife Toads** must also have come from captive stock, but the circumstances are unknown. Fortunately the **Reticulated Python** *Malayopython reticulatus* which escaped in Cambridge in 2019 was quickly recaptured (Allain 2020). **Harlequin Ladybird** was introduced to mainland Europe for the biological control of aphids; once it became established there it spread naturally into Britain.

There is a clear link between the introduction and spread of alien species and climate change, and species such as **Girdled Snail** and **Wasp Spider** have doubtless spread in recent years because the climate is now more favourable to them than it once was. The link is especially clear in the case of the **Greenhouse Slug**, which started out in greenhouses

and then spread out into gardens and has now reached more natural habitats. The **Mealybug Destroyer** has perhaps started out on a similar path.

Some alien plants with no horticultural link are more frequent in towns than in the wider countryside as streets and waste ground provide warm and open habitats in which plants of southerly affinities like **Guernsey Fleabane** can spread. Even weekend binges in Cambridge can play their part, as the **Tomatoes** which can occasionally be found growing by the pavement near city pubs must often owe their origin to what Leslie (2019) delicately calls 'regurgitated fruit'. Some species such as **Mediterranean Nettle** just appear, apparently out of nowhere, and we can only speculate about their origin.

A few alien species have become troublesome. Much effort is put into campaigns to eradicate some of the most problematic (or supposedly problematic) plants, such as **Floating Pennywort, Giant Hogweed** *Heracleum mantegazzianum* and **Himalayan Balsam**. Attitudes to the most conspicuous introduced mammal, **Grey Squirrel**, are very varied. Biologists often oppose its presence on principle as an alien species, or because of its impact as a predator on bird populations, and people resent their garden squirrels taking food intended for the birds. However, the foresters' attempt to brand the species as a 'tree rat' has never been entirely successful and a recent UK survey found that 57% of respondents like (or would like) to see them in their local parks (Dunn *et al.* 2018). It is indeed obvious that many people (including young children) enjoy watching what they see as a charming animal, and at worst regard it with the amused tolerance traditionally afforded to a charming rogue. By contrast **American Mink**, a mammal which (like the **Brown Rat**) has never attained any degree of public affection, has been effectively eliminated from the area in recent years by a programme of targeted trapping. We will presumably have to learn to live with introduced invertebrates such as **Box-tree Moth** and **Scarlet Lily Beetle**. Even biologists regard species such as **Bitterling** and **Midwife Toad** as interesting and valuable additions to the fauna. Most introduced species are noticed only by specialists, and take an unobtrusive place amongst our established wildlife.

Adapting to urban conditions

One aspect of urban wildlife that we have not explored in any detail is the extent to which species may adapt to urban conditions, rather than simply responding to environmental changes by expansions or contractions of range like chess pieces being pushed around on the board. However, microevolution in plant species is well documented and some of the weeds found in Cambridge college lawns, such as **Greater Plantain** and **Yarrow**, are genetically prostrate variants adapted to the closely mown turf (Briggs

2009). The variable **Annual Meadow-grass** in a Cambridge bowling green has similarly been shown to be a perennial, prostrate form which is distinct from annual, upright plants in nearby flower beds. A purplish variant of the annual plant has recently been found in gardens; this is more difficult to spot than the green plant against dark soil and thus more easily missed when gardeners are weeding (Leslie 2019). Studies elsewhere in the world have shown that some of our common street weeds have developed genetic variants which are resistant to commonly used herbicides; it seems likely that these are also present on our streets but as far as we know they have not been studied here (Preston 2020). The invasive genotypes of South African **Narrow-leaved Ragwort** *Senecio inaequidens* are probably those pre-adapted to our climate (Lachmuth *et al.* 2010), and **Oxford Ragwort** evolved as a species in Britain from stock introduced from Sicily.

Anyone seeing the **Carrion Crows** working through the litter bins on Parker's Piece, systematically examining the rubbish and devouring any take-away food they discover, will be struck by the way in which some species can adapt to life in towns by changing their behaviour. Other birds which are much less shy than they once were include **Grey Herons**, standing patiently by fishermen on the river bank, and some **Jays**,

Figure 17.6 One of the Botanic Garden's resident Jays. (PAR).

which will now allow you to approach them closely in the streets. By contrast **Rooks** have disappeared as breeding birds from the town centre within living memory. Although it is possible to suggest specific reasons for this, such as persecution and the loss of elm trees (in which many nested) from disease, it seems that the Rook is simply not able to survive as an urban bird. It has been completely lost from other towns too, notably the central London conurbation (Balmer *et al.* 2013).

The richness of the urban environment

The naturalists taking part in the NHC survey and compiling the chapters for this book have often been surprised at the sheer diversity of wildlife to be found in the area. We have, of course, to be aware of 'shifting baselines', the problem that we might perceive habitats as rich because we did not know them in the past when they were much richer. However, baselines shift in both directions. John Ray and his small team of botanists who did much fieldwork in the town in the 1650s for the first Cambridgeshire plant catalogue (Ray 1660) would no doubt be shocked by the loss of some of their favourite sites, and the loss of species from those that remain, but they would be equally surprised at the species from southern Europe, eastern Asia and the Americas they could now see on the streets. Ornithologists transported into the town from the 1940s would immediately ask what had happened to the Rook colonies in the city's elm trees; lichenologists and bryologists would be astonished at the number of epiphytes now growing on other tree species. However, most of us live in the present, and do not spend much time looking back nostalgically to a former Golden Age or thinking gratefully that we are lucky to be living now. It is clear that Cambridge possesses a rich wildlife, one that continues to provide pleasure to many of its residents and includes more species than any of us can hope to see in a single lifetime. We hope that this book will encourage people to continue to study the city's wildlife, and to ensure that it will continue to delight future generations.

Contributors

Steven Allain has had a passion for amphibians and reptiles for as long as he can remember. This passion became a career following the completion of a zoology degree at Anglia Ruskin in 2015. During his time in Cambridge, Steven became intimately involved with the conservation and monitoring of the county's reptiles and amphibians.

Rachel Bates is a freelance ecological consultant and has been slightly obsessed by bats for several years, helping the Cambridgeshire Bat Group with projects or leading her own independent research. Outside of work and bats she enjoys botanising, with a particular interest in orchids, and has a growing interest in terrestrial invertebrates.

Steve Boreham is a geologist and ecologist who has worked in a wide range of environments. His research interests include the vegetation history of southern England, the flora and fauna of the East Anglian coast, woodland ecology, freshwater ecology and the hydrology and management of chalk springs and streams. He is a long-standing trustee of Hobson's Conduit Trust.

Peter M.J. Brown is an ecologist who teaches at Anglia Ruskin University. He has a particular interest in entomology and since 2009 has co-led the UK Ladybird Survey with Prof. Helen Roy.

Sam Buckton graduated from Cambridge in 2018, then contributed to the University's Biodiversity Action Plan, designing the Cambridge Biodiversity Metric. Currently undertaking an MSc at York, he is a researcher for Jasper Kenter's Global Assessment for a New Economics project. Although a 'pan-species lister', he has a particular fondness for bryophytes and plant parasites.

Chris Donnelly is involved in several local geoconservation projects as a member of Cambridgeshire Geological Society. She has studied Ornithology, Ecology and Landscape with Cambridge ICE followed by Earth and Life Sciences with the OU. In real life, she has spent over 30 years organising and leading wildlife holidays, with a bit of geology thrown in.

Monica Frisch grew up in Cambridge and became actively involved in Cambridge Natural History Society on her return to the city in 2005. She is an enthusiastic amateur botanist, happy to learn about other aspects of natural history and interested in ecology and conservation.

Becky Green has been fascinated by wildlife since her dad took her bird watching as a child. After finishing a degree, she volunteered and worked with a number of different conservation charities across the UK, before landing her current role as Senior Ranger for the Wildlife Trust BCN at Trumpington Meadows.

Jonathan Heath is a naturalist who has lived in Cambridge his whole life. He likes to record all types of fauna and flora, but birds are his main expertise after watching and learning to identify them from an early age. He studied Natural Sciences at the Open University and in 2021 became Cambridgeshire County Bird Recorder.

Chantal Helm completed her formal education in South Africa and undertook a doctorate in the ecology of African savanna trees. Since arriving in the UK in 2011, she has been employed in university ecology teaching, currently at Cambridge University Botanic Garden, and has also developed a strong interest in bat conservation.

Mark Hill came to Cambridge in 1946. For most of his career he was a plant ecologist, studying many habitats including urban ecosystems. For seven years he was head of the Biological Records Centre. Since retirement he has been an active member of the Cambridge Natural History Society (President 2014–16).

Mark Hows has always been keen on natural history and over the last 20 years has been especially interested in mammals – small mammals in particular. This passion has taken him far and wide. He is a long-time active member of the Cambridgeshire Mammal group and county recorder.

Bob Jarman worked as an agronomist for thirty years and has birdwatched most of his life. 'I started at primary school finding coastal waders feeding on my school playing field in Arbury during the winter of 1962/63. I went to Aberystwyth University to be near the UK's only Red Kites, now I see them over Cambridge!'.

Chris Kirby-Lambert has had a lifelong passion for all elements of natural history and is rarely found without a net or camera in hand. He has a particular interest in invertebrates and has worked as a freelance ecological consultant, specialising in entomology, for the last twelve years.

Vince Lea got interested in the natural world as a boy on fishing trips with his dad in Warwickshire. This interest took him into plant genetics, then jobs in the plant breeding industry brought him to Cambridgeshire. Here, he has volunteered with many wildlife organisations and currently works for the Countryside Restoration Trust.

Duncan Mackay spent his childhood catching sticklebacks and caddisflies in Hobson's Conduit. After a degree in Biology, he returned to Cambridge to join the family ironmongery business. He has led numerous expeditions to the Arctic. His interests include dragonflies, moths, mammals, birds and woodland ecology. He was president of the Cambridge Natural History Society 2019–2021.

Jenny Mackay is a Reserves Officer for the Wildlife Trust BCN. She worked for York University Conservation Volunteers during her Biology degree and then volunteered for the trust before being taken on as permanent staff. She is a passionate conservationist, which she also follows on her wildlife-friendly family farm in the fens.

Anne Miller is a kayaker and has been interested in the natural world since childhood. Having spent much of her career leading teams of engineers solving difficult problems, when Floating Pennywort started overwhelming the Cam her natural instinct was to build a team to tackle it.

Nick Owens studied Zoology at Cambridge, which included a PhD on baboons in Tanzania. This was followed by research on Brent Goose behaviour in East Anglia. Thereafter he was a long-serving teacher at Oundle School. On retirement he developed an interest in solitary bees and served as Chairman of the Norfolk and Norwich Naturalists' Society.

Chris D. Preston has been keen on natural history since childhood but did not settle on his main interests, flowering plants and bryophytes, until he came to Cambridge as an undergraduate in 1973. He has rashly taken up microfungi in retirement.

Paul Rule has been interested in wildlife since he was a child growing up in rural Cambridgeshire. After spending the majority of his working life in the telecoms industry, retirement has allowed him to rediscover that small boy and he now spends a large part of each day looking for and photographing invertebrates of every kind.

Jonathan Shanklin is the botanical recorder for Cambridgeshire. He was encouraged in natural history as a child, but studied physics whilst at Cambridge. After joining the British Antarctic Survey he discovered the Antarctic ozone hole. In 2003 he started the CNHS programme of field studies, which became a foundation for this book.

Victoria Smith has been the Local Nature Reserve Officer for Cambridge City Council for nearly ten years. 'To be the caretaker of these precious and somewhat vulnerable spaces is an honour and oftentimes a straight up delight! Having volunteers to help me with this task only adds to the reward.'

Rhona Watson is fortunately interested in all wildlife, but unlucky enough to find there is still too much to learn to be an expert. She is librarian of a college with a nature trail, woods, a water course and several acres of grounds. This can make her lunchtime walks very interesting.

Olwen Williams spent a career as a doctor, before retirement allowed a return to Cambridge undergraduate life to indulge a lifelong passion for natural history. This was followed by a PhD on the impact of veterinary medicines on dung flies. Jack-of-all-trades, she now runs a U3AC naturalists group and writes the NatHistCam monthly blog.

Acknowledgements

Many people have contributed to this book, not just the authors of the text, the creators of the diagrams and the photographers whose contributions are identified elsewhere. The core group of the NatHistCam steering committee kept the project on course and were assisted at various stages by Louise Bacon, Rosie Bleet (née Earwaker), Kevin Hand and Annette Shelford. Guy Belcher, the conservation officer for Cambridge City Council, was very supportive.

Early on, Phil Ricketts and the staff of CPERC created the NatHistCam section on their website enabling people to submit records. Over 2000 records were submitted via the CPERC website with Paul Rule, Garret Maguire and Rob Pople submitting about half of them. CPERC also provided access to the data they hold for Cambridge as well as advice on recording.

We thank the UK Centre for Ecology and Hydrology for permission to use data from their Land Cover Maps 2007 and 2019 (Chapter 1). For Chapter 3, Brian Collins (G. David, Cambridge) gave permission to use the maps in Bryan (2008). The Syndics of Cambridge University Library gave permission for the use of several images and Jacqueline Cox (Keeper of University Archives) advised us on the records of University matriculations. For lichens (Chapter 7) and fish (Chapter 12) we thank Mark Powell and the Environment Agency, who have allowed us to incorporate published material in our text and use their figures.

Sixty private gardeners allowed us to study the weeds in their gardens, and several more provided information about their garden animals (Chapter 5). Likewise 27 college gardeners answered queries and allowed us to visit their gardens (Chapter 15).

For birds (Chapter 13), we especially thank Graham Easy for his inspirational ornithological observations and papers to the Cambridgeshire Bird Club's annual reports and, at least, 21 papers to Nature in Cambridgeshire from the 1960s to the millennium. The bird chapter would not have been possible without the input and dedication of the County Bird Recorders, contributors and editors of the annual Cambridgeshire Bird Reports, bulletins

and records over the years especially Vince Lea who was editor during the course of this project. Also, thanks to Peter Bircham for The Birds of Cambridgeshire (1989) and authors of the first Atlas of the Birds of Cambridgeshire (1994) – Peter Bircham, John Rathmell and Bill Jordan.

Thanks are due to Dr Steve Boreham for his help in clarifying many details of the local geology. Dr P. Friend kindly identified the geological horizons in East Pit. We thank Alan Leslie for his expert identification of difficult plant species and hybrids, many of which are little known. Brian Eversham identified elms. Louise Bacon and Catherine Tregaskes helped in compiling the lichens section; Mark Powell checked it.

Many people contributed to the sections on invertebrates in addition to the named authors. The Botanic Garden helped with regular moth trapping and provided access to all the records on their wildlife database. They gave permission to study bees and wasps on site. Adrian Matthews made his extensive moth trapping data available. Val Perrins and Adrian Parr helped with dragonfly identification. Frankie Owens and Mark Welch made useful comments on bees and wasps which greatly improved Chapter 10. Brian Eversham and Richard Preece gave valuable advice on molluscs (Chapter 11).

We thank our friends who read and commented on draft chapters. David Jones and Peter Jones read drafts of Chapter 3 (Development of the city). Steve Hartley read drafts of Chapters 4–7 (plants and fungi). Mary Wheater read drafts of Chapters 8–11 (invertebrates). Members of the NatHistCam committee also commented on draft chapters. Indeed they could all be regarded as editors of the book, but as that would have made the number of editors too large, Mark Hill, who compiled the text, appears as sole editor.

Special thanks are due to Mackays of Cambridge who hosted the website. Nick Trull ably maintained our twitter feed @NatHistCam even when not living in Cambridge. Sam Motherwell designed our logo. Thanks also to the Cambridge Natural History Society for initial support and for encouragement in the background as we went along.

Photographers

AM	Adrian Matthews		MF	Maria Fremlin
AD	Andrew Dunn		MFPF	Mike Foley
AR	Akua Reindorf		MG	Mark Gurney
AS	Annette Shelford		MH	Mark Hows
ATM	Anne Miller		MM	Michael Massie
BCT	Bat Conservation Trust		MOH	Mark Hill
CD	Chris Donnelly		MP	Mark Powell
CDP	Chris Preston		MS	Mario Shimbov
CKL	Chris Kirby-Lambert		NRM	Neil Mackay
CRS	Robin Stevenson		NWO	Nick Owens
CUBG	Cambridge University Botanic Garden		OW	Olwen Williams
DJM	Duncan Mackay		PAR	Paul Rule
EA	Environment Agency (Great Ouse & Fenland Fisheries team)		PAS	Pete Stroh
			PC	Peter Corbett
FJR	Fred Rumsey		PD	Pat Doody
FWS	Francisco Welter Schultes		PGL	Peter Leonard
GCK	Graham CopeKoga		PJD	Peter Damerell
GM	Garret Maguire		RH	Roger Horton
GO	Geoff Oliver		RJJ	Bob Jarman
GSM	Gilles San Martin		RKW	Rhona Watson
JDS	Jonathan Shanklin		SJB	Sam Buckton
JH	Jon Heath		SJH	Stephen Henry
JMO	John O'Boyle		SJRA	Steven Allain
JS	Jonathan Sleath		SPT	Stephen Tomkins
KL	Keith Lugg		VL	Vince Lea
LKE	Keith Edkins		VS	Victoria Smith
MEF	Monica Frisch		WMB	Wahaj Mahmood-Brown

BAP	Biodiversity Action Plan; the UK BAP (2007) lists threatened species requiring conservation	IUCN	International Union for Conservation of Nature
BAS	British Antarctic Survey	JNCC	Joint Nature Conservation Committee
BASF	BASF Pest Control Solutions UK	lb	pound weight = 0.454 kg
BBC	British Broadcasting Corporation	LNR	Local Nature Reserve
BCT	Bat Conservation Trust	mya	million years ago (geology)
BSBI	Botanical Society of Britain and Ireland	NBN	National Biodiversity Network
CCTV	closed circuit television	NHC	NatHistCam (Natural History of Cambridge)
CiWS	City Wildlife Site	NIAB	National Institute of Agricultural Botany
CNHS	Cambridge Natural History Society	NIAB EMR	National Institute of Agricultural Botany East Malling Research
CP	Country Park (in Birds chapter)		
CPBRC	Cambridgeshire and Peterborough Biological Records Centre	Noc-mig	Nocturnal migration
		NO_x	Nitrogen oxide(s)
		O.D.	Ordnance Datum (= above sea level)
CPERC	Cambridgeshire and Peterborough Environmental Records Centre	OS	Ordnance Survey (mapping)
		pH	a measure of alkalinity-acidity: 7 is neutral; below 7 acid; above alkaline
CPPF	Cambridge Past Present and Future (organisation)		
CRT	Countryside Restoration Trust	PRV	Protected Road Verge
CU	Cambridge University	RPCC	Register of Plants of Conservation Concern
CUBG	Cambridge University Botanic Garden	RSPB	Royal Society for the Protection of Birds
CVF	Cam Valley Forum	RSPCA	Royal Society for the Prevention of Cruelty to Animals
CWS	County Wildlife Site		
DDT	Dichlorodiphenyltrichloroethane, an organochlorine pesticide	SO_2	Sulphur dioxide
		sp., spp.	species (singular and plural)
DNA	Deoxyribonucleic acid, a molecule containing genetic information	SSSI	Site of Special Scientific Interest
		U3AC	University of the Third Age in Cambridge
EA	Environment Agency	WT	Wildlife Trust in this book, the one for Bedfordshire, Cambridgeshire and Northamptonshire
GMS	Garden Moth Scheme		
GPS	Global Positioning System		
GWCT	Game and Wildlife Conservation Trust	y	year (in Birds chapter)
iRecord	A recording scheme using a mobile phone app	ya	years ago (geology)

Glossary

archaeophyte: in botany, a non-native (alien) plant that was introduced by humans, either intentionally or unintentionally, and became naturalised in Britain and Ireland between the start of the Neolithic period and AD 1500

ascocarp: the fruiting body of an ascomycete

ascomycetes: the largest subdivision of the kingdom of fungi

basidiomycetes: the subdivision of the kingdom of fungi which includes many mushrooms and toadstools, rusts and smuts

bioblitz: a public engagement event to record as many species (of all sorts) as possible in a specific area in a given timescale

biotrophic parasites: those that obtain food only from living host cells

blight: a deadly plant disease, typically one caused by fungi or fungoids such as mildews, rusts, and smuts

bryophyte: moss or liverwort

calcifuge, calcicole: calcifuges are plants that avoid calcareous soils preferring more acidic soils; calcicoles prefer alkaline chalk and limestone soils

Cambridgeshire (v.c.29): a county in Eastern England; the vice-county excludes Huntingdonshire and the Soke of Peterborough which are part of the administrative county.

corvid: a member of the bird family which includes crows, ravens and rooks

cryptogam: a plant that reproduces by spores rather than seeds, for example ferns, mosses and liverworts

dicot: in botany, a dicot is a plant which has two seed leaves when it first germinates

electro-fishing: a means of surveying fish populations by using electricity to temporarily stun the fish

epiphyte: a plant growing on another one

eutrophic: of water bodies, rich in nutrients

eutrophication: the process of enrichment

exoskeleton: an external skeleton, such as those of many invertebrates

flyover: in ornithology used to describe birds flying over a location but not landing

fungoid: like a fungus; the oomycetes are fungoids which have evolved a similar life cycle to that of fungi

gemma (plural gemmae): (mosses and liverworts) a single-celled or few-celled vegetative propagule

genotype: an organism with particular genetic characteristics, such as salt-tolerance

hectad: an area 10 km × 10 km

herpetofauna: reptiles and amphibians

hirundine: a group of birds including swallows

hypha: thread-like structures that are part of fungi

in tandem: (of Odonata) joined together but not mating; often the tandem state does not result in mating but it may be post-coital or a prelude to egg laying

kleptoparasite: (of insects) a nest parasite using resources, which may include the host's eggs or larvae, intended for the host species (the same as cuckoo parasite)

legume: a plant in the family Fabaceae (formerly known as Leguminosae), which includes beans and peas

monad: an area 1 km × 1 km

mycelium: a network of hyphae

mycologist: someone who studies fungi

myxomycetes: slime moulds

native: in botany, a plant that arrived naturally, without human assistance in Britain and Ireland since the end of the last glaciation or one that was already present, having persisted during the last Ice Age

NBN Atlas: the UK's National Biodiversity Network collates biological records from diverse sources

necrotrophic parasites: obtain their food from dead hosts

neophyte: in botany, a non-native plant that first escaped into the wild after 1500

nictitating membrane: a transparent or translucent eyelid found in fish, amphibians and reptiles, birds and some mammals

Odonata: damselflies and dragonflies

odonatologist: someone who studies damselflies and dragonflies

ovipositing and oviposit (verb): to lay eggs usually in or on vegetation, used for insects which have a tube-like egg-laying organ, an ovipositor

parthenogenetic (female moths): asexual reproduction without fertilisation

pedicel: the stalk of a flower

phylum: a taxonomic category forming subdivisions of kingdoms

protonema: a thread-like chain of cells that forms an early stage of development in the life cycle of mosses

quadrat: a square area, often 2 m × 2 m, used for surveying vegetation

resupinate fungus: a crust-like fungus

rhizoid: (mosses and liverworts) root-like structure usually attached to the stem

riparian: a species found along the margins of rivers and other watercourses

Skinner moth trap: a foldable, portable moth trap usually fitted with a UV light

tetrad: an area 2 km × 2 km, often used in botanical surveying and recording

Tree-oil: an extract of the Australian *Melaleuca alternifolia* (Myrtaceae)

vascular plant: flowering plants, ferns, horsetails and clubmosses, but not mosses or liverworts

vice-county: one of 112 divisions of Great Britain of more or less similar size, whose boundaries do not change (unlike those of administrative counties) used for botanical (and other) recording

Places mentioned in the text are listed alphabetically with a brief description where appropriate and the monad(s) in which they fall. Where a location is in several monads generally the monad containing the largest portion is given. Street names in Cambridge, which can be looked up on a map, are not given. The local nature reserves and other sites of particular interest are described in more detail in chapter 16. Places outside the NHC study area are in italic. The inclusion of a place in this list does not mean that there is public access.

Adams Road Bird Sanctuary (no public access): west Cambridge TL4358
Addenbrooke's (Hospital): south Cambridge TL4655
Arbury: suburb in north Cambridge
Ascension Parish Burial Ground: off Huntingdon Road TL4359
Babraham Road Park & Ride: south Cambridge TL4754
Baits Bite Lock, on the river Cam north-east of the NHC survey area
Barnwell Abbey: site of historic abbey (priory) TL4659
Barnwell East: nature reserve off Barnwell Road, east Cambridge TL4758
Barnwell Lake: a former pit between the railway and Newmarket Road TL4759
Barnwell Station: now disused, just north of Newmarket Road TL4759
Barnwell West: nature reserve off Barnwell Road, east Cambridge TL4758
Beechwoods: woodland off Worts' Causeway TL4854
Beehive Centre: shopping area south-east of city centre TL4658
Benet House, Hills Road adjoining Botanic Garden: TL4557
Bin Brook: stream flowing into Cambridge from the west at TL4257
Biomedical Campus: south Cambridge TL4654
Bolton's Pit: private site, south of Barton Road TL4357
Botanic Garden (Cambridge University) TL4557
Bottisham: a village east of Cambridge; where the naturalist Leonard Jenyns had his home
Bourn: a village west of Cambridge
Bourn Brook: stream flowing from the west into the NHC area at Byron's Pool TL4254/TL4354
Bramblefields: nature reserve off Laxton Way, Chesterton TL4760
Brook Leys: a lake in the Eddington development in west Cambridge TL4259
Byron's Pool: a stretch of the river Granta and associated woodland TL4354
Cam, River: flows through the NHC area (its source is in Essex). Originally called the Granta, it has two major tributaries – the Rhee (source is in Hertfordshire) which joins it at

Hauxton Junction and the current Granta which joins it further south (source in Cambridgeshire)
Cam Catchment: the area drained by the River Cam and its tributaries
Cam Valley: the area from the headwaters of the Cam and its tributaries, down to the confluence with the River Ouse just north of Wicken
Cambridge Leisure: once Cambridge's cattle market, to the east of the railway TL4656
Cambridge North Station: in Chesterton, north-east of the city centre TL4760
Cambridge Regional College, King's Hedges Road: TL4561
Cambridge Retail Park, Newmarket Road TL4659
Cambridge Sewage Farm/Works, north-east Cambridge TL4761
Catholic Church, Hills Road TL4557
Cherry Hinton: former village now part of Cambridge to the east TL4856/TL4956
Cherry Hinton Brook: a chalk stream flowing from Cherry Hinton TL4856 to the Cam
Cherry Hinton Chalk pit(s): disused Chalk pits (East Pit and West Pit) off Lime Kiln Hill TL4855
Cherry Hinton Hall: parkland in south-east Cambridge TL4856
Cherry Hinton Lakes: three former quarries, now flooded, in east Cambridge TL4757/TL4857/TL4856
Cherry Hinton Recreation Ground: off High Street Cherry Hinton TL4856
Chesterton: former village in north Cambridge TL4660
Chesterton Fen: rough grassland, formerly fen, between Fen Road, Chesterton and the river TL4861
Chesterton sidings: now redeveloped to include Cambridge North Station TL4760
Chippenham Fen National Nature Reserve north-east of Cambridge
Christ's Pieces: public open space TL4558
City Cemetery, Newmarket Road TL4859
Clare College: main site TL4458
Clay Farm: housing development in south-west Cambridge TL4555
Clifton Estate: development east of railway line south of the city centre TL4656

Coe Fen and Sheep's Green: grassland along river Cam TL4457
Coldham's Brook the lower part of Cherry Hinton Brook nearer to the Cam
Coldham's Common TL4758
Corpus Christi College TL4458
Coton Footpath: path leading west from end of Adams Road TL4358
Darwin College TL4457
Darwin Green: development in north of Cambridge TL4360
David Attenborough Building: Pembroke Street TL4458/4558
Dickerson Pit (Milton Country Park)
Ditton Meadows: grassland south of river TL4760
East Cambridge Main Drain: runs across Coldham's Common TL4758
East Pit: large disused chalk pit, Lime Kiln Road TL4855
Eddington: development on western edge of Cambridge TL4259
Eight Acre Wood, Trumpington TL4355
Emmanuel College TL4558
Fen Ditton: village on north-east edge of Cambridge TL4860
Fen Drayton (& RSPB Reserve) north-west of Cambridge
First Public Drain: flows north-west through the Science Park TL4661
Fitzwilliam College TL4359
Foul Anchor: hamlet in north Cambridgeshire
Gamlingay: village in west Cambridgeshire
Giant's Grave, Cherry Hinton: springs here are the source of Cherry Hinton Brook TL4856
Girton: village to the north of Cambridge TL4261
Girton College TL4260
Gog Magog Golf Course: on southern edge of NHC area TL4954
Gog Magog Hills/Gog Magogs: the higher ground to the south-east of Cambridge
Grantchester: village to south-west of Cambridge TL4355
Grantchester Meadows: grassland to west of River Cam between Cambridge and Grantchester TL4355/4356
Great Ouse: the river that the Cam flows into south of Ely
Great Shelford: village south of Cambridge
Guided Busway: runs through north-east Cambridge to St Ives and south-west to Trumpington

Hauxton: village to south-west of
Cambridge

Hauxton Junction: the confluence (SW of
Cambridge) of the River Cam/
Granta with its major tributary the
Rhee (also sometimes known as the
Cam)

Heydon: village south-west of Cambridge

Hill of Health: area of more acidic soils,
now developed, in north Cambridge
off Huntingdon Road

Hinton Moor: formerly an area between
Cambridge and Cherry Hinton, now
developed TL4756

Histon Road Cemetery: a Victorian
landscaped cemetery TL4459

Hobson's Brook: a chalk stream rising
from springs at Nine Wells and
flowing north into Cambridge
TL4554

Hobson's Conduit: the man-made
extension to Hobson's Brook in
central Cambridge TL4557

Hobson's Park TL4554

Horningsea: village to north-east of
Cambridge

Ickleton: village to south of Cambridge

Impington: village to north of Cambridge

Impington Lake: fishing lake, also
called Cawcutts Lake, just north of
the A14 TL4461

Jesus College TL4559

Jesus Ditch: stream separating Jesus
College from Jesus Green to the
north TL4559

Jesus Green: open space south of river
TL4559

Jesus Lock TL4459

Junction 12 of the M11 with the A603
TL4256

King's Hedges: area of north Cambridge
TL4561

Lammas Land: open space and
recreation ground TL4457

Leckhampton: part of Corpus Christi
college on western side of
Cambridge TL4357

Leper Chapel, Newmarket Road:
historic building owned by CPPF
TL4759

Lime Kiln Close, Cherry Hinton:
former chalk pit, now wooded
TL4856

Limekiln Hill: a high point on the
eastern edge of Cambridge TL4855

Little St Mary's churchyard:
Trumpington Street TL4457

Little Shelford: village to south of
Cambridge

Logan's Meadow: grassland north-west of
river TL4659

Magog Down: former arable land restored
mainly to chalk grassland and
woodland south of Cambridge

Market (Ward): the local government
area covering central Cambridge

Midsummer Common: open space south
of river Cam in central Cambridge
TL4559

Mill Pond/Pool: there are several mill
ponds on the river Cam between
Silver Street and Newnham Road,
where there used to be several water
mills TL4457

Mill Road Cemetery TL4658

Milton: village just to north-east of
Cambridge

Milton Country Park: just to north-east
of Cambridge mostly outside the
NHC area

Milton sewage treatment works, now
called Cambridge Water Recycling
Centre TL4761

Museum of Zoology: off Pembroke Street
TL4458

Needingworth: village west of Cambridge,
near St Ives

Newmarket Road Park & Ride: on
eastern edge of Cambridge TL4959

Newnham: district in western Cambridge
TL4457

NIAB Trial Grounds: agricultural land
between Huntingdon Road and
Impington; part now redeveloped as
Darwin Green TL4360

Nightingale Recreation Ground TL4755

Nine Wells: wooded area with chalk
springs which are the source of
Hobson's Brook TL4654

Norman Cement Works: formerly
between railway line and Coldham's
Lane; now demolished TL4757

Observatory, the: Cambridge University
Observatory TL4359

Orchard Park: area of north Cambridge
TL4461

Ouse Fen: RSPB reserve near St Ives

Ouse Washes: area of wetlands in north
Cambridgeshire

Over: village to north of Cambridge

Paradise: wet woodland by the river in
Newnham TL4457

Parker's Piece: public open space in
central Cambridge TL4558

Peterhouse College & Deer Park TL4457

Petersfield: district to south-east of
centre; public open space on East
Road TL4558

Plant Breeding Institute: now
redeveloped as Trumpington
Meadows TL4354

Queens' College: TL4458

Robinson Crusoe Island: small scrub-
covered island in the Cam TL4457

Roman Road: the old Roman Road is a
wide path running south-east from
Worts' Causeway TL4954

Romsey / Romsey Town: district of east
Cambridge TL4657

Rush, the: stream crossing Sheep's Green
TL4457

Science Park TL4661

Sedgwick Museum of Earth Sciences,
Downing Street TL4558

Senate House TL4458

Seven Acre Wood, Trumpington TL4455

Sheep's Green and Coe Fen: open space
either side of the river TL4457

Skaters' Meadow: Wildlife Trust reserve
by Grantchester Meadows TL4456

Snakey Path, Cherry Hinton: path
alongside Cherry Hinton Brook
TL4757

Stapleford: village south of Cambridge

St Andrew's church, Cherry Hinton
TL4857

St Andrew's church, Chesterton TL4659

St Bede's School sports field, Birdwood
Road: TL4757

St Bene't's Church, Bene't Street TL4458

St Edward's churchyard TL4458

St John's College & Fellows' Garden
TL4458

Storey's Field, Eddington open space
TL4259

Stourbridge Common: open space south
of the Cam TL4659/4759

Swaffham Bulbeck: village to east of
Cambridge

Swan's Pit, Chesterton: site of gravel pit,
now developed

TA Pit/lake (Territorial Army Pit): one
of three flooded quarries in east
Cambridge TL4757

Teversham: village east of Cambridge
TL4958

The Backs: the land, mostly owned by
colleges, on the banks of the Cam
TL4458

The Brecks: area of sandy soils in Norfolk
and Suffolk east of Cambridge

Travellers' Rest Pit: geological SSSI at the
edge of Eddington TL4259

Trumpington: former village in south-
west Cambridge TL4454

Trumpington Meadows Country
Park: parkland alongside housing
development in south-west
Cambridge TL4354

University Rugby Club training ground,
Grange Road TL4358

Vicar's Brook: a branch of Hobson's
Brook TL4556

Wandlebury Country Park: owned by
CPPF south of Cambridge

Washpit Brook: small stream flowing
north in north-east Cambridge
TL4259/TL4260

Waterbeach: village to north-east of
Cambridge

West Cambridge Site: area of University
facilities west of the city centre
TL4258/TL4259

West Pit, Cherry Hinton: now a caravan
park off Lime Kiln Road, with a
wooded area and grassland to the
east TL4855

Wicken Fen: National Nature Reserve to
north-east of Cambridge

Zoology Department, Cambridge
University: off Downing St TL4558

References

We have noted that some reports are available on-line but have not cited their URLs as they can be found more easily by googling their titles.

ADAS (2013) *Analysis and interpretation of tree audit data for Cambridge City Council*. Report No. CEN5002. Cambridge City Council, Cambridge. Available on-line.

Allain, S.J.R. (2020) Snakes in the grass: the misidentification of adders in Cambridgeshire. *Nature in Cambridgeshire* 62: 51–53.

Allain, S.J.R. & Goodman, M.J. (2017) Absence of chytrid fungus (*Batrachochytrium dendrobatidis*) in an introduced population of the common midwife toad (*Alytes obstetricans*) in Cambridge, UK. *Herpetological Bulletin* 142: 40–41.

Allain, S.J.R. & Goodman, M.J. (2018a) The absence of the amphibian chytrid fungi in the common midwife toad (*Alytes obstetricans*) from an introduced population in Cambridge, UK. *Herpetology Notes* 11: 451–454.

Allain, S.J.R. & Goodman, M.J. (2018b) Cambridge Amphibian Survey Report 2016. *Nature in Cambridgeshire* 60: 31–36.

Allain, S.J.R. & Goodman, M.J. (2018c) New records of palmate newts (*Lissotriton helveticus*) in Cambridge. *Nature in Cambridgeshire* 60: 36–37.

Allain, S.J.R. & Goodman, M.J. (2019a) New records of midwife toads (*Alytes obstetricans*) in Cambridgeshire. *Nature in Cambridgeshire* 61: 69–70.

Allain, S.J.R. & Goodman, M.J. (2019b) Cambridge Amphibian Survey Report 2017. *Nature in Cambridgeshire* 61: 70–75.

Allain, S.J.R. & Smith, L.T. (2016) Newt mortalities on an urban cycle path. *Herpetological Bulletin* 138: 27–28.

Allain, S.J.R., Goodman, M.J. & Jopling, A.D. (2019) Notes on the successful mitigation-driven translocation of slow worms (*Anguis fragilis*) at Wandlebury Country Park. *Nature in Cambridgeshire* 61: 67–69.

Allain, S.J.R., Smith, L.T. & Miller, G.J. (2017) Introduced non-native amphibians and reptiles in Cambridgeshire 2010–2016. *Nature in Cambridgeshire* 59: 44–50.

Bacon, L. (2015) Invertebrate report 2014. *Nature in Cambridgeshire* 57: 141–143.

Bacon, L., Cooper, A. & Venables, H. (2013) *Cambridgeshire Bird Atlas 2007–2011*. Cambridgeshire Bird Club, Cambridge.

Balmer, D.E., Gillings, S., Caffrey, B.J., Swann, R.L., Downie, I.S. & Fuller, R.J. (2013) *Bird Atlas 2007–2011*. BTO Books, Thetford.

Barnard, P. & Ross, E. (2012) *The adult Trichoptera (caddisflies) of Britain and Ireland*. FSC Publishing, Telford.

Bat Conservation Trust (2020) *National Nathusius' Pipistrelle Project*. On-line article.

Bellamy, J. *et al.* (1986) *Hampstead Heath Flora*. Greater London Council, London.

Bendall, S. (1998) *Baker's Map of the University and Town of Cambridge 1830*. Cambridgeshire Records Society, Cambridge.

Bircham, P.M.M. (1989) *The birds of Cambridgeshire*. Cambridge University Press, Cambridge.

Bircham, P.M.M., Rathmell, J.C.A. & Jordan, W.J. (1994) *An atlas of the breeding birds of Cambridgeshire*. Cambridge Bird Club, Cambridge.

Boreham, S. (1990) Macro-invertebrates as water quality indicators in two Cambridge chalk streams. *Nature in Cambridgeshire* 32: 67–73.

Boreham, S. (1991) Macro-invertebrates as water quality indicators in Bin Brook, a polluted Cambridge clay stream. *Nature in Cambridgeshire* 33: 14–20.

Boreham, S. (1996) Thermokarst landforms in the Cambridge area. *Nature in Cambridgeshire* 38: 16–22.

Boreham, S. (2002a) *The Pleistocene stratigraphy and palaeoenvironments of the Cambridge District*. PhD thesis, Open University.

Boreham, S. (2002b) *A summer survey of the flatworm and caddis-fly fauna of some cold-water springs in South Cambridgeshire and Hertfordshire*. Unpublished report for Natural England.

Boreham, S. (2004) The structure and formation of the Wandlebury area. *Proceedings of the Cambridge Antiquarian Society* 93: 5–8.

Boreham, S. & Leszczynska, K. 2019. The geology of the Middle Cam Valley, Cambridgeshire, UK. *Quaternary* 2: 24.

Boreham, S., White, T.S., Bridgland, D.R., Howard, A.J. & White, M.J. (2010) The Quaternary history of the Wash fluvial network, UK. *Proceedings of the Geologists' Association* 121: 393–409.

Boyd, A.W. (1957) Sewage-farms as bird-habitats. *British Birds* 50: 253–263.

Bradley, S. & Pevsner, N. (2014) *Cambridgeshire*. Yale University Press, New Haven.

Braithwaite, M.E., Ellis, R.W. & Preston, C.D. (2006). *Change in the British Flora 1987–2004*. Botanical Society of the British Isles, London.

Brickell, C., ed. (2006) *Royal Horticultural Society encyclopedia of plants & flowers*, ed. 4. Dorling Kindersley, London.

Briggs, D. (2009) *Plant microevolution and conservation in human-influenced systems*. Cambridge University Press, Cambridge.

Brindley, H.H. (1904) The Mollusca of Cambridgeshire. In J.E. Marr & A.E. Shipley, eds, *Handbook to the natural history of Cambridgeshire*, pp. 114–138, 257–258. Cambridge University Press, Cambridge.

Brown, P.M.J. & Roy, H.E. (2018) Wildlife reports: Ladybirds. *British Wildlife* 29: 290–292.

Brown, P.M.J., Roy, H.E. & Comont, R. (2015) Wildlife reports: Ladybirds. *British Wildlife* 26: 285–287.

Bryan, P. (2008) *Cambridge: the shaping of the city*, ed. 2. G. David, Cambridge.

Bryan, P. & Wise, N. (2005) Cambridge New Town – a Victorian microcosm. *Proceedings of the Cambridge Antiquarian Society* 94: 199–216.

Buckton, S.J. (2021) Pasties and pygmies: the plant galls and leaf-miners of the Cambridge University Botanic Garden. *Nature in Cambridgeshire*: 63: 5–19.

Buczacki, S., Shields, C. & Ovenden, D. (2012) *Collins fungi guide*. Collins, London.

Burkill, I.H. (1893) Notes on the plants distributed by the Cambridge dust-carts. *Proceedings of the Cambridge Philosophical Society* 8: 92–95.

Bushell, W.D. (1938) *Hobson's Conduit*. Cambridge University Press, Cambridge.

Cadbury, C.J. & Oswald, P.O. (2009) Mistletoe (*Viscum album*) undergoes an explosive increase in Cambridge. *Nature in Cambridgeshire* 51: 50–60.

Cambridgeshire Bat Group (2020) *Our bats.* On-line article.

Carroll, L., Sparks, T. & Upson, T. (2008) 100 years of Cambridge meteorological records. *Nature in Cambridgeshire* 50: 10–17.

Catt, J. (2010) *Hertfordshire geology and landscape.* Hertfordshire Natural History Society.

Coombe, D.E. (1994) 'Maritime' plants of roads in Cambridgeshire (v.c. 29). *Nature in Cambridgeshire* 36: 37–60.

Cox, K., Groom, A., Jennings, K. & Mercer, I. (2018) National Parks or Natural Parks: how can we have both? *British Wildlife* 30: 87–96.

CPBRC (2006) *Black poplars* (Populus nigra betulifolia) *in Cambridgeshire.* Cambridgeshire & Peterborough Biological Records Centre. Available on-line.

Crosby, M. (2020) Pallas's Warbler (*Phylloscopus proregulus*) – second record for Cambridgeshire. *Cambridgeshire Bird Club Report (for 2019)* 93: 142.

Davies, N.B. (1992) *Dunnock behaviour and social evolution.* Oxford University Press, Oxford.

Dietz, C. & Keifer, A. (2018) *Bats of Britain and Europe.* Bloomsbury Wildlife, London.

Dunn, M., Marzano, M., Forster, J. & Gill, R.M.A. (2018) Public attitudes towards "pest" management: Perceptions on squirrel management strategies in the UK. *Biological conservation* 222: 52–63.

Easy, G.M.S. (1967) Rookeries in Cambridge. *Cambridge Bird Club Report (for 1966)* 40: 33–34.

Easy, G.M.S. (1987) The Carrion Crow in Cambridgeshire. *Cambridgeshire Bird Club Report (for 1986)* 60: 37–39.

Easy, G.[M.S.] (1991) Black poplars *Populus nigra* in Cambridgeshire. *Nature in Cambridgeshire* 33: 45–49.

Easy, G.[M.S.] (1994) An update on Skua movements inland from the Wash. *Cambridgeshire Bird Club Report (for 1993)* 67: 89–90.

Easy, G.[M.S.] (1996) The Rook *Corvus frugilegus* in Cambridgeshire. *Nature in Cambridgeshire* 38: 55–61.

Easy, G.[M.S.] (2001a) The Milton-Chesterton sidings 1. The origins as a ballast pit and bird habitat. *Nature in Cambridgeshire* 43: 7.

Easy, G.[M.S.] (2001b) The Milton-Chesterton sidings 3. The plant-life of the sidings. *Nature in Cambridgeshire* 43: 11–12.

Easy, G.[M.S.] (2007) Sea bird departures from the Wash: the Cambridgeshire connection. *Nature in Cambridgeshire* 49: 84–88.

Eaton, M., Holling, M. and the Rare Breeding Birds Panel. (2020) Rare breeding birds in the UK in 2018. *British Birds* 113: 737–791.

Environment Agency (2016) *Fish population survey report. The Lower River Cam.* Available on-line.

Environment Agency (2019) *Fish population survey report. The Lower River Cam.* Available on-line.

Evans, C., Lucy, S. & Patten, R. (2018) *Riversides: Neolithic barrows, a Beaker grave, Iron Age and Anglo-Saxon burials and settlement at Trumpington. Cambridge.* McDonald Institute for Archaeological Research, Cambridge.

Fellows, R.B. (1948) *Railways to Cambridge: actual and proposed.* Locomotive papers no. 2. The Oakwood Press, South Godstone. Reprinted in 1976 by The Oleander Press.

Field, R., Perrin, V., Bacon, L. & Greatorex-Davies, N. (2006) *The butterflies of Cambridgeshire.* Butterfly Conservation Cambridge & Essex Branch.

Fitter, R.S.R. (1945) *London's natural history.* New Naturalist 3. Collins, London.

Fox, R. *et al.* (2015) *The state of the UK's butterflies 2015.* Butterfly Conservation and the Centre for Ecology & Hydrology, Wareham.

Friend, P. (2008) *Southern England.* New Naturalist 108. Collins, London.

Gardiner, T. & Didham, R.K. (2020) Glowing, glowing, gone? Monitoring long-term trends in glow-worm numbers in south-east England. *Insect Conservation and Diversity* 13: 162–174.

Gerard, J. (1597) *The herball or generall historie of plantes.* London.

Gibbard, P.L., West, R.G. & Hughes, P.D. (2018) Pleistocene glaciation of Fenland, England, and its implications for evolution of the region. *Royal Society Open Science* 5: 170736.

Godwin, H. & Willis, E.H. (1964) Cambridge University natural radiocarbon measurements VI. *Radiocarbon* 6: 116–137.

Goode, D. (2014) *Nature in towns and cities.* New Naturalist 127. William Collins, London.

Gray, E.A. (1974) Hobson's Brook then and now. *Nature in Cambridgeshire* 17: 24–28.

Gray, E.A. (1977a) The fertility of Hobson's Brook. *Nature in Cambridgeshire* 20: 24–29.

Gray, E.A. (1977b) *Hobson's Conduit: the story of a Cambridgeshire chalk stream.* Bird's Farm Publications, Cambridge.

Guillebaud, P. (2005) The enclosure of Cambridge St Giles: Cambridge University and the Parliamentary Act of 1802. *Proceedings of the Cambridge Antiquarian Society* 94: 185–198.

Guillebaud, P. (2006) Changes in the landscape of west Cambridge after enclosure 1805–1870. *Proceedings of the Cambridge Antiquarian Society* 95: 159–170.

Guillebaud, P. (2007) West Cambridge 1870–1914: building the bicycle suburb. *Proceedings of the Cambridge Antiquarian Society* 96: 193–210.

Guillebaud, P. (2008) West Cambridge: the two World Wars and the inter-war lull. *Proceedings of the Cambridge Antiquarian Society* 97: 179–193.

Guillebaud, P. (2009) Changes in the landscape of west Cambridge, Part V: 1945 to 2000. *Proceedings of the Cambridge Antiquarian Society* 98: 127–142.

Hall, C.P. & Ravensdale, J.R., eds (1976) *The West Fields of Cambridge.* Cambridge Antiquarian Records Society, Cambridge.

Hannant, G. & Sparks, T. (2008) Phenological changes in Cambridgeshire. *Nature in Cambridgeshire* 50: 85–91.

Hawksley, R. & Mungovan, R. (2020) *Greater Cambridge Chalk Streams Project Report.* Wildlife Trust BCN and Wild Trout Trust. Available on-line.

Hayhow, D.B. *et al.* (2016) *State of nature 2016.* State of Nature Partnership. Available on-line.

Hesse, M. (2007) The East Fields of Cambridge. *Proceedings of the Cambridge Antiquarian Society* 96: 143–160.

Hey, R.W. & Perrin, R.M.S. (1960) *The geology and soils of Cambridgeshire.* Cambridge Natural History Society, Cambridge.

Hill, M.[O.] (2016) A natural history of Cambridge. *Nature in Cambridgeshire* 58: 108–110.

Hill, M.O. & Preston, C.D. (2015) Disappearance of boreal plants in southern Britain: habitat loss or climate change? *Biological Journal of the Linnean Society* 115: 598–610.

Hill, M.O., Preston C.D. & Roy, D. B. (2004) *PLANTATT. Attributes of British and Irish plants: status, size, life history, geography and habitats.* Centre for Ecology & Hydrology, Huntingdon.

Hill, M.O., Preston, C.D. & Shanklin, J.D. (2020) Geographical patterns in the flora of Cambridgeshire. *British & Irish Botany* 2: 285–308.

Hodgetts, N. & Lockhart, N. (2020) Checklist and country status of European bryophytes – update 2020. *Irish Wildlife Manuals* 123: 1–214.

Horn, P.W. (1923) Notes on the fishes of the London Docks. *London Naturalist* 1922: 19–21.

Hows, M., Pilbeam, P., Conlan, H. & Featherstone, R., eds (2016) *Cambridgeshire mammal atlas 2016*. Cambridgeshire Mammal Group.

Huang, Z. *et al.* (2019) Longitudinal comparative transcriptomics reveals unique mechanisms underlying extended healthspan in bats. *Nature ecology & evolution* 3: 1110–1120.

Hudson, W.H. (1898) *Birds in London*. Longmans, Green, and Co., London.

Ingram, D. & Robertson, N. (1999) *Plant disease*. New Naturalist 85. HarperCollins, London.

Jarman, B. (2012) The disappearance of three species of woodland breeding birds in Cambridgeshire. *Cambridgeshire Bird Report (for 2011)* 85: 163–167.

Jarman, B. (2014) House Sparrow survey of Cambridge. *Cambridgeshire Bird Club (for 2013)* 87: 162–169.

Jarman, B. & Preston, C.D. (2020) Cambridge Rooks (*Corvus frugilegus*). *Cambridgeshire Bird Club Report* (for 2019) 93: 150–152.

Jefferies, D.J., Strachan, R. & Strachan, C. (2004) The catastrophic 99.8% crash of the water vole *Arvicola terrestris* population of Cambridgeshire (v.c. 29) between 1989 and 1997. *Nature in Cambridgeshire* 46: 3–11.

Kerney, M.P. (1976) *Atlas of the non-marine mollusca of the British Isles*. Institute of Terrestrial Ecology, Cambridge.

Kerney, M.P. (1999) *Atlas of the land and freshwater molluscs of Britain and Ireland*. Harley Books, Colchester.

Keynes, M.E. (1976) *A house by the river*. Darwin College, Cambridge.

King, W.B.R. & Nicholson, H.H. (1946) *Geology and soils of Cambridgeshire*. Cambridge Natural History Society, Cambridge.

Kirk, K. & Cotton, C. (2016) *The Cambridge phenomenon: global impact*. Third Millennium Publishing, London.

Kirtland, C. (1995) Black-headed Bunting in Cambridge – a first for the county. *Cambridgeshire Bird Club Report (for 1993)* 67: 75–77.

Koepp, R. (2002) *Clusters of creativity*. John Wiley & Sons, Chichester.

Korsten, E., Jansen, E.A., Boonman, M., Schillemans, M.J. & Limpens, H. (2016) Swarm and switch: on the trail of the hibernating common pipistrelle. *Bat News* 110: 8–10.

Kowarik, I. (2020) Herbert Sukopp – an inspiring pioneer in the field of urban ecology. *Urban ecosystems* 23: 445–455.

Lachmuth, S., Durka, W. & Schurr, F.M. (2010) The making of a rapid plant invader: genetic diversity and differentiation in the native and invaded range of *Senecio inaequidens*. *Molecular ecology* 19: 3952–3967.

Lee, J.R., Woods, M.A. & Moorlock, B.S.P., eds (2015) *British regional geology. East Anglia*, ed. 5. British Geological Survey, Keyworth.

Leedham-Green, E. (1996) *A concise history of the University of Cambridge*. Cambridge University Press, Cambridge.

Leslie, A.C. (2015) Vascular plant records 2014. *Nature in Cambridgeshire* 57: 129–139.

Leslie, A.C. (2019) *Flora of Cambridgeshire*. Royal Horticultural Society, Peterborough.

Lobel, M.D., ed (1975) *The atlas of historic towns. Volume 2 Bristol:Cambridge:Coventry:Norwich*. Scholar Press, London.

MacCallum, F. (1986) The natural history and conservation status of Nine Wells. *Nature in Cambridgeshire* 28: 50–53.

Marr, J.E. (1920) The Pleistocene deposits around Cambridge. *Quarterly Journal of the Geological Society* 75: 204–244.

Marr, J.E. & Gardner, E.W. (1916) On some deposits containing an arctic flora in the Pleistocene Beds of Barnwell, Cambridge. *Geological Magazine* 3: 339–343.

Marr, J.E. & Shipley, A.E., eds (1904) *Handbook to the natural history of Cambridgeshire*. Cambridge University Press, Cambridge.

Marren, P. (1995) *The new naturalists*. New Naturalist 82. HarperCollins, London.

Mason, S.C., Palmer, G., Fox, R., Gillings, S., Hill, J.K., Thomas, C.D. & Oliver, T.H. (2015) Geographical range shifts of many taxonomic groups continue to shift polewards. *Biological Journal of the Linnean Society* 115: 586–597.

McGill, J. (2015) *East Romsey Town Cement Works*. Mill Road History Project Building Report. Available on-line.

Meed, J. (2021) *The value of the green belt south of Cambridge to populations of farmland birds (2020)*. Available on-line.

Morris F.O. (1870) *A history of British butterflies*, ed. 3. Bell and Daldy, London.

Morris, P. (2018) *Hedgehog*. New Naturalist 137. William Collins, London.

Morrison, M.B. (2015) *The links on the hills: a history of the Old Course at the Gogs*. Gog Magog Golf Club, Cambridge.

Morrison, M.B. (2016) *The worst golf course ever*. Privately published.

Morton, R.D., Marston, C.G., O'Neil, A.W. & Rowland, C.S. (2020) *Land Cover Map 2019 (25m rasterised land parcels, GB)*. NERC Environmental Information Data Centre. Available on-line.

Morton, R.D., Rowland, C.S., Wood, C.M., Meek, L., Marston, C.G. & Smith, G.M. (2014) *Land Cover Map 2007 (1km percentage aggregate class, GB) v1.2*. NERC Environmental Information Data Centre. Available on-line.

Naggs, F., Raheem, R. & Budha, P. (2008) The carnivorous slug *Testacella* in Cambridgeshire. *Nature in Cambridgeshire* 50: 48–51.

Napier, J. (2001) The Milton-Chesterton sidings 4. The butterflies of the sidings. *Nature in Cambridgeshire* 43: 12–14.

Neal, E. (1948) *The badger*. New Naturalist monograph. Collins, London.

Newton, A.E. (1986) Bryophyte sites in Cambridgeshire. *Nature in Cambridgeshire* 28: 23–28.

Owen, J. (2010) *Wildlife of a garden: a thirty-year study*. Royal Horticultural Society, Peterborough.

Payne, R.M. (2005) The flora of walls and buildings in the Isle of Ely. *Nature in Cambridgeshire* 47: 43–58.

Pescott, O.L., Simkin, J.M., August, T.A., Randle, Z., Dore, A.J. & Botham, M.S. (2015) Air pollution and its effects on lichens, bryophytes, and lichen-feeding Lepidoptera: review and evidence from biological records. *Biological Journal of the Linnean Society* 115: 611–635.

Petrovan, S.O. & Schmidt, B.R. (2016) Volunteer conservation action data reveals large-scale and long-term negative population trends of a widespread amphibian, the common toad (*Bufo bufo*). *PLoS One* 11: e0161943.

Pollard, E. (1973) Introductions of the Roman Snail in Cambridgeshire. *Nature in Cambridgeshire* 16: 25–28.

Powell, M. & Cambridge Lichen Group (2012) The lichens of Cambridge walls. *Nature in Cambridgeshire* 54: 56–60.

Preece, R.C. & Sparks, T.H., eds (2012) *Fauna Cantabrigiensis. The vertebrate and molluscan fauna of Cambridgeshire by the Rev. Leonard Jenyns (1800–1893): transcript and commentaries*. Ray Society, London.

Preece, R.C. & White, T.S. (2012) Land and freshwater molluscs in the Cambridge Botanic Garden. *Nature in Cambridgeshire* 54: 53–56.

Preston, C.D. (2008) The aquatic plants of the River Cam and its riparian commons, Cambridge, 1660–1999. *Nature in Cambridgeshire* 50: 18-37.

Preston, C.D. (2018) Where was the Hill of Health, and what plants grew there? *Nature in Cambridgeshire* 60: 53–60.

Preston, C.D. (2020) The phenology of an urban street flora: a transect study. *British & Irish Botany* 2: 1–26.

Preston C.D. & Hill, M.O. (2019) *Cambridgeshire's mosses and liverworts – a dynamic flora*. Pisces Publications, Newbury.

Preston, C.D. & Sheail, J. (2007) The transformation of
the riparian commons of Cambridge from undrained
pastures to level recreation areas, 1833–1932. *Nature in
Cambridgeshire* 49: 70–84.

Preston, C.D., Sheail, J., Armitage, P. & Davy-Bowker, J.
(2003) The long-term impact of urbanisation on aquatic
plants: Cambridge and the River Cam. *Science of the Total
Environment* 314–316: 67–87.

Rackham, O. (2015) Brandon Park fungi 1959–2014. Change and
stability in occurrence. *Suffolk Natural History* 51: 26–32.

Ranger, W. (1849) *Report to the General Board of Health on a
preliminary enquiry into the sewage, drainage, and supply
of water, and the sanitary condition of the inhabitants of
the town of Cambridge.* Her Majesty's Stationery Office,
London.

Ray, J. (1660) *Catalogus plantarum circa Cantabrigiam
nascentium.* Cambridge & London.

Ray, J. (1670) *Catalogus plantarum Angliae, et insularum
adjacentium.* London.

Rishbeth, J. (1948) The flora of Cambridge walls. *Journal of
Ecology* 36: 136–148.

Rivers, M. *et al.* (2019) *European red list of trees.* International
Union for Conservation of Nature and Natural Resources,
Cambridge & Brussels.

Rivington, R.T. (2012) *The history and techniques of punting in
Cambridge.* Oleander Press, Cambridge.

Roach, J.P.C., ed. (1959) *A history of the county of Cambridge
and the Isle of Ely. Volume III. The City and University of
Cambridge.* Oxford University Press, London.

Roy, H.E. and Brown, P.M.J. (2018) *Field guide to the ladybirds
of Great Britain and Ireland.* Bloomsbury Wildlife, London.

Segal Quince Wicksteed (1985) *The Cambridge phenomenon.*
Segal Quince Wicksteed, Swavesey.

Sell, P.D. & Murrell, G. (1996–2018) *Flora of Great Britain and
Ireland.* 5 vols. Cambridge University Press, Cambridge.

Shanklin, J. D. (2020) *Register of plants of conservation concern
in Cambridgeshire (v.c.29),* ed. 8. Updated annually;
available on-line.

Shanklin, J. & Tribe, H. (2017) Fungi in the Cambridge
University Botanic Garden. *Nature in Cambridgeshire* 59:
3–6.

Shipton, P. (1961) Rookeries in Cambridge 1945–1960. *Nature in
Cambridgeshire* 4: 42–43.

Sibthorp, J. (1794) *Flora oxoniensis.* Oxford.

Sparks, T., Atkinson, S. & Lewthwaite, K. (2013) Snow,
snowdrops, lawns and observers. Topics from Nature's
Calendar/UK Phenology Network. *British Wildlife* 24:
265–268.

Stace, C.A. (2019) *New flora of the British Isles,* ed. 4. C & M
Floristics, Middlewood Green.

Stewart, A.J.A., Bantock, T.M., Beckmann, B.C., Botham,
M.S., Hubble, D. & Roy, D.B. (2015) The role of ecological
interactions in determining species ranges and range
changes. *Biological Journal of the Linnean Society* 115:
647–663.

Storrie, J. (1886) *The flora of Cardiff.* Cardiff Naturalists'
Society, Cardiff.

Sukopp, H. (2002) On the early history of urban ecology in
Europe. *Preslia* 74: 373–393.

Tansley, A.G. (1939) *The British Islands and their vegetation.*
Cambridge University Press, Cambridge.

Taylor, A. (1999) *Cambridge: the hidden history.* Tempus
Publishing, Stroud.

Tanner, J.R., ed. (1917) *The historical register of the University
of Cambridge.* Cambridge University Press, Cambridge.

Teeling, E. (2019) Limiting the damage: molecular basis of
extended health span in bats. *Nature Portfolio Ecology &
Evolution Community.* On-line commentary on Huang *et
al.* (2019).

Tribe, H. (2001) The Milton-Chesterton sidings 2. The sidings in
the railway years. *Nature in Cambridgeshire* 43: 8–11.

Turner, I.M., Chua, K.S., Ong, J.S.Y., Soong, B.C. & Tan,
H.T.W. (1996) A century of plant species loss from an
isolated fragment of lowland tropical rain forest. *Biological
Conservation* 10: 1229–1244.

UK Beetle Recording (2020) *Polistichus connexus* (Geoffroy in
Fourcroy, 1785). Available on-line.

Ward, M. (2005) The first confirmed breeding of Little Egrets
in Cambridgeshire. *Cambridgeshire Bird Club Report (for
2004)* 78: 161.

West, R.G. & Gibbard, P.L. (2017) The Observatory Gravels and
the Travellers' Rest Pit, Cambridge, England. *Proceedings
of the Yorkshire Geological Society* 61: 313–322.

Williamson, M., Gaston, K.J. & Lonsdale, W.M. (2001) The
species-area relationship does not have an asymptote!
Journal of Biogeography 28: 827–830.

Wilson, K. & Jarman, R.J. (1995) The birds of Cherry
Hinton Chalk Pit and Cherry Hinton Hall, Cambridge.
Cambridgeshire Bird Club Report (for 1993) 67: 79–85.

Woodward, I., Aebischer, N., Burnell, D., Eaton, M., Frost,
T., Hall, C., Stroud, D.A. & Noble, D. (2020) Population
estimates of birds in Great Britain and the United
Kingdom. *British Birds* 113: 69–104.

Worssam, B.C. & Taylor, M.A. (1969) *Geology of the country
around Cambridge.* Memoirs of the Geological Survey of
Great Britain. Her Majesty's Stationery Office, London.

Wright, A.P.M. (1989) Chesterton. In A.P.M. Wright & C.P.
Lewis, eds, *A history of the county of Cambridge and the Isle
of Ely. Volume IX. Chesterton, Northstowe, and Papworth
Hundreds (North and North-west of Cambridge),* pp. 5–39.
Oxford University Press, Oxford.

Wundsch, H.H. (1943) Die Seen der mittleren Havel als
Glyptotendipes-Gewässer und die Metamorphose von
Glyptotendipes paripes Edwards. *Archiv für Hydrobiologie*
40: 362–380.

Yalden, D. (1999) *The history of British mammals.*
T & AD Poyser, London.

Page numbers in **bold** refer to pictures and those followed by 'm' refer to maps. See also the section on Contributors (p. 290) and the Gazetteer (p. 297) for further details of authors and of localities mentioned in the text.

Temperature 20, 21, 22
  trends 23
Tench (*Tinca tinca*) 199, 200, 201
Tenebrio molitor (Mealworm Beetle) **133**
Tenthredo maculata see Tenthredo, Large
  Yellow-girdled
  mesomela see Tenthredo, Common Green
  scrophulariae (Figwort Sawfly) 169
Tenthredo, Common Green (*Tenthredo mesomela*)
  169
  Large Yellow-girdled (*Tenthredo maculata*) 169
Tephritis divisa **256**, 258
  formosa 182
Tern, Black 216
  Common **208**, 210, 216, 284
  Little 216
  Sandwich 208, 216
Testacella haliotidea (Eared Shelled Slug) **194**
Tetragnatha extensa 190, **191**
  montana 190
Teversham churchyard 261
  lichens 101
Thecaphora seminis-convolvuli 99
Theodoxus fluviatilis (Freshwater Nerite) 195
Thereva nobilitata (Common Stiletto Fly) **256**
Thistle, Creeping (*Cirsium arvense*) 59
  Dwarf (*Cirsium acaule*) 261
  Marsh (*Cirsium palustre*) 56, 281
  Slender (*Carduus tenuiflorus*) 60
  Spear (*Cirsium vulgare*) 59
Thorn, Feathered (*Colotois pennaria*) **123**, **247**
  Canary-shouldered (*Ennomos alniaria*) **118**, 119
Thread-moss, Archangelic (*Bryum archangelicum*)
  89
  Cape (*Orthodontium lineare*) 84
  Capillary (*Bryum capillare*) 85, 86
  Nodding (*Pohlia nutans*) 84
  Pale Glaucous (*Pohlia wahlenbergii*) 83
Threadwort, Common (*Cephaloziella divaricata*) 89
Thrush, Mistle 2, 223; vector of Mistletoe 63, 209,
  224
  Song 208, 224, 244, 245
Thuidium tamariscinum (Common Tamarisk-
  moss) 3, **83**
Thyme, Basil (*Clinopodium acinos*) 60
  Large (*Thymus pulegioides*) 60
  Wild (*Thymus drucei*) 47, 60
Thyme-moss, Woodsy (*Plagiomnium cuspidatum*)
  89
Thymelicus lineola (Essex Skipper) **112**
  sylvestris (Small Skipper) 112
Thymus drucei (Wild Thyme) 47, 60
  pulegioides (Large Thyme) 60
Tiger, Jersey (*Euplagia quadripunctaria*) 3, **125**, 286
Tilia × europaea (Common Lime) **63**, 265
  spp. (Limes) 41, 62, 63
Timandra comoa (Blood Vein) 248
Tinca tinca (Tench) 199, 200, 201
Tinea pellionella (Case-bearing Clothes Moth) **123**
Tineola bisselliella (Common Clothes Moth) 123
Tinodes waeneri 128
Tipula oleracea see Tipula, Marsh Brown-edged
Tipula, Marsh Brown-edged (*Tipula oleracea*) 182
Tit, Bearded 221
  Blue 220, 244
  Coal 211, 220, 244
  Great 220, 244
  Long-tailed 221, 244, 264

Toad, Common (*Bufo bufo*) 202m, 243, 244, 264,
  273; sex ratio 206
  Midwife (*Alytes obstetricans*) **203**, 287, 288
Toadflax, Ivy-leaved (*Cymbalaria muralis*) 77, 78,
  279
  Purple (*Linaria purpurea*) 61, 66, 252
Tomato (*Solanum lycopersicum*) 287
Tomkins, Stephen 179
Tomocerus minor **257**
Toothwort, Purple (*Lathraea clandestina*) **48**
Torilis arvensis (Spreading Hedge-parsley) 50
Tortella tortuosa (Frizzled Crisp-moss) 88, 89, 249
Tortoiseshell, Small (*Aglais urticae*) 111
Tortula muralis (Wall Screw-moss) 85, **87**
  vahliana (Chalk Screw-moss) 88
Tottenhill glaciation 16
Totternhoe Stone (Burwell Rock) 13
Trachemys scripta elegans (Red-eared Slider) 205,
  287
Trametes gibbosa (Lumpy Bracket) 94
  versicolor (Turkeytail) 94
Travellers' Rest Pit 16
Treecreeper 223
Tree-of-heaven (*Ailanthus altissima*) 41
Trees 7, 41
  planted 54
Trefoil, Lesser (*Trifolium dubium*) 68
Triaenodes bicolor 128, 129
Trichoptera *see* Caddisflies
Trichostegia minor 128, 129
Trifolium arvense (Hare's-foot Clover) 60, **61**
  dubium (Lesser Trefoil) 68
  fragiferum (Strawberry Clover) 261
  ochroleucon (Sulphur Clover) 56
  ornithopodioides (Bird's-foot Clover) 51
  repens (White Clover) 67, 73, 74, 75
  scabrum (Rough Clover) **51**
Trinity College, foundation 28
Tripleurospermum inodorum (Scentless Mayweed)
  64, 65
Trisetum flavescens (Yellow Oat-grass) 59, 262
Triturus cristatus (Great Crested Newt) 203, 204m
Trochulus sericeus (Hairy Snail) 195
Trombidium sp. (Red Velvet Mite) **254**, 255
Trooping Funnel (*Clitocybe geotropa*) 93
Trout, Brown (*Salmo trutta*) 199, **200**, 201, 273
True Bugs (Hemiptera), aquatic 151
  Botanic Garden 247
  diversity 149
  garden 149
  hedgerow 152
  household 149
  meadow 7, 152
  NatHistCam recording dates 3
  new colonists 154
  Paul Rule's garden 149, 251
  tree 152
  wetland 151
  woodland 152
True Flies (Diptera), Botanic Garden 247
  climate change 185, 186
  diversity 180
  garden 181
  hedgerow 183
  household 181
  meadow 181
  NatHistCam recording dates 3
  new colonists 185

  rare species 186
  wetland 184
  woodland 183
True Weevils (Curculionidae) 142
Trumpington 35, 38
  churchyard 261
Trumpington Meadows 6, 7, 8, 38, 268m, 269, 272
  birds 209
  dragonflies 163
  fish 209
  habitat creation 271, 284
  history 271
  meadows 273
  ponds 273
  R. Cam restoration project 273
Truncatellina cylindrica (Cylindrical Whorl Snail)
  195
Tuberolachnus salignus (Large Willow Aphid) 152,
  153
Tufted-sedge (*Carex elata*) 58
Tulip Tree (*Liriodendron tulipifera*) 54
Tulostoma brumale (Winter Stalkball) 92
Turf-moss, Springy (*Rhytidiadelphus squarrosus*)
  86
Turkeytail (*Trametes versicolor*) 94
Turnstone 216
Turritis glabra (Tower Mustard) 49
Tussilago farfara (Colt's-foot) 65
Tussock, Pale (*Calliteara pudibunda*) **118**, 119
Twayblade, Common (*Neottia ovata*) 56, 264
Twite 210
Typha angustifolia (Lesser Bulrush) 265
  latifolia (Bulrush) 58
Tyria jacobaeae (Cinnabar Moth) 114, **115**
Tytthaspis sedecimpunctata (16-spot Ladybird) **144**,
  145
Ulmus glabra (Wych Elm) 45
  minor (Small-leaved Elm) 265
  × *hollandica* 'Cicestria' (Chichester Elm) 7, 44,
  243
  × *vegeta* (Huntingdon Elm) **44**
  spp. (Elms) 44, 45, 142, 171
Umber, Mottled (*Erannis defoliaria*) **123**
Umbilicus rupestris (Navelwort) 49, 279
Uncertain (*Hoplodrina alsines*) 122
Underwing, Broad-bordered Yellow (*Noctua
  fimbriata*) **122**
  Large Yellow (*Noctua pronuba*) **122**
  Lesser Broad-bordered Yellow (*Noctua janthe*)
  122
  Lesser Yellow (*Noctua comes*) 122
  Lunar (*Omphaloscelis lunosa*) **122**
Unio pictorum (Painter's Mussel) 196
Urban ecology, history 279
Urban habitats 5m, 6, 9
  adaptation to 288
  complexity 280
  conservation 280
  ladybirds 144
  lichens 105
  richness 289
  vascular plants 61, 70
Urocystis eranthidis **100**
Urophora stylata (Spear Thistle Gall Fly) **182**
Urtica dioica (Common Nettle) 54, 55, 59, 69, 77,
  78, 243, 251
  membranacea (Mediterranean Nettle) 72, **73**,
  287